BASIC ELECTRONICS FOR SCIENTISTS

BASIC ELECTRONICS FOR SCIENTISTS

JAMES J. BROPHY

IIT Research Institute

McGRAW-HILL BOOK COMPANY   New York · St. Louis · San Francisco

Toronto · London · Sydney

BASIC ELECTRONICS FOR SCIENTISTS

34567-HDBP-10987

DEDICATED TO MURIEL

PREFACE

It is clear that electronic measurements pervade all corners of experimental science and engineering. The great power and versatility of electronic devices and, consequently, their widespread application make it imperative for science and engineering students to obtain a working familiarity with electronics. Yet this familiarity need not be as intensive as that attempted in the training of electronic engineers.

This text is written to provide the undergraduate science major with a basic understanding of electronic devices and circuits. This understanding should be sufficient to appreciate the operation and characteristics of the many electronic instruments he will use in his professional career. The analysis of circuits, rather than their design, is emphasized since such a student will be required to design only the simplest of circuits. On the other hand, he must thoroughly understand the operation of quite complicated instruments. In this connection the physical basis for the equivalent circuits of both active and passive components is stressed, and thus, some of the mystery that seems to surround such circuits is removed.

In order to display adequately the physical origin of electronic circuits, it is necessary in several instances to employ a few simple differential equations. The solutions are always immediately given in the text, however, so that a knowledge of differential equations is not necessary. The author feels that this approach results in a more satisfying exposition for the scientifically oriented student than, for example, simply assuming the validity of Ohm's law. Complex-number representation is absolutely necessary in ac-circuit theory, but sample manipulations of addition and multiplication are explained when complex impedances are first introduced. It is assumed that the student possesses a general acquaintance with electricity and properties of materials as covered in beginning physics courses. Circuit theory is treated by starting with direct currents, however, so that parts of the early chapters may be used as refresher material.

Since this text is written from the point of view of an experimentalist, concurrent laboratory experience is highly recommended. Almost all of the circuits analyzed give actual component values and can easily form the basis for suitable experiments. No attempt has been made to suggest such experiments in detail because of the diversity of equipment likely to be found in different university laboratories. On the other hand, the problems have been chosen to demand quantitative answers and therefore may substitute in some measure for laboratory work where a separate laboratory course is not possible. In later chapters a number of complex instruments are treated in terms of block diagrams of individual circuits previously described. This should make it clear to the student how he can approach the analysis of other complete circuits and gain an understanding of their operation.

For many years I have felt that a working familiarity with electronics contributes immeasurably to a professional scientific career. If this text makes it possible for others to attain such familiarity, I will be well satisfied. I am deeply indebted to many colleagues who, through their publications, have provided much background material for this book. Where appropriate, these contributions are recognized in the text. I must also express my deep thanks to those who kindly read and criticized the manuscript, particularly Prof. Howard Carr of Auburn University. Finally, the work could not possibly have been completed were it not for the selfless encouragement provided by my wife, Muriel. This extends far beyond preparation of the typescript, which she also did with boundless enthusiasm.

JAMES J. BROPHY

CONTENTS

BASIC ELECTRONICS FOR SCIENTISTS

1

DIRECT CURRENT CIRCUITS

The operation of any electronic device, be it as complicated as a television receiver or as simple as a flashlight, can be understood by determining the magnitude and direction of electric currents in all parts of its functional unit, the circuit. In fact, it is not possible to appreciate how any given circuit functions without a detailed knowledge of the currents in its individual components.

Even the most complicated circuits can be examined in easy stages by first considering each part separately and subsequently noting how the various subcircuits fit together. Therefore, circuit analysis should start by treating elementary configurations under the simplest possible conditions. Circuits in which the currents are steady and do not vary with time are called direct-current circuits. Such dc circuits, which are considered in this chapter, are important and relatively simple to understand.

INTRODUCTORY CONCEPTS

1-1 Potential difference

One of the fundamental properties of electrons is their electric charge, which has the magnitude 1.6029×10^{-19} coul. If two electric charges (such as two electrons) are near one another, they exert a force on each other given by *Coulomb's law*

$$F = \frac{1}{4\pi\epsilon_0} \frac{q_1 q_2}{r^2} \tag{1-1}$$

where F is the force in newtons, q_1 and q_2 are the electric charges, r is the distance in meters between the charges, and $\epsilon_0 = 8.85 \times 10^{-12}$ coul²/newton-m² is a constant which depends upon the system of units used to measure the force, charge, and distance. The particular system of units chosen in Eq. (1-1) is called the *rationalized meter-kilogram-second system* (*mks* system). It is selected here because the conventional electrical quantities important in circuit analysis are part of this system.

The experimental fact that an electric charge experiences a force due to another charge located some distance away may be usefully represented by saying that the first charge sets up an *electric field* in the surrounding space and that the field produces the observed force on the second charge. Thus, we may say that the force on q_2 corresponding to Eq. (1-1) is caused by an electric field $\mathscr{E}$ at the position of q_2 such that

$$F = q_2 \mathscr{E} \tag{1-2}$$

This relation defines an electric field as the force per unit charge

$$\mathscr{E} = \frac{F}{q_2} \tag{1-3}$$

and the units of electric field are clearly newtons per coulomb. The direction of the electric field at any point is simply the direction of the force on a positive charge at that point.

The idea of an electric field removes the conceptual difficulty of how two objects can "push" each other even though they are separated by some distance. It also makes it possible to determine the force on an electric charge using Eq. (1-2) in situations where the electric field in a region is known, whereas the geometric arrangement of charges generating the field is not. This situation is very common in electric-circuit analysis.

Suppose an electric charge q is placed in an electric field $\mathscr{E}$. According to Eq. (1-2) a force $q\mathscr{E}$ is exerted on the charge by the field. This means that the charge has potential energy by virtue of being located in the field. The change in potential energy of the charge in moving from point a to point b in the electric field is simply the mechanical work required to move it from *a* to *b* against the force due to the field. If there is no friction or acceleration, the electric force $q\mathscr{E}$ must be balanced by an externally

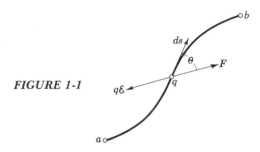

FIGURE 1-1

applied force *F* at all points along the path, as in Fig. 1-1. Then, from the usual definition of work

$$W = \int_a^b F \cos \theta \, ds \qquad (1\text{-}4)$$

where θ is the angle between the applied force *F* and the direction of motion *ds*. Using Eq. (1-2)

$$W = -q \int_a^b \mathscr{E} \cos \theta \, ds \qquad (1\text{-}5)$$

The integral in Eq. (1-5) is defined as the electric *potential difference V* between *a* and *b*, and is given by

$$V = \frac{W}{q} \qquad (1\text{-}6)$$

Notice that the units of potential difference are work per unit charge, newton-meters per coulomb or joules per coulomb. Because potential difference is used so frequently in electric circuits, the unit joules per coulomb has been named a *volt*, in honor of the early worker in electricity, Alessandro Volta.

Note that *V* is the potential difference between the two points *a* and *b* and that it is incorrect to speak of the potential of one point without reference to another point. The point *b* is said to be at a higher potential than point *a* if work is done against electric forces when a positive charge is moved from *a* to *b*. In circuit analysis it is common to consider the potential of several points all with reference to one given place, usually taken to be at zero potential and called the *ground*. In this case it is satisfactory to speak of the potential at a point, so long as the implied reference point is clearly understood.

According to Eq. (1-5), the potential difference *V* is

$$V = -\int_a^b \mathscr{E} \cos \theta \, ds \qquad (1\text{-}7)$$

The quantity $\mathscr{E} \cos \theta$ is simply the component of the field in the direction of the path s, which we call $\mathscr{E}_s$. Notice that if we write

$$\mathscr{E}_s = -\frac{dV}{ds} \tag{1-8}$$

and substitute Eq. (1-8) into Eq. (1-7)

$$V = -\int_a^b \mathscr{E}_s \, ds = \int_a^b \frac{dV}{ds} \, ds = \int_a^b dV = V_b - V_a = V \tag{1-9}$$

That is, Eq. (1-7) is satisfied by an expression of the form of (1-8). This means that Eqs. (1-7) and (1-8) are alternative expressions relating potential difference and electric field. In particular, Eq. (1-8) states that the component of electric field in a given direction is just the negative of the space rate of change of the potential in that direction. This rate of change is called the *potential gradient* and is measured in volts per meter. According to Eq. (1-8) the same units of measurement are appropriate for electric field as well.

1-2 Current and current density

The motion of electric charges, as, for example, in response to an electric field, constitutes an electric *current*. Specifically, current is defined as the time rate at which charge is transported past a given point, so that

$$I = \frac{dq}{dt} \tag{1-10}$$

Many materials, most notably metals such as copper and silver, contain free electrons which can move when acted upon by an electric field. Consider the section of copper wire shown in Fig. 1-2 in which there is an electric field $\mathscr{E}$ directed from right to left.

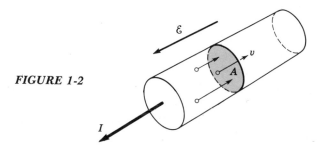

FIGURE 1-2

Because the electronic charge is negative, the free electrons in the metal are urged from left to right and their motion constitutes an electric current in the wire.

Suppose each electron moves with an average velocity v as the net result of the accelerating force due to the field and collisions within the metal. Then in a small interval of time dt each electron advances a distance $v\,dt$. The electrons which cross the shaded plane during this interval are those contained in a section of wire of length $v\,dt$ or volume $Av\,dt$, where A is the cross section of the wire. If there are n free electrons per cubic meter, the number is $nAv\,dt$. Denoting by e the electronic charge, the total charge dq crossing the plane in time dt is therefore

$$dq = nevA\,dt \tag{1-11}$$

According to Eq. (1-10), the current resulting from the electronic motion is

$$I = \frac{dq}{dt} = nevA \tag{1-12}$$

Current is expressed in coulombs per second, which is termed an *ampere* in honor of the French scientist André Marie Ampère.

Note that the direction of the current is opposite to the motion of the electrons. Although this may seem incongruous, the current in gaseous and liquid conductors, for example, is transported by charges of both signs, and these move in opposite directions. Obviously, whichever direction is assigned to the current, one or the other of the charges moves in the opposite direction. By common agreement the current direction was arbitrarily defined to be the direction of motion of positive charges. This convention was settled upon before it was known that the free charges in metals are electrons. Actually, Benjamin Franklin's original definitions of positive and negative electricity determined that the electronic charge is a negative quantity, although the existence of electrons was unknown at the time.

In many instances it is useful to consider the *current density* in a conductor, the ratio of the current to the cross-sectional area. Thus, in the case of the wire discussed above, the current density J is

$$J = \frac{I}{A} - nev \tag{1-13}$$

in which the right side is independent of the geometry of the conductor.

1-3 Ohm's law

Each free electron in a wire carrying a current is accelerated by the electric field until it loses its velocity as the result of a collision within the metal. After every collision the electron starts from rest as sketched in Fig. 1-3 and then accelerates once more so that the net result is an average velocity v. This average velocity increases linearly with the applied field $\mathscr{E}$ (see Exercise 1-3) so that

$$v = \mu \mathscr{E} \tag{1-14}$$

where the quantity μ is called the *mobility* of the electron. The mobility is a property of the material; it is large for materials which are good conductors and small for those which are poor conductors, if n is the same in both cases.

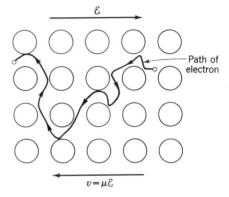

FIGURE 1-3   *Path of free electron in solid conductor is result of acceleration caused by electric field and many collisions.*

Substituting Eq. (1-14) into (1-13)

$$J = ne\mu \mathscr{E} \tag{1-15}$$

and the ratio of the current density to the electric field $J/\mathscr{E}$, which depends only upon the wire material, is called the *conductivity* σ of the metal.

$$\frac{J}{\mathscr{E}} = \sigma = ne\mu \tag{1-16}$$

The left side of Eq. (1-16) is one form of *Ohm's law,* named after the German scientist Georg Simon Ohm, who first discovered experimentally the proportionality between the current density

TABLE 1-1

CONDUCTIVITIES AND RESISTIVITIES OF METALS AND ALLOYS

Material	*Conductivity,* $10^6 \ \Omega\text{-m}^{-1}$	*Resistivity,* $10^{-8} \ \Omega\text{-m}$
Aluminum	38	2.6
Brass	17	6
Carbon	0.029	3.5×10^2
Constantan (Cu 60, Ni 40)	2.0	50
Copper	58	1.7
Manganin (Cu 84, Mn 12, Ni 4)	2.3	44
Nichrome	1.0	100
Silver	68	1.5
Tungsten	18	5.6

and the electric field in a metallic conductor. The conductivities of several metals at room temperature are listed in Table 1-1, together with corresponding values of the reciprocal of the conductivity, called the *resistivity* $\rho = 1/\sigma$, which is also commonly used.

Consider now the metallic conductor L m long in Fig. 1-4 hav-

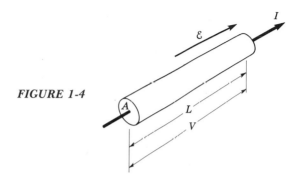

FIGURE 1-4

ing a cross-sectional area of A m² which is carrying a current of I amp. The magnitude of the electric field $\mathscr{E}$ may be written, according to Eq. (1-8), in terms of the potential difference V between the ends of the wire as

$$\mathscr{E} = \frac{V}{L} \tag{1-17}$$

Substituting this expression into Ohm's law, Eq. (1-16), results in

$$J = \frac{\sigma}{L} V \tag{1-18}$$

From the definition of current density, Eq. (1-13),

$$J = \frac{I}{A} = \frac{\sigma}{L} V \tag{1-19}$$

After rearranging and introducing resistivity as the reciprocal of the conductivity, Eq. (1-19) becomes

$$V = \frac{\rho L}{A} I \tag{1-20}$$

The quantity $\rho L/A$ is known as the *resistance* of the conductor. Specifically, the resistance R is

$$R = \frac{\rho L}{A} \tag{1-21}$$

According to Eq. (1-21) the resistance of a wire depends not only upon the material of the wire, through its resistivity, but also upon its cross-sectional area and length. That is, a long thin wire has a greater resistance than a short thick wire of the same material. The unit of resistance is called the *ohm* and the commonly adopted symbol used to designate a resistance in ohms is the Greek letter omega, Ω. Equation (1-21) shows that resistivity is given in *ohm-meters* and, correspondingly, the units of conductivity are termed *reciprocal ohm-meters*. The reciprocal of resistance is *conductance*, which is measured in units of reciprocal ohms, often called *mhos*.

Finally, from Eq. (1-20), Ohm's law may be written

$$V = RI \tag{1-22}$$

This more familiar form, which is fundamental to circuit analysis, states that whenever a conductor of resistance R carries a current I, a potential difference V must be present across the ends of the conductor. Note that, according to Eq. (1-22), an ohm is equivalent to a volt per ampere.

1-4 Joule's law

The kinetic energy of the electrons in a conductor, which results from acceleration by the electric field, is dissipated in inelastic collisions within the conductor and converted to heat energy. Consequently the temperature of a conductor carrying a current must increase slightly, and it is apparent that electric power is expended in forcing a current through the resistance of the conductor.

In order to calculate the rate at which energy must be supplied to the conductor of Fig. 1-4, note that a charge dq goes through a potential difference V in moving from one end of the wire to the other. According to Eq. (1-6), the energy dW required is

$$dW = V \, dq \tag{1-23}$$

which, from the definition of current, Eq. (1-10), is

$$dW = VI \, dt \tag{1-24}$$

Therefore, the rate at which energy is converted to heat, that is, the power P, is

$$P = \frac{dW}{dt} = IV \tag{1-25}$$

This expression may be written in terms of the resistance of the conductor using Ohm's law. The result,

$$P = I^2 R \tag{1-26}$$

is known as *Joule's law*, after Sir James Prescott Joule, who discovered experimentally that the rate of development of heat in a resistance is proportional to the square of the current.

According to Joule's law, electric power is dissipated in a conductor whenever it carries an electric current. This effect is put to use in incandescent lamps, where a thin metal filament is heated to white heat by the current, and also in electric fuses, in which the conductor melts when the current exceeds a predetermined value. On the other hand, the size of wires, and therefore their resistance, is selected so that the power loss will be small and the temperature rise negligible when the wire is carrying less than the maximum design current. The joule heat in a conductor is commonly spoken of as the "*I*-squared-*R*" loss. Note that the unit of power, according to Eq. (1-25), is a joule per second, which is called a *watt*, in honor of James Watt, developer of the steam engine.

CIRCUIT ELEMENTS

1-5   Resistors

An electrical component very frequently used in electronic circuits is the *resistor,* which is a circuit element having a specified value of resistance. Resistance values commonly encountered range from a few ohms to thousands of ohms, or *kilohms* (abbreviated as kΩ), and even millions of ohms, or *megohms* (designated by MΩ). Lumped resistances that resistors introduce into a circuit are large compared with those of wires and contacts between wires. According to Ohm's law, a potential difference develops across the resistor as a result of current in it at the place in the circuit where the resistor is inserted. The conventional symbol for a resistor in a circuit diagram is a zigzag line, as illustrated in Fig. 1-5.

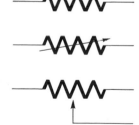

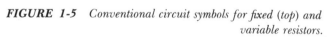

FIGURE 1-5   *Conventional circuit symbols for fixed (top) and variable resistors.*

Some resistors are constructed from a long, very fine wire wound on an insulating support. Resistance values can be increased by decreasing the cross-sectional area of the wire and by increasing its length, as Eq. (1-21) shows, and by selecting wire materials having a large resistivity (see Table 1-1). Such *wire-wound* resistors commonly employ metal-alloy wires which have resistivities relatively independent of temperature. Typical materials are manganin and constantan. Wire-wound resistors are used where it may be necessary to dissipate sufficient joule heat for the temperature of the resistor to rise significantly. The resistance of wire-wound resistors can be determined quite precisely by choosing the proper wire length, so wire-wound resistors are also useful in applications where accurate resistance values are desired.

Thin-film resistors are made by depositing a thin film of a metal on a cylindrical insulating support. High resistance values are a consequence of the thinness of the film. Because of the difficulty in producing uniform films, it is not possible to control resistance values as precisely as in the case of wire-wound resistors. However, thin-film resistors are free of troublesome inductance effects common in wire-wound units (Chap. 3), and this is important in high-frequency circuits. Thin-film resistors fabricated from nonmetallic materials, particularly finely divided carbon granules, are also common. Carbon itself has very high resistivity, as do the points of contact between the granules. In fact, it is possible to achieve such high resistance values with carbon granules that in many situations it is unnecessary to employ thin films at all and the resistance element is a simple rod of pressed carbon granules. Such units are known as *composition* resistors.

Both thin-film and composition resistors are provided with insulation and wire leads to facilitate inserting them into circuits. It is common practice to provide colored markings which denote the resistance value of each unit according to the universal *resistor color code* shown in Appendix 1. In addition, the physical size of the resistor is a rough indication of the maximum permissible power the unit is capable of dissipating without appreciable increase in temperature caused by joule heating. Thus, for example, common resistor power ratings are 1 watt, $1/2$ watt, and $1/4$ watt, although other values are used as well. Examples of typical thin-film and composition resistors are shown in Fig. 1-6.

It is often necessary to vary the resistance of a resistor while it is permanently connected in a circuit. Such *variable resistors* employ a mechanical slider or arm which rides over the resistance element, thus selecting the length of the element included in the circuit. Both wire-wound and composition resistance elements are commonly made circular so that the position of the slider may be adjusted by rotation of a shaft. The circuit symbols for variable resistors are of two types, as in Fig. 1-5, depending upon whether two or three terminals are provided for external connections. A variable resistor having two terminals is called a *rheostat,* while one with three is known as a *potentiometer.* Obviously, a potentiometer, with its terminals at each end of the resistance element and a third terminal attached to the slider, can be used as a rheostat if one of the resistance-element terminals is ignored.

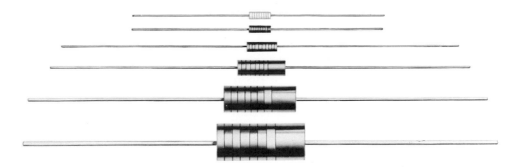

FIGURE 1-6 *Typical composition resistors. (Courtesy Allen-Bradley Co.)*

1-6 Batteries

According to Joule's law, electric energy is dissipated in any conductor when it carries a current. In simple dc circuits the source of this energy, which must be supplied in order to maintain the current, is often a chemical *battery*. Other sources of dc electric power will be considered in a later chapter. In a battery, chemical energy is converted into electric energy, and the chemical reactions maintain a potential difference between the battery terminals whether or not a current is present. This potential difference is commonly referred to as an *electromotive force*, abbreviated *emf*, in order to distinguish it from the potential difference which appears across a resistance in accordance with Ohm's law. As a battery continues to supply the energy necessary to maintain current in a circuit, the chemical constituents eventually become depleted and the battery is said to be *discharged*. Depending upon the particular chemical nature of the battery, it may be possible to *charge* it, that is, return it to its original chemical composition, by passing a current between its terminals in a direction opposed to the internal emf. The symbol for a battery in circuit diagrams, Fig. 1-7,

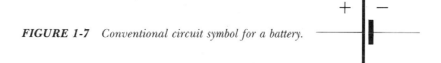

FIGURE 1-7 *Conventional circuit symbol for a battery.*

consists of a short heavy line parallel to a longer thin line. It is always assumed, if not explicitly indicated, that the longer line represents the higher, or positive, terminal of the internal emf. Since the internal emf is a potential difference, its unit is the volt.

The carbon-zinc battery is by far the most common, and least expensive, source of electrical energy. Although it is conventionally referred to as a *dry cell,* it actually consists of a moist paste of zinc chloride, ammonium chloride, and manganese dioxide (called the *electrolyte*) contained between a zinc electrode and a carbon electrode. The zinc and carbon electrodes serve as the terminals of the battery. The operation of such a cell is briefly as follows. At the zinc electrode, zinc atoms are dissolved into solution as doubly charged zinc ions. The zinc electrode becomes negatively charged because each zinc atom leaves behind two electrons. At the carbon electrode ammonium ions reacting with manganese dioxide withdraw electrons from the carbon, and thus it becomes charged positively. If the negative zinc electrode is connected externally through a circuit to the positive carbon electrode, electrons can flow between them to complete the chemical reaction.

Notice that in order for the chemical reaction to continue, zinc ions must move away from the negative electrode and the reaction products near the positive terminal must likewise move away from the carbon electrode. Thus, current is carried internally to the battery by means of ions moving in the electrolyte, and this is a source of internal resistance. Current in the internal resistance has the effect of reducing the terminal voltage of the battery. The terminal voltage of the dry cell slowly decreases with use as the internal resistance increases because of depletion of the manganese dioxide. The internal resistance eventually becomes so large that the battery is useless.

If the dry cell is left idle for some time before it is completely discharged, the internal resistance gradually reduces because of internal diffusion of the ions. On the other hand, if a dry cell is allowed to age for extended periods (more than one year) internal ionic diffusion increases the internal resistance so much that the cell becomes inoperative, even though it may never have been used. The emf of a freshly prepared dry cell is 1.5 volts. Higher voltages are conventionally obtained by connecting a number of individual units (Fig. 1-8); in fact the term *battery* originated from

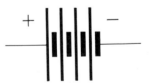

FIGURE 1-8   Four batteries connected in series.

just such assemblies. Dry-cell batteries of 1.5, 9, 22.5, 45, 67.5 and 90 volts are most commonly available.

The familiar lead-acid *storage battery* used in automobiles is an example of a battery that can be repeatedly recharged. The positive electrode of a fully charged storage battery is a porous coat of lead dioxide on a grid of metallic lead. The negative electrode is metallic lead, and both electrodes are immersed in a liquid sulfuric acid electrolyte at a specific gravity of about 1.3. During discharge the lead dioxide is converted to lead sulfate, which is poorly soluble and clings to the positive plate. This reaction withdraws electrons from the electrode, thus charging it positively. At the negative electrode, sulfate ions from solution produce lead sulfate and release electrons. Again the lead sulfate adheres to the electrode and at discharge both electrodes are nearly entirely converted to lead sulfate. The loss of sulfate ions from solution during discharge reduces the specific gravity to about 1.16, so that the condition of the battery may be determined by measuring the specific gravity of the electrolyte.

These chemical reactions are easily reversible, and current directed into the positive terminal acts to return the electrodes to their original chemical composition. Charging requires an external source to furnish electric energy, after which the battery again can supply energy during discharge. Thus, the storage battery may be said to store electric energy in chemical form. In addition, the internal resistance of the lead-acid battery is very low and the battery is capable of delivering currents of several hundred amperes for short times. The fully charged cell has an emf of about 2.1 volts, and commercial units are available as 6-, 12-, and 24-volt batteries. It is important to maintain an idle storage battery fully charged, for otherwise the electrodes slowly become converted to a sulfate which cannot be returned to the original chemical composition by a charging current. In this condition, the electric energy capacity of the battery is reduced.

The internal resistance of the recently developed *mercury battery* does not change appreciably during discharge. This means that the terminal voltage remains essentially constant throughout the useful life. It then falls precipitously when the battery is exhausted, as illustrated in Fig. 1-9. The constant-voltage charac-

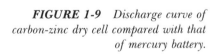

FIGURE 1-9 *Discharge curve of carbon-zinc dry cell compared with that of mercury battery.*

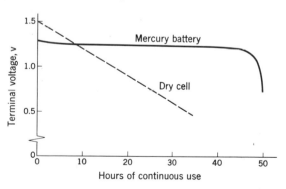

teristic of mercury batteries is important in those electronic applications where the proper operation of a circuit depends critically upon the battery voltage. Such situations are not uncommon in vacuum-tube and transistor circuits. In addition, the constant-voltage feature means that the mercury battery is useful as a voltage standard in electrical measurement circuits. The mercury battery has a zinc amalgam for one electrode and mercuric oxide and carbon for the other. The chemical reactions at the electrodes are somewhat similar to those of the dry cell, and the potential developed is 1.35 volts.

Other recent battery types include the *alkaline* battery and the *nickel-cadmium* battery. The alkaline battery is chemically quite similar to the dry cell, but has a strongly basic electrolyte between the electrodes. This, together with a modified electrode structure, lowers internal resistance, increases energy capacity, and improves shelf life. The nickel-cadmium battery can be repeatedly recharged like the lead storage battery, but is completely sealed, since gas evolution during charging acts as a self-regulating mechanism to prevent the buildup of a large gas pressure. This feature, and the fact that a liquid electrolyte is not required, compensates for the high cost of this battery. Typical modern batteries are illustrated in Fig. 1-10.

FIGURE 1-10 *Typical modern batteries. (Courtesy Union Carbide Co.)*

SIMPLE CIRCUITS

1-7   Series circuits

If several electric components, such as resistors, are connected so that the current is the same in every one, the components are said to be in a *series* circuit. Consider the simple series circuit comprising the battery and three resistors illustrated in Fig. 1-11a.

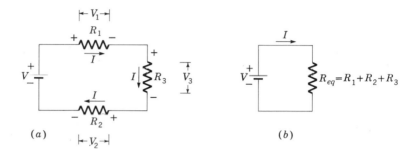

FIGURE 1-11   (a) *Simple series circuit, and* (b) *its equivalent.*

The current I results in a potential difference between the terminals of each resistor which is given by Ohm's law. That is,

$$V_1 = R_1I \qquad V_2 = R_2I \qquad \text{and} \qquad V_3 = R_3I \qquad (1\text{-}27)$$

Clearly, the sum of these voltages is equal to the battery emf (refer to Exercise 1-7), or

$$V = V_1 + V_2 + V_3 \qquad (1\text{-}28)$$

Equation (1-28) is a simple example of a principle of electronic circuits which is considered in greater detail in the next section. The equation states that the algebraic sum of the potential differences around any complete circuit is equal to zero. Note the polarity distinction between the potential difference at the terminals of a resistor compared with that of a source of emf such as a battery: the current direction is *into* the positive terminal of a resistance while it is *out of* the positive terminal of an emf source. Since, according to Fig. 1-4, the potential decreases in the direction of the current through a resistance, the potential difference is commonly referred to as the *IR drop* across the resistor.

If the *IR* drops of Eq. (1-27) are inserted into Eq. (1-28), the result is

$$V = IR_1 + IR_2 + IR_3 = I(R_1 + R_2 + R_3) \qquad (1\text{-}29)$$

Thus, the current in the series circuit is

$$I = \frac{V}{R_1 + R_2 + R_3} = \frac{V}{R_{eq}} \qquad (1\text{-}30)$$

where the equivalent resistance R_{eq} is defined as

$$R_{eq} = R_1 + R_2 + R_3 \qquad (1\text{-}31)$$

Evidently the equivalent resistance of any number of resistors connected in series equals the sum of their individual resistances. Insofar as the current is concerned, the circuit of Fig. 1-11b containing the one single resistor R_{eq} is equivalent to that of Fig. 1-11a, which has three resistors.

A useful circuit based on the series connection of resistors is the *potential divider,* Fig. 1-12, in which the junction between each

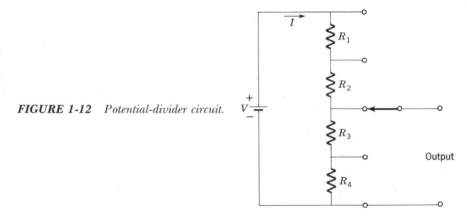

FIGURE 1-12 *Potential-divider circuit.*

pair of resistors is connected to a terminal of a *multiple-tap* selector switch. By positioning the switch on each of its various taps it is possible to present a given fraction of the battery voltage V at the output terminals. The division of the·potential V among the various taps depends upon the magnitudes of the resistances in the potential divider (see Exercise 1-9). Obviously, if the series resistors are replaced by a potentiometer, the output voltage may be set at any desired fraction of V. This is the principle of the volume control in radio and television receivers.

1-8 Parallel circuits

Another way of connecting electric components, such as resistors, is shown in Fig. 1-13. Here the potential difference across

FIGURE 1-13 *Parallel-connected resistors.*

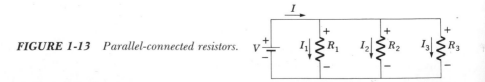

each resistor in the circuit is the same; this form of connection is called a *parallel circuit*. The current in each resistor is given by Ohm's law as

$$I_1 = \frac{V}{R_1} \qquad I_2 = \frac{V}{R_2} \qquad \text{and} \qquad I_3 = \frac{V}{R_3} \qquad (1\text{-}32)$$

In this case, the sum of the currents equals the battery current (Exercise 1-11), or

$$I = I_1 + I_2 + I_3 \qquad (1\text{-}33)$$

Substituting for the currents from Eq. (1-32), this becomes

$$I = \frac{V}{R_1} + \frac{V}{R_2} + \frac{V}{R_3} = V \left(\frac{1}{R_1} + \frac{1}{R_2} + \frac{1}{R_3} \right) \qquad (1\text{-}34)$$

Now, in order to determine the equivalent resistance for parallel resistors, we define R_{eq}, using Ohm's law, as

$$V = IR_{eq} \qquad (1\text{-}35)$$

Inserting Eq. (1-35) into Eq. (1-34)

$$I = \frac{V}{R_{eq}} = V \left(\frac{1}{R_1} + \frac{1}{R_2} + \frac{1}{R_3} \right) \qquad (1\text{-}36)$$

So that

$$\frac{1}{R_{eq}} = \frac{1}{R_1} + \frac{1}{R_2} + \frac{1}{R_3} \qquad (1\text{-}37)$$

which states that for any number of resistors in parallel the reciprocal of the equivalent resistance equals the sum of the reciprocals of the individual resistances.

Consider the special case of two resistors in parallel,

$$\frac{1}{R_{eq}} = \frac{1}{R_1} + \frac{1}{R_2} = \frac{R_2 + R_1}{R_1 R_2} \qquad (1\text{-}38)$$

so that

$$R_{eq} = \frac{R_1 R_2}{R_1 + R_2} = \frac{R_1}{1 + R_1/R_2} \qquad (1\text{-}39)$$

Suppose now R_1 is fixed and R_2 can take any value; according to Eq. (1-39) R_{eq} is always less than R_1. A similar argument applies if R_2 is fixed and R_1 can vary. This proves that the equivalent resistance of the combination of two resistors in parallel is smaller than that of either resistor. The same result holds for any number of parallel resistors.

1-9 Networks

Network connections of series and parallel resistances can be analyzed by successive applications of Eqs. (1-31) and (1-37). Consider, for example, the network of Fig. 1-14*a* with the resistance

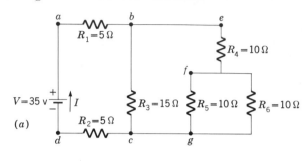

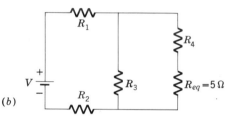

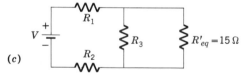

FIGURE 1-14   *Network reduction by series and parallel equivalents.*

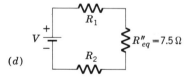

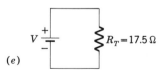

values as marked on the circuit diagram. The parallel combination of R_5 and R_6, each of which is 10 Ω, may be replaced by a 5-Ω resistor since according to Eq. (1-37)

$$\frac{1}{R_{eq}} = \frac{1}{R_5} + \frac{1}{R_6} = \frac{1}{10} + \frac{1}{10} = \frac{2}{10} \tag{1-40}$$

$$R_{eq} = 5 \ \Omega$$

Therefore the network is reduced to that shown in Fig. 1-14*b*. Next, the combination of R_{eq} with R_4 ($= 10 \ \Omega$) is, by Eq. (1-31),

$$R'_{eq} = R_{eq} + R_4 = 5 + 10 = 15 \ \Omega \qquad (1\text{-}41)$$

and the network is now Fig. 1-14*c*. R'_{eq} and R_3 are in parallel, so that their equivalent is

$$R''_{eq} = \frac{R'_{eq}R_3}{R'_{eq} + R_3} = \frac{15 \times 15}{15 + 15} = \frac{225}{30} = 7.5 \ \Omega \qquad (1\text{-}42)$$

Lastly, the series combination of R''_{eq}, R_1, and R_2 is simply

$$R_T = R''_{eq} + R_1 + R_2 = 7.5 + 5 + 5 = 17.5 \ \Omega \qquad (1\text{-}43)$$

and the entire network of Fig. 1-14*a* may now be replaced by its simple equivalent, Fig. 1-14*e*, where R_T represents the resistance of the entire network. The current in the battery is therefore

$$I = \frac{V}{R_T} = \frac{35}{17.5} = 2 \text{ amp} \qquad (1\text{-}44)$$

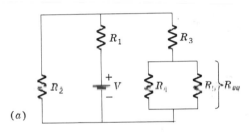

(a)

FIGURE 1-15 *Second example of network reduction by series and parallel equivalents.*

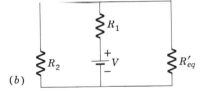

(b)

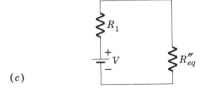

(c)

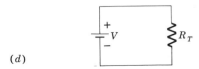

(d)

Suppose it is desired to determine the current I_3 in R_3. This is accomplished by first calculating the potential difference V_3 between points b and c in the circuit diagram. The IR drop across R_1 is $IR_1 = 2 \times 5 = 10$ volts, and a similar value applies to the IR drop across R_2. According to Eq. (1-28)

$$V = V_1 + V_3 + V_2 \tag{1-45}$$

Thus

$$V_3 = V - V_1 - V_2 = 35 - 10 - 10 = 15 \text{ volts} \tag{1-46}$$

The current in R_3 is therefore

$$I_3 = \frac{V_3}{R_3} = \frac{15}{15} = 1 \text{ amp} \tag{1-47}$$

By similar reasoning it is possible to determine the current in each resistor (see Exercise 1-13).

As a second example, note the network reduction illustrated in Fig. 1-15a to d. Resistors R_4 and R_5 are in parallel and their equivalent in combination with R_3 results in R'_{eq}. Using the definition of parallel resistors, R_2 and R'_{eq} are seen to be in parallel and therefore may be replaced by R''_{eq}. Finally, R_T is simply the sum of R''_{eq} and R_1. Again, the current in each resistor may be determined by successive application of Eq. (1-28).

CIRCUIT ANALYSIS

1-10   Kirchhoff's rules

It is not possible to reduce many of the networks important in electronics to simple series-parallel combinations, so that more powerful analytical methods must be used. Two simple extensions of Eqs. (1-28) and (1-33), known as *Kirchhoff's rules*, are most helpful in this connection. Consider first the simple parallel circuit, Fig. 1-13, redrawn as in Fig. 1-16 to illustrate the idea of a *branch point*, or *node*, of a circuit. A node is the point at which three (or

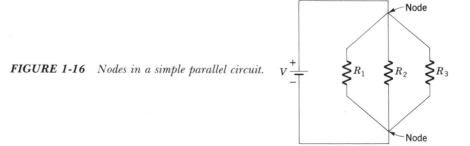

FIGURE 1-16   *Nodes in a simple parallel circuit.*

more) conductors are joined. Kirchhoff's first rule is that the algebraic sum of the currents at any node is zero. Symbolically

$$\Sigma I = 0 \tag{1-48}$$

Note that Eq. (1-48) is essentially a statement of continuity of current; it may also be looked upon as a result of the conservation of electric charge.

Kirchhoff's second rule has already been applied implicitly in using Eq. (1-28) to calculate I_3 in Fig. 1-14a. It states that the algebraic sum of the potential differences around any complete loop of a network is zero. Symbolically

$$\Sigma V = 0 \tag{1-49}$$

A loop of a network is understood to be any closed path such as $abcda$ in Fig. 1-14a which returns to the same point. Other examples of complete loops in the same network are $befgcb$ and $daefgd$. Equation (1-49) is a consequence of the conservation of energy, as illustrated in Exercise 1-7.

In applying Kirchhoff's rules to any network the first step is to assign a current of arbitrary direction to each of the resistances in the network. The polarity of the potential difference across each resistor is then marked on the circuit diagram using the convention already noted that the current enters the positive terminal of a resistance. The polarity of emf sources are, of course, specified in advance from the circuit diagram itself. Kirchhoff's rules are then applied to the various nodes and circuit loops to obtain a sufficient number of simultaneous equations to solve for the total number of unknown currents.

It is true that if a network contains m nodes and n unknown currents there are $m - 1$ independent equations which result from Eq. (1-48). Similarly, there are $n - (m - 1) = n - m + 1$ independent equations derived from Eq. (1-49). The total number of independent equations obtained from Kirchhoff's rules applied to any network is therefore $(m - 1) + n - (m - 1) = n$. This is just the number of unknown currents and the network solution is therefore completely determined. It is generally possible to write down more node and loop equations than are needed but only n of them are truly independent.

The solution of these independent equations often results in certain of the currents being negative. This means that the original arbitrarily assigned current direction is, in fact, incorrect and the current is actually in the opposite direction. Thus, it is not necessary to know the true current direction in advance. Once the various currents have been calculated, the IR drops in any portion of the circuit are determined using Ohm's law.

The technique of applying Kirchhoff's rules to a network can best be illustrated with a few examples. Consider first the simple parallel-resistor circuit of Fig. 1-17. The current direction in

each resistor has been arbitrarily selected and the polarity of the
IR drops marked in accordance with these assigned directions.
Note that this network has only two nodes, one at *b* and the other

FIGURE 1-17

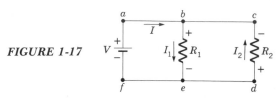

at *e*.   Therefore, there is only $2 - 1 = 1$ independent node equation.   Considering the branch point at *b*, Eq. (1-48) yields

$$I - I_1 + I_2 = 0 \qquad (1\text{-}50)$$

Notice at branch point *e* the current equation is

$$-I + I_1 - I_2 = 0 \qquad (1\text{-}51)$$

Clearly Eq. (1-51) is simply the negative of (1-50) and the two relations are therefore not independent.   Either equation may be used
in the solution of the network.

Consider now the loop *abef*.   According to Eq. (1-49)

$$V - I_1 R_1 = 0 \qquad (1\text{-}52)$$

Similarly, around the loop *abcdef*

$$V + I_2 R_2 = 0 \qquad (1\text{-}53)$$

Since there are three unknown currents, there must be $3 - 2 +
1 = 2$ independent loop equations and these are (1-52) and (1-53).
Note, however, that around loop *bcde*

$$I_1 R_1 + I_2 R_2 = 0 \qquad (1\text{-}54)$$

This is not an independent relation, as may be shown by subtracting Eq. (1-52) from (1-53).   The result is Eq. (1-54).   Thus these
three loop equations are not independent, and any two may be
used in solving the network.

Choose Eqs. (1-50), (1-52), and (1-54) as the three independent
equations to solve for the three unknown currents.   The solution is accomplished by first solving Eq. (1-52) for I_1,

$$I_1 = \frac{V}{R_1} \qquad (1\text{-}55)$$

Next, I_2 is determined from (1-54),

$$I_2 = -\frac{I_1 R_1}{R_2} \qquad (1\text{-}56)$$

Substituting (1-56) into (1-50),

$$I - I_1 - \frac{I_1 R_1}{R_2} = 0 \qquad (1\text{-}57)$$

Substituting from (1-55) for I_1,

$$I - \frac{V}{R_1} - \frac{VR_1}{R_1R_2} = I - V\left(\frac{1}{R_1} + \frac{1}{R_2}\right) = 0 \qquad (1\text{-}58)$$

The current I is therefore

$$I = V\left(\frac{1}{R_1} + \frac{1}{R_2}\right) \qquad (1\text{-}59)$$

which is quite equivalent to the solution corresponding to Eq. (1-34) arrived at by considering parallel resistors.

Finally, I_2 is determined by substituting for I_1 in Eq. (1-56),

$$I_2 = -\frac{VR_1}{R_1R_2} \qquad (1\text{-}60)$$

or

$$I_2 = -\frac{V}{R_2} \qquad (1\text{-}61)$$

According to the minus sign in Eq. (1-61), this current is actually in the opposite direction to that assumed in Fig. 1-17. Correspondingly, the IR drop across R_2 has the opposite polarity from that shown on the circuit diagram.

More complicated networks require more than three equations, and it is usually desirable to employ the standard method of determinants to solve the set of simultaneous equations. This technique, illustrated in the following section, has the considerable advantage that it is possible to solve directly for only those currents that are of interest. Often, only one or two of the currents in a network are of direct concern, and in this case a complete solution for all the unknowns is superfluous.

1-11 Wheatstone bridge

In this section Kirchhoff's rules are used to analyze the *Wheatstone bridge* circuit illustrated in Fig. 1-18. This extremely useful circuit was developed in 1843 by Charles Wheatstone and is widely used in electrical measurements to determine values of unknown resistances. The manner in which it is used may be understood from an analysis of the circuit. According to Kirchhoff's rule for branch points a, b, and d,

$$I - I_1 - I_2 = 0$$

$$I_1 - I_3 + I_5 = 0 \qquad (1\text{-}62)$$

$$I_3 + I_4 - I = 0$$

Because there are four branch points in the Wheatstone bridge circuit, these three current equations are independent, so the fourth one, which could be written for branch point c, is not used.

Applying Kirchhoff's rule to loops $abdefa$, $acba$, and $bcdb$, the equations are

$$-I_1R_1 - I_3R_3 + V = 0$$

$$-I_2R_2 - I_5R_5 + I_1R_1 = 0 \qquad\qquad (1\text{-}63)$$

$$I_5R_5 - I_4R_4 + I_3R_3 = 0$$

Note carefully the indicated polarities of the various IR drops as they are encountered in traversing each loop. Since there are six

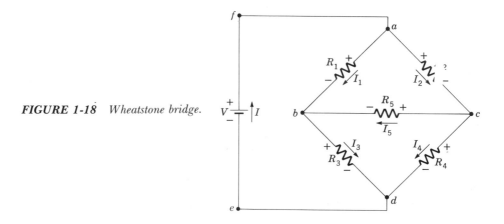

FIGURE 1-18 *Wheatstone bridge.*

unknown currents, $6 - 4 + 1 = 3$ loop equations are needed here and any others are redundant.

Equations (1-62) and (1-63) are six equations in six unknowns. Therefore, in applying the method of determinants to these simultaneous equations it is necessary to evaluate two sixth-order determinants in calculating each current. The total solution involves seven different such determinants. While the evaluation of a sixth-order determinant is straightforward and a number of standard approaches exist to reduce the order before final evaluation, the complete solution of seven sixth-order determinants is quite laborious. Therefore, although the solution to the set of Eqs. (1-62) and (1-63) is in principle accomplished, it is useful to seek alternative methods.

The analysis of complex networks can usually be simplified by the use of *loop currents*. This technique, known as *Maxwell's method*, after James Clerk Maxwell, in effect applies both Kirchhoff's rules simultaneously and thereby reduces the number of simultaneous equations needed. The loop currents are drawn around any complete loop as the three illustrated for the case of the Wheatstone bridge in Fig. 1-19. After the polarity of the IR drops are indicated in accordance with the current directions, the usual voltage equations around each loop are written. Thus, with reference to Fig. 1-19

$$V - R_1(I_a - I_b) - R_3(I_a - I_c) = 0$$
$$-R_2I_b - R_5(I_b - I_c) + R_1(I_a - I_b) = 0 \qquad (1\text{-}64)$$
$$R_3(I_c - I_a) + R_5(I_c - I_b) + R_4I_c = 0$$

Here again, note the polarity of the IR drops and the current directions. Upon rearranging

$$-(R_1 + R_3)I_a + R_1I_b + R_3I_c = -V$$
$$R_1I_a - (R_1 + R_2 + R_5)I_b + R_5I_c = 0 \qquad (1\text{-}65)$$
$$-R_3I_a - R_5I_b + (R_3 + R_4 + R_5)I_c = 0$$

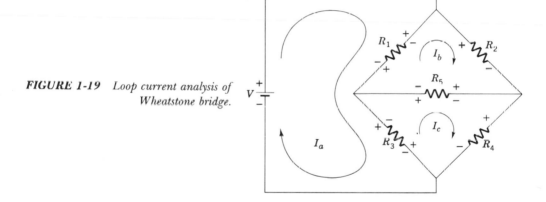

FIGURE 1-19   *Loop current analysis of Wheatstone bridge.*

The solution of Eqs. (1-65) for any current, say I_b, using determinants is found by forming a ratio in which the denominator is the determinant of the coefficients of the currents and the numerator is a similar determinant with the coefficients of the unknown current replaced by the right side of the equation. That is, the solution for I_b is

$$I_b = \frac{\begin{vmatrix} -(R_1 + R_3) & -V & R_3 \\ R_1 & 0 & R_5 \\ -R_3 & 0 & R_3 + R_4 + R_5 \end{vmatrix}}{\begin{vmatrix} -(R_1 + R_3) & R_1 & R_3 \\ R_1 & -(R_1 + R_2 + R_5) & R_5 \\ -R_3 & -R_5 & R_3 + R_4 + R_5 \end{vmatrix}}$$

$$= \frac{VR_5R_3 + VR_1(R_3 + R_4 + R_5)}{\Delta} \qquad (1\text{-}66)$$

where Δ signifies the denominator. Similarly, I_c is

$$I_c = \frac{\begin{vmatrix} -(R_1 + R_3) & R_1 & -V \\ R_1 & -(R_1 + R_2 + R_5) & 0 \\ -R_3 & -R_5 & 0 \end{vmatrix}}{\Delta}$$

$$= \frac{VR_1R_5 + VR_3(R_1 + R_2 + R_5)}{\Delta} \tag{1-67}$$

Now, the current through R_5, which in Fig. 1-18 is labeled I_5, is

$$I_5 = I_b - I_c$$

$$= \frac{V}{\Delta} (R_5R_3 + R_1R_3 + R_1R_4 + R_1R_5 - R_1R_5 - R_1R_3$$

$$- R_2R_3 - R_5R_3) \tag{1-68}$$

$$I_5 = \frac{V}{\Delta} (R_1R_4 - R_2R_3)$$

Equation (1-68) is a most important relation for the Wheatstone bridge. Note that if

$$R_1R_4 = R_2R_3$$

or

$$\frac{R_1}{R_2} = \frac{R_3}{R_4} \tag{1-69}$$

then I_5 is zero, independent of the applied voltage. If the resistances in the arms of the bridge obey the ratios indicated in Eq. (1-69), the bridge is said to be *balanced*. Thus, for example, if R_1, R_2, and R_3 are known resistances and I_5 is zero, the value of R_4 may be immediately calculated from the condition for balance, Eq. (1-69).

In the common version of a Wheatstone bridge, resistances R_1 and R_2 are connected to a switch to give decade values of the ratio R_2/R_1, and R_3 is a continuously variable calibrated resistor. Once the bridge is balanced by adjusting R_3, the value of the unknown R_4 is simply $(R_2/R_1)R_3$. The decade values of the ratio (R_2/R_1) may range from 10^{-3}, 10^{-2}, and 10^{-1} to 1, 10, 10^2, and 10^3, so that a very wide range of resistance values can be measured. In practice, a current-indicating instrument is connected in the position of R_5 to indicate balance. Note that this meter need not be calibrated, since it is only used to indicate the balance condition, that is, a zero current.

Equation (1-68) is an example of a case in which useful information concerning the circuit is derived without carrying through the complete solution for all currents. It is often possible to draw the loop currents in such a way that only one current need be determined (see Exercise 1-20). Actually, the facility of choosing loop currents that will minimize the effort required to solve any given network is only attained with experience. The techniques discussed above are sufficiently powerful to analyze all of the circuits studied in this book.

1-12   Potentiometer circuit

A very accurate way to compare two potential differences uses the *potentiometer circuit*, a simple version of which is illustrated in Fig. 1-20. Here an accurately variable precision potentiometer

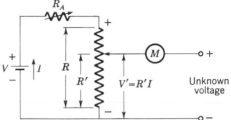

FIGURE 1-20   Simple potentiometer circuit for measuring unknown voltage.

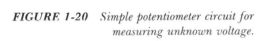

is connected in series with a variable resistance and a battery. The slider of the precision resistor is connected to one external terminal through a current-indicating meter and one end of the resistor is connected to the other output terminal. Suppose a specific value of the current $I = V/(R + R_A)$ is selected by adjusting the variable resistor R_A. Then, the potential V' of the slider on R is simply IR', where R' is the resistance between the end of the resistor and the slider. Since I and R are known, the position of the slider can be calibrated in terms of potential difference in volts. If now an unknown voltage, as for example a battery, is connected to the output terminals, and the slider is adjusted until the current indicated by the meter M is zero, the value of the unknown voltage is equal to IR'.

The potentiometer is a comparison measuring device which determines the value of the unknown potential difference in terms of the voltage of a standard battery. To show how this is accomplished, refer to the practical circuit in Fig. 1-21. Here, V_S is the emf of a standard such as a mercury battery or, more usually, a *Weston cell*, which is a special battery with an extremely stable emf. Suppose now R_A is adjusted until the meter M_1 indicates zero current. This means that

$$IR_S = V_S \qquad\qquad (1\text{-}70)$$

In this circuit the precision variable resistance is composed of nine identical series resistors, each of value R, and a variable resistance R'. The current in the output circuit, indicated by M_2, is adjusted

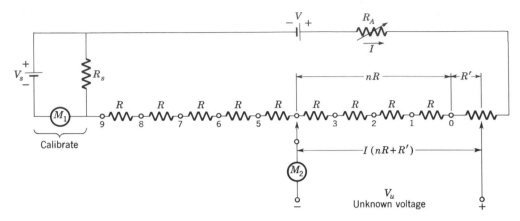

FIGURE 1-21   *Practical potentiometer circuit.*

to zero with the unknown voltage source V_u connected to the output terminals. This is done by selecting the proper switch position for the switch and the slider. When the current in M_2 is zero

$$V_u = I(nR + R') \tag{1-71}$$

where n is the tap number of the selector switch. Substituting
for I in Eq. (1-71) from Eq. (1-70)

$$V_u = V_S \frac{nR + R'}{R_S} \tag{1-72}$$

According to this expression, the unknown voltage is determined
entirely in terms of the standard emf and the resistances of the
potentiometer circuit. Rearranging (1-72)

$$\frac{V_u}{V_S} = \frac{nR + R'}{R_S} \tag{1-73}$$

which demonstrates directly how the unknown and standard voltages are compared in terms of resistances. Note, particularly,
that neither the current I nor the battery voltage V need be known.
   The accuracy of the potentiometer circuit depends upon the
precision with which the various resistors are constructed and the
mechanical stability of the slider on the variable resistance. Accuracy can be improved by combining fixed resistors selected by a
tap switch together with the continuously variable resistor, as in
Fig. 1-21. This is so because the potential drop across the variable resistor is only 1/10 of that, say, in the circuit of Fig. 1-20 and
voltage errors caused by mechanical irregularities in the slider are
reduced by the same factor. The variable resistor is ordinarily
a wire of uniform resistance wound in the form of a helix. The
moving slider is attached to a shaft so that the slider travels along
the helix as the shaft is rotated.
   A great virtue of the potentiometer circuit is that no current
flows in the measuring circuit at balance. This means that the

unknown potential is measured under effectively open-circuit conditions and the measurement is unperturbed by internal IR drops. Actually, a small current may be present, depending upon the sensitivity of the null indicator, and sensitive electronic amplifiers are often used in place of the meter to minimize the null current.

EQUIVALENT CIRCUITS

1-13 Thévenin's theorem

Many times the analysis of electronic circuits is facilitated by replacing all or part of a network by an *equivalent circuit* which, for certain purposes, has the same characteristics as the original. An example of this possibility has already been discussed in connection with series and parallel combination of resistors. There, an entire network of resistances was replaced by a single equivalent resistance in order to calculate the current. In other situations, particularly in connection with vacuum-tube and transistor circuits, equivalent circuits may be used to represent the behavior of electronic devices. By replacing, say, a vacuum tube with its equivalent circuit it becomes possible to determine the electric characteristics of the device by circuit analysis.

One of the most useful equivalent circuits is the one that results from *Thévenin's theorem*, which shows how to replace any network of resistors and batteries by a single series combination of a resistor and a battery. Consider, for example, the current in the

FIGURE 1-22

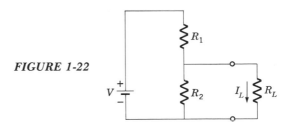

load resistor R_L connected to the simple circuit of Fig. 1-22. Using Kirchhoff's rules, I_L is (Exercise 1-25)

$$I_L = V \frac{R_2}{R_1 R_2 + R_L(R_1 + R_2)} \tag{1-74}$$

After dividing through by $R_1 + R_2$, Eq. (1-74) can be put in the form

$$I_L = \frac{V R_2/(R_1 + R_2)}{R_L + R_1 R_2/(R_1 + R_2)} \tag{1-75}$$

If now an equivalent battery V_{eq} is defined as

$$V_{eq} = \frac{VR_2}{R_1 + R_2} \qquad (1\text{-}76)$$

and an equivalent resistor R_{eq} is defined as

$$R_{eq} = \frac{R_1 R_2}{R_1 + R_2} \qquad (1\text{-}77)$$

then Eq. (1-75) becomes

$$I_L = \frac{V_{eq}}{R_L + R_{eq}} \qquad (1\text{-}78)$$

This equation also represents the current through R_L in the simple series circuit shown in Fig. 1-23. Therefore, insofar as the current through the output load resistor is concerned, the circuit of Fig. 1-23 is entirely equivalent to the circuit of Fig. 1-22 and it is called the *Thévenin equivalent circuit.*

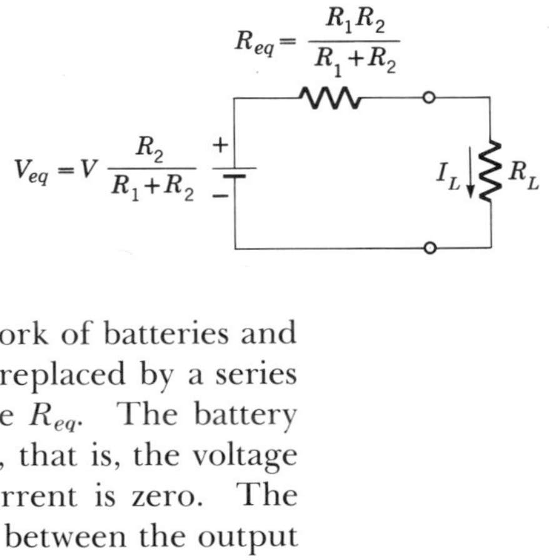

FIGURE 1-23 *Thévenin equivalent of circuit in Fig. 1-22.*

$$R_{eq} = \frac{R_1 R_2}{R_1 + R_2}$$

$$V_{eq} = V \frac{R_2}{R_1 + R_2}$$

According to Thévenin's theorem any network of batteries and resistors having two output terminals can be replaced by a series combination of a battery V_{eq} and a resistance R_{eq}. The battery V_{eq} is the open-circuit voltage of the network, that is, the voltage at the output terminals when the output current is zero. The resistance R_{eq} is the resistance of the network between the output terminals with the batteries of the network short-circuited or replaced by a zero resistance (or by their internal resistances, if these are appreciable).

Note that according to the previous paragraph the equivalent battery for the circuit of Fig. 1-22 is the IR drop across R_2. Since the current in R_2 is $V/(R_1 + R_2)$ when the output current $I_L = 0$, Eq. (1-76) for V_{eq} follows directly. Similarly, R_{eq} is the parallel combination of R_1 and R_2 when the battery V is replaced with a zero resistance, and this is precisely Eq. (1-77). Note that the output voltage, that is, the voltage across R_L, is, from Eq. (1-78),

$$V_L = I_L R_L = \frac{V_{eq} R_L}{R_L + R_{eq}} = \frac{V_{eq}}{1 + R_{eq}/R_L} \qquad (1\text{-}79)$$

This shows that if R_L is large compared with R_{eq}, the output voltage is essentially equal to V_{eq}.

To illustrate the power of the equivalent-circuit method, consider the Wheatstone-bridge circuit of Fig. 1-24a. The current through R_5 is determined by first replacing the remainder of the circuit with its Thévenin equivalent. Replacing the battery with a short circuit puts R_3 in parallel with R_1 and this combination in series with the parallel combination of R_2 and R_4 across the out-

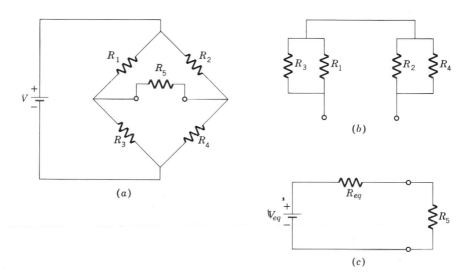

(a)

(b)

(c)

FIGURE 1-24   (a) *Conventional Wheatstone bridge circuit, (b) after replacing battery with a short circuit in order to calculate R_{eq}, (c) the Thévenin equivalent.*

put terminals, as illustrated in Fig. 1-24b. Therefore, R_{eq} in the equivalent circuit, Fig. 1-24c, is

$$R_{eq} = \frac{R_1 R_3}{R_1 + R_3} + \frac{R_2 R_4}{R_2 + R_4} \tag{1-80}$$

The open-circuit voltage at the output terminals is simply the po-tential difference between the junction of R_1 and R_3 and the junc-tion of R_2 and R_4. This potential difference is found by subtracting the IR drop across R_2 from the IR drop across R_1. Therefore the equivalent battery is

$$V_{eq} = \frac{V R_1}{R_1 + R_3} - \frac{V R_2}{R_2 + R_4} \tag{1-81}$$

Finally, according to the equivalent circuit, Fig. 1-24c, the current through I_5 is

$$I_5 = \frac{V_{eq}}{R_{eq} + R_5} \tag{1-82}$$

The ease and rapidity with which this result is obtained should be compared with that necessary using Kirchhoff's rules. The equivalence of Eq. (1-82) with Eq. (1-68) is proved by evaluating the determinant in the denominator of (1-68) in Exercise 1-26.

1-14   Norton's theorem

A second form of equivalent circuit useful in situations as, for example, transistor circuits where current sources, rather than emfs, are of major interest is one given by *Norton's theorem.* Norton's theorem states that any network of batteries and resistors having two output terminals can be replaced by a parallel combination of a current source I_{eq} and a resistance R_{eq}.   The current source I_{eq} is the short-circuit current in the output terminals of a circuit, that is, the load current when the load resistance is zero.   The resistance R_{eq} is the same as for Thévenin's theorem.

Norton's equivalent circuit is shown in Fig. 1-25, where the tri-

FIGURE 1-25   *Norton equivalent circuit.*

angle represents the current source I_{eq}.   No simple electric component acts as a current source the way a battery acts as a voltage source.   Nevertheless, the idea of a current source is conceptually very useful in circuit analysis.   Note that in Fig. 1-25 the voltage across the load resistor R_L is simply

$$V_L = I_{eq} \frac{R_{eq}R_L}{R_{eq} + R_L} \qquad (1\text{-}83)$$

and the output current in R_L is

$$I_L = \frac{V_L}{R_L} = I_{eq} \frac{R_{eq}}{R_{eq} + R_L} = \frac{I_{eq}}{1 + R_L/R_{eq}} \qquad (1\text{-}84)$$

According to Eq. (1-84), if R_L is small compared with R_{eq}, the output load current is approximately equal to I_{eq}.   This corresponds to Eq. (1-79) for the Thévenin equivalent circuit.

Since it is possible to represent any network by either the Thévenin or the Norton equivalent circuit, it must be possible to convert from one equivalent circuit to the other.   Referring to Fig. 1-26*a* and *b*, the short-circuit current through the load is V_{eq}/R_{eq} for the Thévenin equivalent circuit, and, according to Eq. (1-84), is equal to I_{eq} for the Norton equivalent circuit.   For both circuits to represent the same network, it must be true that

$$I_{eq} = \frac{V_{eq}}{R_{eq}} \qquad (1\text{-}85)$$

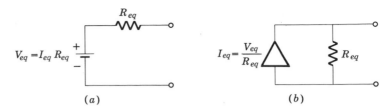

(a) (b)

FIGURE 1-26 *Relationship between (a) Thévenin equivalent circuit and (b) Norton equivalent circuit.*

Thus, it is a simple matter to convert from one equivalent circuit to another. Which circuit is used to represent any given network is entirely a matter of choice and convenience.

1-15 Maximum power transfer

In many electronic circuits, such as a radio transmitter or phonograph amplifier, it is important to transfer efficiently the maximum amount of electric power from the circuit to the load, which may be an antenna or loudspeaker. Therefore, it is of interest to determine circuit conditions for which it is possible to achieve the maximum power transfer. Suppose the network is represented by its Thévenin equivalent circuit shown in Fig. 1-27 and that the

FIGURE 1-27 *Thévenin's equivalent circuit used to examine maximum power transfer to load resistance R_L.*

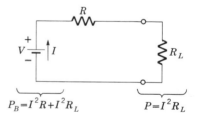

load connected to the output terminals is represented by the resistance R_L. The subscripts on the equivalent battery and equivalent resistance have been eliminated for convenience.

According to Joule's law, the power delivered to the load resistance is

$$P = I^2 R_L = \left(\frac{V}{R + R_L}\right)^2 R_L$$

$$= \frac{V^2/R_L}{(1 + R/R_L)^2} \tag{1-86}$$

The numerator of (1-86) is the power that the battery V would generate in the load resistance if the internal resistance R were equal to zero. That is, it is the maximum power P_M. Thus

$$P = \frac{P_M}{(1 + R/R_L)^2} \tag{1-87}$$

Equation (1-87) shows that P is smaller than P_M. This is so because of the power expended in the internal resistance of the network. Note that the power in the load is zero if the load resistance is very small and is also zero when the load resistance is very large. Thus, there must be an optimum load resistance for which the power in R_L is a maximum.

To find the condition for *maximum power transfer*, differentiate Eq. (1-86) with respect to R_L and equate the result to zero,

$$\frac{dP_L}{dR_L} = \frac{V^2}{R_L}\frac{2R/R_L^2}{(1 + R/R_L)^3} + \frac{V^2}{(1 + R/R_L)^2}\frac{-1}{R_L^2} = 0 \tag{1-88}$$

$$\frac{2R}{R_L} = 1 + \frac{R}{R_L}$$

so that

$$R_L = R \tag{1-89}$$

This means that maximum power is delivered to the load when the load resistance is equal to the internal resistance of the network delivering the power. When the load resistance is equal to the internal resistance of the network, the load is said to be *matched* to the circuit. Note that with a matched load the ratio of the maximum power transferred to the power taken from the battery, $I^2R + I^2R_L$, is

$$\frac{P_{max}}{P_B} = \frac{I^2R_L}{I^2R_L + I^2R_L} = \frac{1}{2} \tag{1-90}$$

which means that half of the power is lost in the internal resistance of the network and that the maximum efficiency is therefore 50 percent.

Since the equivalent circuit of Fig. 1-27 represents any network, the results represented by Eqs. (1-89) and (1-90) apply equally well to all circuits. The use of the equivalent-circuit concept in this connection has thus made it possible to prove a very general result quite easily. Finally, the maximum power transferred should not be confused with the maximum power P_M which can be dissipated in a given resistor. The former is the maximum power that a practical network can deliver to any load, while the latter is simply the power that can be dissipated in a given fixed load by a network with zero internal resistance.

ELECTRICAL MEASUREMENTS

1-16   D'Arsonval meter

By far the most common design for electric current–measuring instruments is the *d'Arsonval meter,* named after its inventor.   A multiturn coil of fine wire wound on an aluminum frame is pivoted between the poles of a horseshoe permanent magnet (Fig. 1-28*a*).

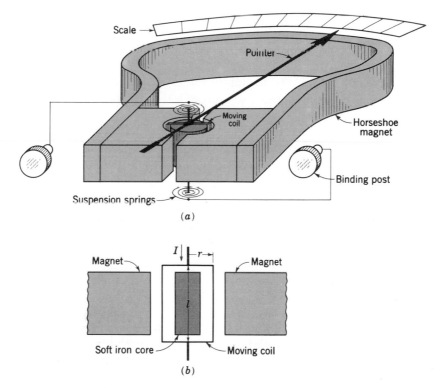

FIGURE 1-28   (*a*) *Sketch of the essential features of d'Arsonval meter, and* (*b*) *a cross section of moving coil and magnet structure.*

Two fine spiral springs serve to position the coil and to carry the current to be measured.   A pointer attached to the coil indicates the current on a scale as the coil rotates in response to the inter-action between the current in the coil and the magnetic field of the magnet.   A soft iron pole piece is fitted between the poles of the magnet so that the sides of the coil move in a radially directed field.

In considering the torque on a one-turn coil (Fig. 1-28*b*) note that the force on the left-hand conductor is IlB (refer to Chap. 2). This force is directed out of the plane of the figure.   A similar force, oppositely directed, is exerted on the right-hand conductor. Therefore, the mechanical torque on the coil caused by the current I is simply $IlB \times 2r = IBA$, where A is the area of the coil. For a coil of n turns the total torque is n times this value.

The torque of restitution exerted by the two spiral springs is proportional to the angular deflection θ and may be written $K\theta$, where K is the spring constant. Equating this to the torque on the coil,

$$nIBA = K\theta \tag{1-91}$$

from which

$$\theta = \frac{nAB}{K} I \tag{1-92}$$

which means that the deflection of the pointer is directly proportional to the current. According to Eq. (1-92) the sensitivity, that is, the deflection for a given current, of a d'Arsonval meter is improved by increasing the magnetic field of the magnet, the coil area, and the number of turns on the coil, or by decreasing the torque constant of the springs.

The size of the coil and springs is dictated by mechanical ruggedness, since a large coil suspended by weak springs is subject to damage from mechanical shock and vibration. Also, it is not desirable to increase n inordinately in an effort to improve sensitivity, since the resistance of the coil is increased thereby. This may adversely affect the operation of the meter, as explained in a later section. The magnetic field is limited to that available from conventional permanent magnets. In spite of these practical limitations, common d'Arsonval meters have full-scale deflections for currents as small as 10^{-3} amp (1 *milliampere*, abbreviated ma), or even 50×10^{-6} amp (50 *microamperes*, abbreviated μa). Laboratory instruments, which may be shock-mounted and therefore designed for maximum sensitivity, are capable of measuring 10×10^{-12} amp, or 10 *picoamperes*.

1-17 Ammeters and voltmeters

The d'Arsonval meter is a current-sensitive device, or *ammeter*. It is often convenient to change the current required for full-scale deflection in order to increase the range of currents over which the meter is useful. This is accomplished by *shunting* a portion of the current around the ammeter with a parallel resistance, as diagramed in Fig. 1-29. Note that the internal resistance of the ammeter's coil R_m is indicated explicitly. Following Kirchhoff's rules, $I = I_m + I_s$ and $I_m R_m = I_s R_s$, so that the current to be determined is

$$I = I_m + \frac{I_m R_m}{R_s} = I_m \left(1 + \frac{R_m}{R_s}\right) \tag{1-93}$$

If, for example, the shunt resistance is one-ninth of the meter resistance, $1 + R_m/R_s = 10$ and the full-scale deflection is extended to ten times the inherent sensitivity of the meter.

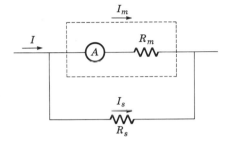

FIGURE 1-29   *Increasing range of an ammeter by using shunt resistor in parallel with meter resistance.*

It is always necessary to consider the effect of the meter resistance on the circuit. Suppose it is desired to measure the current in R_L of the Thévenin equivalent circuit of Fig. 1-30 using an

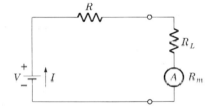

FIGURE 1-30   *Effect of ammeter resistance on current in circuit.*

ammeter having an internal resistance of R_m. With the ammeter connected into the circuit the current is

$$I = \frac{V}{R + R_L + R_m} \tag{1-94}$$

Unless $R_m \ll R + R_L$, the current indicated by the ammeter is different from the true current. For this reason it is always desirable that the internal resistance of an ammeter be small. On the other hand, in circumstances where the internal resistance may not be small compared with circuit resistances, it is possible to correct for the disturbing influence of the meter resistance and thus determine the true current (see Exercise 1-30).

Since the full-scale deflection of an ammeter may be attributed to the voltage $V_m = R_m I$ across the meter resistance R_m, a d'Arsonval meter also is a *voltmeter*. Here again it is useful to change the range of any given voltmeter by introducing a resistance in series with the meter. Referring to the circuit of Fig. 1-31, the voltage to be measured is

$$V = I_m(R_m + R_s) \tag{1-95}$$

and it is obvious that the series resistance R_s increases the maxi-

mum full-scale voltage of a given meter. It is common practice
to provide several such series resistance *multipliers* to allow a given
meter to be used over a wide range of voltages.

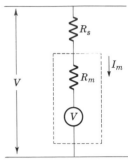

FIGURE 1-31   *Using d'Arsonval meter as voltmeter with series
resistor multiplier.*

The effect of a voltmeter on the circuit to which it is attached
must be considered, just as in the case of an ammeter. This is so
because the voltmeter requires a small current to deflect the
pointer and this current must be supplied by the circuit. If the
meter current is not negligible compared with the normal currents in the circuit, the voltmeter is said to *load* the circuit and a
correction must be applied to the indicated meter reading to determine the true voltage in the absence of the disturbing meter
influence.

Sensitive d'Arsonval meters are useful as voltmeters since they
require only a very small current to achieve full-scale deflection.
It is common practice to specify the sensitivity of a voltmeter in
terms of the ratio of its internal resistance to the full-scale voltage
in units of *ohms per volt*. Note that, according to Eq. (1-95), the
ratio of $R_m + R_s$ to the voltage required for full-scale deflection
is simply the current sensitivity of the meter, and therefore the
two specifications are quite equivalent. For example, a voltmeter
which uses a d'Arsonval meter having a full-scale sensitivity of
1 ma is rated at $1/10^{-3} = 1000$ Ω/volt. This means that, for example, the voltmeter has an internal resistance of 100,000 Ω on the
100-volt scale, etc. Similarly, a 20,000-Ω/volt voltmeter (employing a 50-μa meter) has a resistance of 2 megohms (MΩ) on its 100-
volt scale.

A convenient technique for determining the resistance of a portion of a network is to measure both the current and the voltage
and then apply Ohm's law. There are two distinct ways that the
meters can be connected in this *voltmeter-ammeter method* (Fig. 1-32a
and *b*). The choice between the two possibilities depends upon
the relative values of the meter resistances and the circuit resistances, as can be shown in the following way. Consider first the
circuit in Fig. 1-32*a*. From Kirchhoff's rules

$$V = IR + IR_A \qquad (1\text{-}96)$$

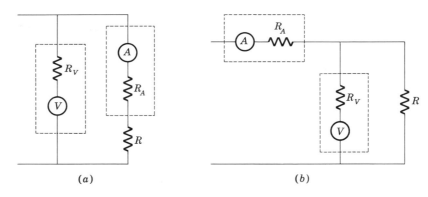

FIGURE 1-32 *Two ways of connecting voltmeter and ammeter to measure resistance R.*

where V and I are the meter readings. The unknown resistance is given by

$$R = \frac{V}{I} - R_A \qquad (1\text{-}97)$$

which shows that the true resistance is smaller than the indicated V/I ratio.

Similarly, in the circuit of Fig. 1-32b, the current I divides between the parallel paths R and R_V so that

$$V = \frac{R_V R}{R_V + R} I \qquad (1\text{-}98)$$

Solving for the unknown resistance, the result is, after some rearrangement,

$$R = \frac{V}{I} \frac{1}{1 - (V/I)/R_V} \qquad (1\text{-}99)$$

According to Eqs. (1-97) and (1-99) the first circuit is most useful when the ammeter resistance is small compared with the unknown (or to V/I), while the second circuit applies when the voltmeter resistance is large compared with the unknown. In either case, the unknown resistance is then given simply by the ratio V/I.

1-18 Ohmmeters and multimeters

A simple extension of the voltmeter-ammeter circuit can be used as an *ohmmeter* in which the meter scale is calibrated directly in ohms. In a typical circuit (Fig. 1-33) the same meter is used successively to measure first the voltage across the unknown resistor and then the current in it. The way the meter scale is calibrated directly in ohms can be understood from the following analysis. First, suppose the terminals a and b in Fig. 1-33 (which are usually connected to *test leads* to facilitate connecting the ohmmeter to the unknown resistor) are shorted together. The voltmeter then measures the battery voltage V.

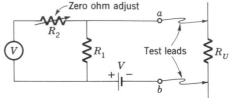

FIGURE 1-33   *A simple ohmmeter circuit.*

Next, the test leads are connected to the unknown resistance. If the voltage across R_1, as measured by the meter, is now V_R, Ohm's law gives

$$R_U + R_1 = \frac{V}{V_R/R_1} \tag{1-100}$$

Solving for R_U

$$R_U = R_1 \left(\frac{V}{V_R} - 1 \right) \tag{1-101}$$

According to Eq. (1-101) the unknown resistance can be calculated directly from the two meter readings, but it is more useful to calibrate the meter scale directly in ohms in the following way.

The variable resistance R_2 is used to adjust the meter reading to full-scale when the test leads are first shorted together. This point on the scale is then "zero ohms," and is so marked. Suppose that when the test leads are connected to the unknown resistor, the meter deflects to half-scale. This means $V_R = V/2$ and, according to Eq. (1-101), $R_U = R_1$. Thus, the midpoint on the scale can be marked with the resistance corresponding to R_1. Similarly, note that the quarter-scale reading, $V_R = V/4$, corresponds to $3R_1$, while a zero reading indicates an open circuit, or infinite ohms. The scale of an ohmmeter is clearly nonlinear (see Exercise 1-34), although it is not difficult to use since it is direct-reading in ohms.

According to Eq. (1-101) the midscale reading of an ohmmeter depends upon R_1, so that by selecting different values for R_1 it is possible to encompass a wide range of unknown resistances. Equation (1-101) assumes that the meter current is negligible, which may not be true on high resistance ranges where R_1 is large. Therefore, practical ohmmeter circuits are slightly more complicated than the elementary one illustrated by Fig. 1-33, but the principle of operation is identical. Note that an ohmmeter cannot be used to determine resistance values in a circuit which is in operation, for erroneous readings result due to IR drops in the circuit itself.

It is convenient to include the functions of a voltmeter, ammeter, and ohmmeter within one instrument since all three employ the same basic d'Arsonval meter. In such an instrument, commonly termed a *multimeter* or *VOM* (volt-ohm-milliammeter), switches or a number of terminals select the function and range to be used. The circuit in Fig. 1-34 is an example of an elementary instrument which has four voltage ranges, two current ranges, and a single ohms scale. By carefully tracing through the connections on this circuit diagram it is possible to draw the simple functional circuits for each use (Exercise 1-35), and in this way subdivide the analysis of the circuit into easy stages.

The VOM circuit of Fig. 1-34 employs a multitap switch with three wipers which are mechanically linked to move together. More elaborate multimeters have considerably more complicated switching arrangements in order to accommodate additional ranges and other functions.

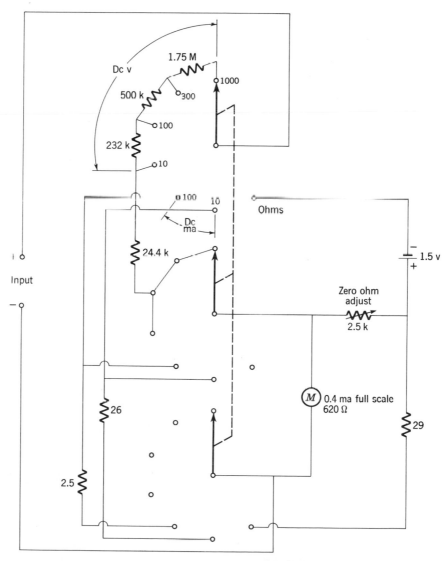

FIGURE 1-34 *Circuit diagram of a simple volt-ohm-milliammeter.*

SUGGESTIONS FOR FURTHER READING

A. M. P. Brookes: "Basic Electric Circuits," The Macmillan Company, New York, 1963.

Leigh Page and Norman Ilsley Adams: "Principles of Electricity," D. Van Nostrand Company, Inc., Princeton, N.J., 1931.

M. E. Van Valkenburg: "Network Analysis," Prentice-Hall, Inc., Englewood Cliffs, N.J., 1955.

EXERCISES

1-1 Determine an expression for the strength of the electric field resulting from a point charge using Coulomb's law and the definition of electric field. If the point charge is an electron, what is the magnitude of the field at a distance of 1 angstrom (10^{-10} m)? What is the direction of the field?

Ans.: 1.44×10^{11} volts/m; toward the electron

1-2 A copper wire 1 mm in diameter carries a current of 20 amp. What is the average velocity of carriers in the wire if the free-electron density in copper is 8.5×10^{28} electrons/m³? Using the conductivity listed in Table 1-1, calculate the mobility of the free electrons.   *Ans.*: 1.85×10^5 m/sec; 4.25×10^{-3} m²/volt-sec

1-3 Show that the mobility of an electron is given by

$$\mu = \frac{e\tau}{m}$$

where τ is the time between collisions. Do this by computing the average velocity of an electron in the time τ caused by an electric field. Using the result of Exercise 1-2, calculate τ for copper.

Ans.: 2.42×10^{-14} sec

1-4 Calculate the resistance of a copper wire 1 m long and 0.5 mm in diameter. Repeat for a similar-sized nichrome wire.

Ans.: 8.65×10^{-2} Ω; 2.55 Ω

1-5 What is the maximum current that can be in a 1-watt 1-MΩ resistor? In a ½-watt 10,000-Ω resistor?

Ans.: 10^{-3} amp; 7.07×10^{-3} amp

1-6 Given that the maximum current capability of a flashlight dry cell is 0.5 amp, what is the internal resistance of the cell? Compare with the internal resistance of a storage battery, if the maximum current in this case is 500 amp.   *Ans.*: 3 Ω; 4.2×10^{-2} Ω

1-7 Prove Eq. (1-28) for the sum of the voltages in a series circuit by computing the joule heat in each of the resistors and equating the total to the power supplied by the battery.

1-8 Assume that Fig. 1-11a represents a battery power source connected to a load R_3 by means of copper wires of resistance R_1 and R_2. If $V = 10$ volts, the load is 5 Ω, and the wires are 0.5 mm in diameter and 100 m long, calculate the current, the power delivered to the load, the power lost in the wires, and the voltage across the load resistor.

Ans.: 1.64 amp; 13.5 watts; 2.9 watts; 8.2 volts

1-9 Design a voltage divider (Fig. 1-12) in which the output voltages possible are 1.0, 2.0, 5.0, and 10.0 volts, if the battery voltage is 10 volts and no current is taken by the output terminals.

1-10 Determine the current in the circuit of Fig. 1-35. *Ans.*: 0.3 amp

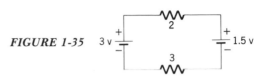

FIGURE 1-35 3 v ⎓   1.5 v

1-11 Prove Eq. (1-33) for parallel-connected resistors by equating the total joule heat in the resistors to the electrical power supplied by the battery.

1-12 How many identical 1-watt resistors, and of what resistance value, are needed to yield an equivalent 1000-Ω 10-watt resistor? Obtain two different solutions.

Ans.: Ten 10-kΩ resistors in parallel; ten 2.5-kΩ resistors in series-parallel

1-13 Determine the current through each resistor of Fig. 1-14a. Verify that the total I^2R loss in the resistors equals the power delivered by the battery

Ans.: 2 amp in R_1 and R_2; 1 amp in R_3 and R_4; 0.5 amp in R_5 and R_6

1-14 In Fig. 1-15a, if $R_1 = 2\ \Omega$, $R_2 = 5\ \Omega$, $R_3 = 2\ \Omega$, $R_4 = 5\ \Omega$, $R_5 - 10\ \Omega$, and $V = 10$ volts, find the total current supplied by the battery.

Ans.: 2.18 amp

1-15 Find the resistance of the network in Fig. 1-36 between the input terminals. What voltage applied to the input results in a 1-amp current in the 4-Ω resistor? *Ans.*: 8 Ω; 72 volts

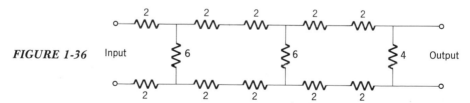

FIGURE 1-36 Input   Output

1-16 Using Kirchhoff's rules find the current in the 4-Ω resistor in the network in Fig. 1-37. *Ans.*: 0.12 amp

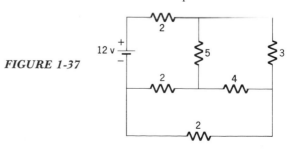

FIGURE 1-37

1-17 Find the current in each resistor of the circuit in Fig. 1-38.

Ans.: 1.15 amp; 0.883 amp; 0.267 amp

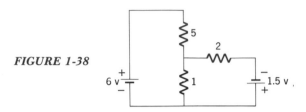

FIGURE 1-38

1-18 Derive an expression that compares the current in the battery of a Wheatstone bridge to that in the unknown resistor at balance.

1-19 Note that in the Wheatstone bridge (Fig. 1-19) at balance $I_5 = 0$. Using this condition, compare the voltage drops in corresponding arms of the bridge and thus derive the balance condition, Eq. (1-69).

1-20 Solve the Wheatstone-bridge network of Fig. 1-19 by drawing loop currents such that there is only one current in R_5. Use the expression for this current to derive the balance condition.

1-21 Suppose that three arms of a Wheatstone bridge are 10-Ω resistors while the fourth is 10.1 Ω. If the battery voltage is 1.5 volts, what is the current in a 100-Ω detector? Repeat if two of the three arms are 100-Ω resistors, while the third is 10 Ω.

Ans.: 7.5×10^{-5} amp; 5.4×10^{-3} amp

1-22 Design a potentiometer circuit (Fig. 1-20) which is capable of measuring unknown voltages up to 2 volts.

1-23 Describe how you would use a potentiometer to determine the ratio of two unknown voltages even if you had no means of standardizing the current in the potentiometer.

1-24 The detector in a potentiometer has a minimum sensitivity of 0.005 μa and an internal resistance of 25 Ω. What is the minimum error possible in measuring the voltage of an unknown?

Ans.: 1.25×10^{-7} volt

1-25 Show how Eq. (1-74) is obtained using Kirchhoff's rules applied to the circuit of Fig. 1-22. Derive the same expression using Thévenin's theorem.

1-26 Show that Eq. (1-82) is equivalent to Eq. (1-68).

1-27 Determine the Norton equivalent circuit for the Wheatstone bridge in Fig. 1-24. Calculate the output current and compare with Eq. (1-82).

1-28 Plot the power delivered to the load divided by the maximum power as a function of the ratio of the source resistance to the load resistance, Eq. (1-87). Why is this maximum equal to $\frac{1}{4}$ when Eq. (1-90) shows that the maximum power transfer ratio is $\frac{1}{2}$?

1-29 Design an *Ayrton shunt* as in Fig. 1-39 for a 50-μa meter which has an internal resistance of 1000 Ω, if the desired current ranges are 10 ma, 100 ma, 1 amp, and 10 amp.

Ans.: 4.9975 Ω; 2.27×10^{-3} Ω; 2.27×10^{-4} Ω; 2.53×10^{-5} Ω

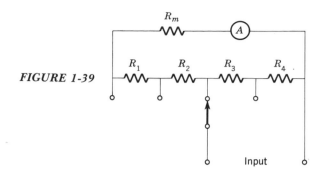

FIGURE 1-39

1-30 Suppose, in the circuit of Fig. 1-30, $R = 1000 \ \Omega$, $R_L = 5000 \ \Omega$, and $R_m = 1000 \ \Omega$. If the indicated current is 1.5 ma, what is the true current when the ammeter is not present? *Ans.*: 1.75 ma

1-31 The voltage in a circuit as measured with a 20,000-Ω/volt meter on the 500-volt scale is 200 volts. On the 100-volt scale the reading is 95 volts. What is the true voltage? *Ans.*: 278 volts

1-32 What are the meter readings in the two versions of the voltmeter-ammeter method of Fig. 1-32 if the voltmeter is 1000 Ω/volt, the internal resistance of the ammeter is 100 Ω, the "unknown" resistance is 1000 Ω, and the applied voltage is 10 volts? Which of the two versions is more satisfactory?
Ans.: 10 volts, 9.1×10^{-3} amp; 9.008 volts, 9.92×10^{-3} amp; circuit *b* is better

1-33 Show how the voltmeter-ammeter method may be used to determine the power in a resistance. Take into consideration the loading effect of the meter resistances.

1-34 Draw the scale of an ohmmeter, assuming $R_1 = 10,000 \ \Omega$ in Eq. (1-101).

1-35 Draw and analyze separately the voltmeter, ammeter, and ohmmeter functions of the VOM in Fig. 1-34. Justify the various component values indicated, given those for the meter.

2
ALTERNATING CURRENTS

The currents and voltages in most practical electronic circuits are not steady but vary with time. For example, when a circuit is used to measure some physical quantity, such as the temperature of a chemical reaction, the voltage or current in the circuit representing the temperature may vary arbitrarily. Similarly, detection of nuclear disintegrations results in a series of rapid voltage pulses of very short duration. In order to understand such effects it is necessary to study the properties of time-varying currents.

The simplest time-varying current alternates direction periodically and accordingly is called an alternating current, abbreviated ac. Obviously an ac circuit is one in which alternating currents are active, but direct currents may be present as well. Most of the concepts developed for dc circuits in the previous chapter carry over to ac circuits. Two new elements in addition to resistance are important in ac circuits and these are treated in this chapter.

SINUSOIDAL SIGNALS

2-1   Frequency, amplitude, and phase

The simplest alternating waveform is *sine-wave* voltage or current, which varies sinusoidally with time. A sinusoidal waveform is generated by the variation of the vertical component of a vector rotating counterclockwise with a uniform angular velocity ω as in Fig. 2-1. One complete revolution is termed a *cycle* and the time

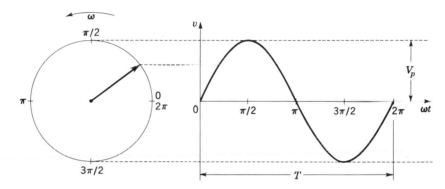

FIGURE 2-1   *Generation of sine wave by vertical component of rotating vector.*

interval required for one cycle is called the *period T*. The number of cycles per second is the *frequency f*, and therefore

$$f = \frac{1}{T} \tag{2-1}$$

The scope of frequencies encountered in electronic circuits is quite large, ranging from the subaudible range of a few cycles per second (cps) through *kilocycle* (10^3 cps) and *megacycle* (10^6 cps) frequencies, on up to the *gigacycle* range (10^9 cps).

Since there are 2π radians in one complete revolution and this requires T sec,

$$\omega = \frac{2\pi}{T} = 2\pi f \tag{2-2}$$

If the length of the vector is V_p, the instantaneous value at any time t is just

$$v = V_p \sin \omega t \tag{2-3}$$

The value V_p is the *maximum* or *peak amplitude* of the sine wave.

If two sinusoidal waveforms have the same frequency but pass through zero at different times, they are said to be out of *phase*, and the angle between the two rotating vectors is called the *phase angle*. In Fig. 2-2 the voltage v_2 is *leading* the sine-wave voltage v_1

because it passes through zero first and the phase difference is the angle ϕ. Note that it is only possible to specify the phase angle between two sine waves if they have the same frequency. A voltage sine wave is completely described by its frequency and amplitude

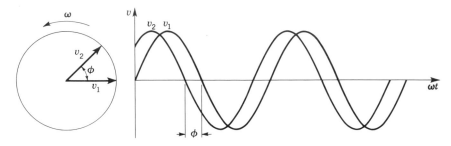

FIGURE 2-2 *Illustrating phase angle between two sinusoidal voltages.*

unless it is compared with another signal of the same frequency. In this case the most general equation for the voltage must include the phase angle

$$v = V_p \sin (\omega t + \phi) \tag{2-4}$$

Note that lowercase symbols are used to indicate time-varying voltages (and currents), while capital letters refer to constant values or to dc quantities.

2-2 Rms value

It is often necessary to compare the magnitude of a sine-wave current with a direct current. This is accomplished by comparing the joule heat produced in a resistor by the two currents. That is, the *effective* value of a sinusoidal current is equal to the direct current which produces the same joule heating as the alternating current. To determine this value, the heating effect of an alternating current is calculated by averaging the I^2R losses over a complete cycle. Therefore, the average power is given by

$$P = \frac{1}{T} \int_0^T i^2R \ dt = \frac{I_p{}^2R}{T} \int_0^T \sin^2 \omega t \ dt \tag{2-5}$$

The integral of $\sin^2 \omega t$ is a standard form evaluated in integral tables, so that

$$P = \frac{I_p{}^2R}{T} \left[\frac{t}{2} - \frac{\sin 2\omega t}{4\omega} \right]_0^T = \frac{I_p{}^2RT}{2T} \tag{2-6}$$

Since the joule heating in a resistor caused by a direct current is equal to I^2R, the effective value of an alternating current I_e is simply

$$I_e{}^2 R = \frac{I_p{}^2 R}{2} \tag{2-7}$$

or

$$I_e = \frac{I_p}{\sqrt{2}} \tag{2-8}$$

According to Eq. (2-8) the effective value of a sine wave is simply its peak value divided by the square root of two. The effective value is commonly referred to as the *root-mean-square* or *rms* value. Voltmeters and ammeters capable of measuring ac signals are almost universally calibrated in terms of rms readings to facilitate comparison with dc meter readings. It is generally understood that ac currents and voltages are characterized by their rms values, unless stated otherwise.

2-3 Power factor

Suppose that the current and voltage in some portion of a circuit are given by

$$i = I_p \sin \omega t$$
$$v = V_p \sin (\omega t + \phi) \tag{2-9}$$

where the phase angle ϕ is introduced to account for the possibility that the current and voltage are not in phase. The instantaneous power p is then

$$p = vi = V_p I_p \sin \omega t \sin (\omega t + \phi) \tag{2-10}$$

According to Eq. (2-10) the instantaneous power in this part of the circuit varies with time and may even become negative, as illustrated by the waveforms in Fig. 2-3. The interpretation of negative power in Eq. (2-10) is that during some portion of a cycle this part of the circuit gives up electrical power to the rest of the cir-

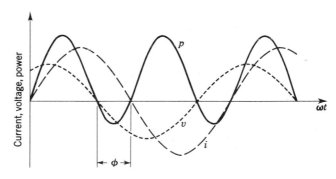

FIGURE 2-3 *Instantaneous power in an ac circuit.*

cuit. For the remainder of the cycle the circuit delivers power to the part under investigation.

The average power is found by averaging Eq. (2-10) over a complete cycle,

$$P = \frac{1}{T} \int_0^T vi \; dt = \frac{V_p I_p}{T} \int_0^T \sin \omega t \sin (\omega t + \phi) \; dt \tag{2-11}$$

The second factor under the integral is expanded using a standard trigonometric identity

$$P = \frac{V_p I_p}{T} \left(\cos \phi \int_0^T \sin^2 \omega t \; dt + \sin \phi \int_0^T \sin \omega t \cos \omega t \; dt \right) \tag{2-12}$$

Both integrals are standard forms and may be evaluated directly to give

$$P = \frac{V_p I_p}{2} \cos \phi \tag{2-13}$$

$$P = VI \cos \phi \tag{2-14}$$

where V and I are rms values.

The meaning of Eq. (2-14) is that the useful power in ac circuits depends not only upon the current and voltage in the circuit but also upon the phase difference between them. The term $\cos \phi$ is called the *power factor* of the circuit. Note that when the phase angle is 90° the power factor is zero and no useful electrical power is developed. Therefore, it is possible for the current and voltage to be very large and, consequently, the instantaneous power large, yet the average power to be zero. On the other hand, when the current and voltage are in phase, the power factor is unity and the power is equal to the current times the voltage, as in a dc circuit.

CAPACITANCE

2-4 Origin of capacitance

According to Coulomb's law, Eq. (1-1), and the definition of electric field, Eq. (1-2), the electric field due to a point charge is

$$\mathscr{E} = \frac{1}{4\pi\epsilon_0} \frac{q}{r^2} \tag{2-15}$$

Using the relation between field and potential gradient, Eq. (1-8),

$$\frac{dV}{ds} = -\frac{1}{4\pi\epsilon_0 r^2} q \tag{2-16}$$

which may be written in the form

$$dV = \frac{-ds}{4\pi\epsilon_0 r^2} q \qquad (2\text{-}17)$$

Note that the potential difference in Eq. (2-17) increases linearly with q. Insofar as the relation between potential difference and charge is concerned, the value of the fraction depends only upon the geometry of the situation and is a constant for a given shape and arrangement of conductors and charges. This geometric constant, the ratio of charge to potential difference, is called the *capacitance C*. Therefore, the relation between charge and potential difference is written as

$$Q = CV \qquad (2\text{-}18)$$

Capacitance is important in ac circuits because a voltage which changes with time gives rise to a time-varying charge according to Eq. (2-18), and this is equivalent to a current. For example, differentiating both sides of Eq. (2-18) with respect to time, and using the definition of current, Eq. (1-10), the result is

$$\frac{dv}{dt} = \frac{1}{C}\frac{dq}{dt} = \frac{i}{C} \qquad (2\text{-}19)$$

Integrating Eq. (2-19)

$$v = \frac{1}{C}\int_0^t i\, dt \qquad (2\text{-}20)$$

According to Eq. (2-20), a voltage is present across a capacitance whenever a current which varies with time is present.

The unit of capacitance is the *farad*, named in honor of Michael Faraday. It is equal to a coulomb per volt, according to (2-18). Actually the magnitude of the farad is too large to be convenient so that practical values are 10^{-6} farad (1 *microfarad*, abbreviated μf) or even 10^{-12} farad (1 *picofarad*, abbreviated pf).

2-5 The parallel-plate capacitor

To illustrate the concepts of the previous section, we determine the capacitance of a parallel-plate *capacitor*. This consists of two parallel conducting plates separated by a small air gap or solid insulating material. It is the basis for most of the capacitors used in electronic circuits. Consider the portions of two large flat conductors shown in Fig. 2-4 in which a charge density of $+\sigma$ coul/m² is present on the lower plate and $-\sigma$ coul/m² on the upper. The capacitance is determined by calculating the potential difference between the plates and then applying the definition of capacitance.

The potential difference is determined by first calculating the electric field between the plates, using Coulomb's law for each

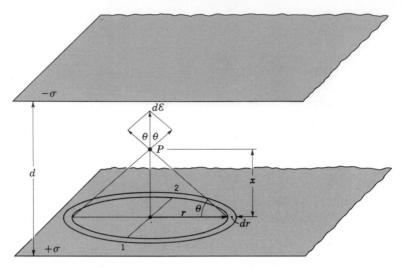

FIGURE 2-4 *Calculating electric field between two oppositely charged parallel plates.*

small region of charge on the plates, and then adding up the effect of the entire charged plates. Consider the electric field at point P a distance x above the lower plate and concentrate first of all on the lower plate. Note that in the ring of radius r, the effect of the charge element at, say, the place marked 1 is very similar to that due to the charge element at the place marked 2 on the opposite diameter of the ring. In particular, the horizontal components of the electric field at P resulting from these two elements cancel. The same is true for all corresponding pairs of elemental charged regions on the ring, so that the net result of the charged ring is only a vertical field at P. The magnitude of the field at P can be calculated from Coulomb's law using $2\pi r \times dr \times \sigma$ for the total charge on the ring. Since this charge is located a distance $\sqrt{r^2 + x^2}$ away, the field $d\mathscr{E}$ due to the ring is

$$d\mathscr{E} = \frac{\sigma}{4\pi\epsilon_0} \frac{2\pi r\, dr}{x^2 + r^2} \cos\theta \qquad (2\text{-}21)$$

The factor $\cos\theta$ is included to give the vertical component of the field, since the horizontal components cancel. Referring to Fig. 2-4, $\cos\theta$ may be expressed as

$$\cos\theta = \frac{x}{(x^2 + r^2)^{1/2}} \qquad (2\text{-}22)$$

Now the total field at P is the sum of all individual rings, so that, inserting Eq. (2-22) into Eq. (2-21) and integrating over the entire area, the total electric field is

$$\mathscr{E} = \frac{\sigma x}{2\epsilon_0} \int_0^\infty \frac{r\, dr}{(x^2 + r^2)^{3/2}} = \frac{\sigma x}{2\epsilon_0} \left[\frac{-1}{(x^2 + r^2)^{1/2}} \right]_0^\infty = \frac{\sigma}{2\epsilon_0} \qquad (2\text{-}23)$$

This result means that the electric field is independent of the height of P above the lower plate, that is, the field between the plates is uniform. Therefore, the field due to the charge density $-\sigma$ coul/m² on the upper plate is also uniform and is also directed upward, since the charge is negative. The electric field between the plates is the sum of that due to the charge on the lower plate plus that due to the charge on the upper plate, or

$$\mathscr{E} = \frac{\sigma}{\epsilon_0} \tag{2-24}$$

Because the field is uniform, the potential difference between the plates is, by Eq. (1-8),

$$V = \mathscr{E}d = \frac{\sigma d}{\epsilon_0} \tag{2-25}$$

where d is the separation of the plates. Consider now an area A of the plates which has a total charge Q. The charge density is $\sigma = Q/A$, and Eq. (2-25) becomes

$$V = \frac{Qd}{A\epsilon_0} \tag{2-26}$$

or

$$Q = \frac{\epsilon_0 A}{d} V \tag{2-27}$$

Comparing Eq. (2-27) with Eq. (2-18), the capacitance of a parallel-plate capacitor is

$$C = \frac{\epsilon_0 A}{d} \tag{2-28}$$

According to Eq. (2-28), the capacitance is increased by making the area of the plates larger and the separation between plates smaller. Note that the capacitance depends only upon geometric factors, as discussed in connection with Eq. (2-17).

It turns out that a solid insulating material between the parallel plates increases the capacitance of the capacitor. The insulator, in effect, permits a greater charge on the plates at a given voltage. The increased capacitance is accounted for by multiplying the right side of Eq. (2-28) by the *dielectric constant* of the insulator. For example, the dielectric constant of mica is about 6 and of paper is about 2, so that the capacitances of capacitors made from these materials are greater by factors of 6 and 2, respectively, than a parallel-plate capacitor with air between the plates.

Conventional capacitors are made of two thin metal foils separated by a thin insulator or *dielectric*, such as paper or mica. This sandwich is then rolled or folded into a compact size and covered with an insulating coating. One axial wire lead is attached to each plate. In order to increase the capacitance, it is desirable for the insulator to be as thin as possible. This can only be done at the expense of reducing the maximum voltage that can be applied before the insulator ruptures because of the intense electric field. Another important factor is the resistivity of the insulator. Thin, large-area shapes increase the *leakage* resistance between the plates and thus degrade the capacitor. Mica and paper dielectric capacitors are available in capacitances ranging from 0.001 to 1 μf and can be used in circuits where the maximum voltage is of the order of hundreds of volts.

Ceramic and plastic-film capacitors are also used, generally with metal-film plates deposited directly on the dielectric. Plastic dielectrics have very high resistivity, which means that the leakage resistance is extremely small. The large dielectric constant of many ceramic materials provides large capacitance values in a small package.

In several applications, most notably transistor circuits, very large capacitance values are desirable and leakage resistances are of secondary concern. *Electrolytic* capacitors made of an oxidized metal foil in a conducting paste or solution are used to achieve high capacitance values. The thin oxide film is the dielectric between the metal foil and the solution. Because the film is extremely thin the capacitance is quite large. Several metals, such as tantalum and aluminum, can be used in electrolytic capacitors, and capacitance values range from 1 to 10^3 μf. The largest capacitances are useful in circuits where the applied voltage does not exceed a few volts, because the oxide dielectric is so thin. Electrolytic capacitors can only be used in circuit situations where the metal foil never becomes negative with respect to the solution. If the foil becomes negative, electrolytic action destroys the film and the capacitor becomes useless. Some typical capacitors are shown in Fig. 2-5.

It is often convenient to vary the capacitance in a circuit without removing the capacitor. The components described above are *fixed* capacitors, since it is clearly not easy to vary their capacitance. The common *variable* capacitor is made of two sets of interleaved plates, one immobile and the other set attached to a shaft. Rotating the shaft effectively changes the area in Eq. (2-28), thus changing the capacitance. Because the dielectric is air and it is necessary to make the separation between plates relatively large to assure that they do not touch, maximum capacitance values are limited to about 500 μf. In the fully unmeshed state a 500-μf variable capacitor may have a minimum capacitance of 10 μf or so. Mica *trimmer* capacitors use a mica dielectric. The separation between plates is adjusted with a screwdriver. They are commonly used where variation in capacitance is only occasionally necessary. The range of capacitance values is about the same as for air dielectric capacitors.

Conventional symbols for capacitors in circuit diagrams are reminiscent of the parallel-plate construction, as illustrated in

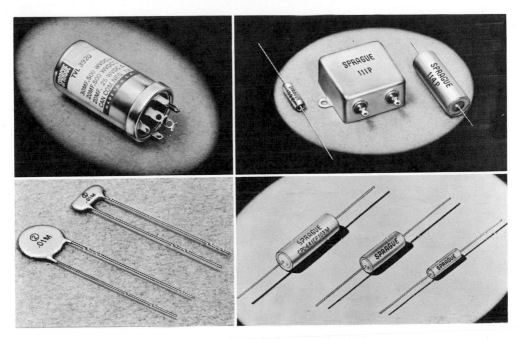

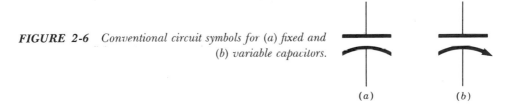

FIGURE 2-5   *Typical capacitors.   (Courtesy Sprague Electric Company.)*

Fig. 2-6. The slightly curved plate is the negative terminal in the case of electrolytic capacitors, and the outside plate on foil capacitors. This is sometimes significant in electronic circuits in order to connect the capacitor properly, even though foil capacitors are not sensitive to voltage polarity.

FIGURE 2-6   *Conventional circuit symbols for (a) fixed and (b) variable capacitors.*

(a)   (b)

2-6   Series and parallel capacitors

Consider the equivalent capacitance C_{eq} of three separate capacitors connected in series as shown in Fig. 2-7. The sum of the

FIGURE 2-7   *Capacitors in series.* V

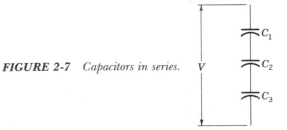

voltages across each capacitor is the total potential V, so that using Eq. (2-18)

$$V = \frac{Q_1}{C_1} + \frac{Q_2}{C_2} + \frac{Q_3}{C_3} \qquad (2\text{-}29)$$

Since the capacitors are connected in series, the same electrical charge $Q = C_{eq}V$ resides on each one. This is so because, for example, the charge on the left plate of C_2 must have come from the right plate of C_1, etc. Therefore, $Q = Q_1 = Q_2 = Q_3$, and

$$\frac{Q}{C_{eq}} = \frac{Q}{C_1} + \frac{Q}{C_2} + \frac{Q}{C_3} \qquad (2\text{-}30)$$

so that

$$\frac{1}{C_{eq}} = \frac{1}{C_1} + \frac{1}{C_2} + \frac{1}{C_3} \qquad (2\text{-}31)$$

Evidently the reciprocal of the equivalent capacitance of any number of capacitors connected in series equals the sum of the reciprocals of the individual capacitances.

The equivalent of parallel-connected capacitors, Fig. 2-8, is

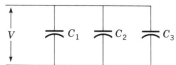

FIGURE 2-8 *Capacitors in parallel.*

found using similar reasoning. Obviously the voltage across all the capacitors is the same, while the total charge is the sum of the individual charges on each capacitor,

$$Q = Q_1 + Q_2 + Q_3 \qquad (2\text{-}32)$$

Therefore

$$\frac{Q}{V} = \frac{Q_1}{V} + \frac{Q_2}{V} + \frac{Q_3}{V}$$

and

$$C_{eq} = C_1 + C_2 + C_3 \qquad (2\text{-}33)$$

This means that the total equivalent capacitance of any number of capacitors connected in parallel is equal to the sum of the individual capacitances.

2-7 *RC* filter

An elementary but very useful circuit employs a capacitor and resistor connected in series, as shown in Fig. 2-9. This series combination is connected to a source of a sinusoidal voltage symbolized on the circuit diagram by a circle containing a one-cycle sine wave. If this voltage is represented by

$$v_i = V_p \sin \omega t \qquad \text{(2-34)}$$

the current in the circuit is determined in the following way. According to Kirchhoff's rules the sum of the voltages around the

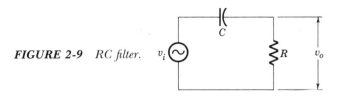

FIGURE 2-9   *RC filter.*

loop must be equal to zero at every instant. This means that the source voltage must equal the voltage across the capacitor plus the IR drop across the resistor, or

$$v_i = \frac{Q}{C} + Ri \qquad \text{(2-35)}$$

where i is the instantaneous current. After differentiating each term with respect to time and putting $i = dQ/dt$, Eq. (2-35) becomes

$$\frac{i}{C} + R\frac{di}{dt} = \frac{dv_i}{dt} = \omega V_p \cos \omega t \qquad \text{(2-36)}$$

Rearranging

$$R\frac{di}{dt} + \frac{1}{C}i = \omega V_p \cos \omega t \qquad \text{(2-37)}$$

The solution of this differential equation is the circuit current i.

To solve this circuit differential equation, note that, because the applied signal has the form of Eq. (2-34), it is likely that the current is also sinusoidal of frequency ω. Therefore, we assume that the current is given by

$$i = I_p \sin (\omega t + \phi) \qquad \text{(2-38)}$$

where I_p and ϕ are to be determined. Differentiating Eq. (2-38)

$$\frac{di}{dt} = \omega I_p \cos (\omega t + \phi) \qquad \text{(2-39)}$$

Now Eqs. (2-38) and (2-39) are substituted into the circuit differential equation, Eq. (2-37). The result is

$$R\omega I_p \cos (\omega t + \phi) + \frac{I_p}{C} \sin (\omega t + \phi) = V_p \omega \cos \omega t \qquad \text{(2-40)}$$

and the equation is solved by choosing values for I_p and ϕ that make Eq. (2-40) true for all values of t. This substitution has changed the differential equation into a trigonometric equation. The values for I_p and ϕ which satisfy Eq. (2-40) are found by first expanding each term in Eq. (2-40) using a trigonometric identity. This gives, after dividing through by ωI_p,

$$R(\cos \omega t \cos \phi - \sin \omega t \sin \phi) + \frac{1}{\omega C} (\sin \omega t \cos \phi$$

$$+ \cos \omega t \sin \phi) = \frac{V_p}{I_p} \cos \omega t \qquad (2\text{-}41)$$

Collecting terms in $\sin \omega t$ and $\cos \omega t$,

$$\left(R \cos \phi + \frac{1}{\omega C} \sin \phi - \frac{V_p}{I_p}\right) \cos \omega t$$

$$+ \left(\frac{1}{\omega C} \cos \phi - R \sin \phi\right) \sin \omega t = 0 \qquad (2\text{-}42)$$

Now consider that $t = 0$; then $\sin \omega t = 0$ and

$$R \cos \phi + \frac{1}{\omega C} \sin \phi - \frac{V_p}{I_p} = 0 \qquad (2\text{-}43)$$

Similarly, suppose $t = \pi/2$, so that $\cos \omega t = 0$. Then

$$\frac{1}{\omega C} \cos \phi - R \sin \phi = 0 \qquad (2\text{-}44)$$

In order that Eq. (2-42) be satisfied for all values of t, both Eqs. (2-43) and (2-44) must be true. Equation (2-44) may be solved immediately for ϕ,

$$\frac{1}{\omega C} \cos \phi = R \sin \phi$$

$$\tan \phi = \frac{\sin \phi}{\cos \phi} = \frac{1}{R \omega C}$$

so that

$$\phi = \arctan \frac{1}{R \omega C} \qquad (2\text{-}45)$$

The solution for ϕ is used in Eq. (2-43) to solve for I_p. This is done with the aid of the diagram in Fig. 2-10, which can be used to evaluate $\sin \phi$ and $\cos \phi$. The sides of the triangle in Fig. 2-10 follow directly from Eq. (2-45). Substituting into Eq. (2-43)

$$R\left[\frac{R}{\sqrt{R^2 + (1/\omega C)^2}}\right] + \frac{1}{\omega C}\left[\frac{1/\omega C}{\sqrt{R^2 + (1/\omega C)^2}}\right] - \frac{V_p}{I_p} = 0 \qquad (2\text{-}46)$$

FIGURE 2-10

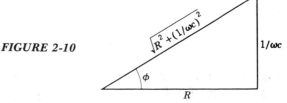

So finally

$$I_p = \frac{V_p}{\sqrt{R^2 + (1/\omega C)^2}} \qquad (2\text{-}47)$$

Thus the current in the circuit is

$$i = \frac{V_p}{\sqrt{R^2 + (1/\omega C)^2}} \sin\,(\omega t + \phi) \qquad (2\text{-}48)$$

where

$$\phi = \arctan \frac{1}{\omega RC}$$

That Eq. (2-48) is indeed a solution of the circuit differential equation may be verified by directly substituting into Eq. (2-37) (see Exercise 2-3).

Note that according to Eq. (2-45), the phase angle is positive. This means that the current leads the voltage, which is characteristic of a capacitive circuit. When $1/\omega RC \rightarrow 0$ at high frequencies, the phase angle is zero and the current is in phase with the voltage. At very low frequencies, $1/\omega RC \rightarrow \infty$ and the phase angle approaches $\pi/2$.

Suppose the voltage across the resistance is considered as an output voltage while v_i is the input voltage. The output voltage is, from Ohm's law,

$$v_0 = Ri = RI_p \sin\,(\omega t + \phi) \qquad (2\text{-}49)$$

Consider only the peak value of v_0, which is, using Eqs. (2-49) and (2-47),

$$V_0 = \frac{RV_p}{\sqrt{R^2 + (1/\omega C)^2}}$$

The ratio of the output voltage to the input voltage is then

$$\frac{V_0}{V_p} = \frac{1}{\sqrt{1 + (1/\omega RC)^2}} \qquad (2\text{-}50)$$

A plot of Eq. (2-50), Fig. 2-11, shows that the output voltage V_0 is very small at low frequencies and is equal to the input voltage at high frequencies. Since low frequencies are attenuated while high

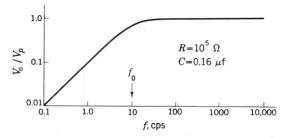

FIGURE 2-11   *Frequency characteristic of an RC high-pass filter.*

frequencies are not, this circuit is called an *RC high-pass filter*. Consider the frequency f_0 where

$$2\pi f_0 RC = 1 \tag{2-51}$$

According to Eq. (2-50) this is where

$$\frac{V_o^2}{V_p^2} = \frac{1}{2}$$

Since the output power in R is proportional to the voltage squared, f_0 is called the *half-power* frequency.

2-8 Differentiating and integrating circuits

Suppose that the series resistance and capacitance in the simple *RC* filter are small enough to make $\omega RC \sim 0$ over a given frequency range. Under this condition the output voltage is, from Eqs. (2-49) and (2-50),

$$v_o = V_p \omega RC \sin(\omega t + \pi/2)$$
$$v_o = V_p \omega RC \cos \omega t \tag{2-52}$$

But, note that the time derivative of the input signal is

$$\frac{dv_i}{dt} = \omega V_p \cos \omega t \tag{2-53}$$

Therefore, combining Eqs. (2-52) and (2-53),

$$v_o = RC \frac{dv_i}{dt} \tag{2-54}$$

The interpretation of Eq. (2-54) is that when $\omega RC \sim 0$ the *RC* filter circuit performs the operation of differentiation. That is, the output voltage signal is the time derivative of the input voltage. This useful property is applied extensively in electronic circuits, most notably in electronic computers.

Correspondingly, the voltage across the capacitor is, by Eq. (2-20), the integral of the current. Therefore, the voltage across the capacitor v_c is, ignoring the limits of integration in Eq. (2-20) for the moment,

$$v_c = \frac{1}{C} \int I_p \sin(\omega t + \phi)\, dt = -\frac{I_p}{\omega C} \cos(\omega t + \phi) \tag{2-55}$$

Suppose now $\omega RC \sim \infty$, which may be accomplished by making R and C very large. Then, $I_p = V_p/R$, $\phi = 0$, and Eq. (2-55) becomes

$$v_c = -\frac{V_p}{RC\omega} \cos \omega t \tag{2-56}$$

Introducing the integral of the input voltage results in

$$v_c = \frac{1}{RC} \int v_i \, dt \qquad\qquad (2\text{-}57)$$

which means that under these conditions the *RC* circuit performs the operation of integration.

It is permissible to ignore the limits of integration in deriving Eq. (2-57), because we are only concerned with steady-state conditions after any initial transient voltages which may accompany turning on the input voltage have died away. The possibility of transient effects in *RC* circuits is considered in a later section. The *RC* circuit is a *low-pass* filter when the output voltage signal is taken from the capacitor (see Exercise 2-5). That is, the circuit as drawn in Fig. 2-12 severely attenuates high-frequency signals and

FIGURE 2-12　*RC low-pass filter.*

transmits low-frequency signals undiminished. The transition frequency from one domain to the other is marked approximately by the half-power frequency, where $\omega_0 RC = 1$ as in the case of the high pass filter.

The output voltage is only a small fraction of the input voltage when the circuit is used to differentiate or integrate, according to Eqs. (2-54) and (2-57). This is not a serious disadvantage in practical applications, however, since the output signal may be subsequently increased in magnitude using vacuum-tube or transistor amplifier circuits described in later chapters.

INDUCTANCE

2-9　Origin of inductance

All the properties of both dc and ac circuits examined so far stem primarily from the force between two electric charges at rest, as expressed by Coulomb's law. It is an experimental fact that two charges in motion, that is, two electric currents, exert forces on each other in addition to the Coulomb force. As in the case of stationary charges, the force between currents exists even though the two currents are separated by a distance. This effect is interpreted by introducing the idea of a *magnetic field* set up in the space surrounding an electric current. The interaction of this field with the second current is said to produce the force. The analogy between the magnetic field of currents and the electric field of charges in the respective situations of charges in motion and at rest is quite obvious. It should be emphasized that both the magnetic field and the electric field are manifestations of the fundamental properties of electrons but that the idea of magnetic and electric fields in no way really explains these fundamental properties. The fields are a great conceptual aid in dealing with the behavior' of electrons, however.

The experimental relation giving the magnetic field B at a point P which is r meters away from a current I in a conductor of length l is called *Ampère's law*,

$$B = \frac{\mu_0}{4\pi} \frac{Il \sin \theta}{r^2} \tag{2-58}$$

In Eq. (2-58) μ_0 is a constant equal to 12.57×10^{-7} weber/amp-m in mks units. The angle θ between the current direction and the radius vector is illustrated in Fig. 2-13. By definition, the direction

FIGURE 2-13 *Magnetic field resulting from a current.*

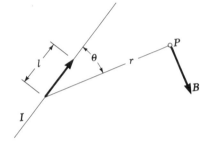

of the magnetic field at P is perpendicular to the plane containing l and r. The magnetic field, in the mks system, is measured in webers per square meter.

The force between two currents is derived from considering the force on a current in a magnetic field. This is given by

$$F = IlB \sin \theta \tag{2-59}$$

where F is the force on a current I in a conductor l meters long in a magnetic field B webers/m². In Eq. (2-59) θ is the angle between the current direction and the magnetic field. The direction of the force is always perpendicular to the plane containing B and I, as illustrated in Fig. 2-14 for the case where $\theta = 90°$.

Note that Ampère's law gives the magnetic field due to a current in a conductor of length l and, correspondingly, Eq. (2-59) gives

FIGURE 2-14 *Force on conductor in magnetic field.*

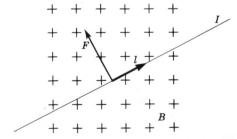

the force on a current in a conductor of length l. In applying these relations to any complete circuit it is necessary to sum up the contributions resulting from every such elementary length in the entire circuit. This may be cumbersome, but, nevertheless, it is possible for many cases of practical interest. For example, Eq. (2-59) is used in Chap. 1 to calculate the torqué on the coil of a d'Arsonval ammeter.

Next, consider what happens when a conductor is moved in a magnetic field. It is found experimentally that whenever a conductor moves in a magnetic field an emf is generated in the conductor; if there is a complete circuit a current exists. Ampère's law is used to determine the magnitude of this *induced* emf. Suppose, as in Fig. 2-15, a conductor of length L is moved at a velocity

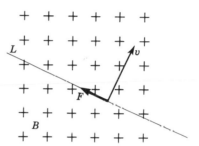

FIGURE 2-15   *Electric charges in conductor moving in magnetic field experience force caused by field.*

v in a direction perpendicular to the uniform magnetic field B. The conductor moves a distance $l = v \times dt$ in a time interval dt. If the total free electric charge in the conductor (considered to be positive charge for simplicity) is Q, the motion of the conductor is equivalent to a current $I = Q/dt$ in the direction of the velocity v. Therefore, according to Eq. (2-59) the free charges experience a force given by

$$F = \frac{Q}{dt} v \ dtB \qquad\qquad (2\text{-}60)$$

where $\sin \theta = 1$, since $\theta = 90°$ in Fig. 2-15. The direction of the force is at right angles to v and B and is therefore along the conductor. Canceling dt in Eq. (2-60) gives

$$F = QvB \qquad\qquad (2\text{-}61)$$

The force exerted on the charges in the direction of the conductor may be expressed in terms of an electric field in the conductor using the definition of electric field, Eq. (1-3),

$$\mathscr{E} = \frac{F}{Q} \qquad\qquad (2\text{-}62)$$

The electric field may be written in terms of the potential gradient along the wire $-V/L$, so that

$$F = \mathscr{E}Q = -VQ/L \qquad\qquad (2\text{-}63)$$

Inserting Eq. (2-63) into Eq. (2-61) and solving for V,

$$-VQ/L = QvB$$

$$V = -LvB \qquad (2\text{-}64)$$

According to Eq. (2-64), an emf LvB is generated in a conductor of length L moving at a velocity v perpendicular to a magnetic field B.

This equation can be put in a more useful form by noting that the area swept out by the moving conductor in a time dt is $Lv\,dt$. Since the conductor is part of a circuit, this means that the area enclosed by the circuit is increasing at the rate

$$\frac{dA}{dt} = Lv \qquad (2\text{-}65)$$

Introducing Eq. (2-65) into Eq. (2-64),

$$V = -\frac{dA}{dt} B = -\frac{d}{dt} AB \qquad (2\text{-}66)$$

Finally, the quantity AB is the total magnetic flux passing through the area of the circuit, which is designated N. Thus

$$V = -\frac{dN}{dt} \qquad (2\text{-}67)$$

which is known as Faraday's law, after Michael Faraday who first investigated induced emfs.

Faraday's law states that whenever a complete circuit loop experiences a changing magnetic flux, an emf is generated in the circuit and the magnitude of this emf is given by the rate of change of magnetic flux. Faraday's law is the basis for electric generators which convert mechanical energy to electric energy. Such generators contain coils of wire rotating in a magnetic field. As a coil rotates, magnetic flux passing through the coil varies from a maximum value when the plane of the coil is perpendicular to the magnetic field to zero when the plane of the coil is parallel to the magnetic field. Consequently an emf is induced in the coil and, since the area of the coil perpendicular to the magnetic field varies as the sine of the angle of rotation, a sinusoidal emf is generated.

Faraday's law may be put into a more useful form for circuit analysis by writing Ampère's law, Eq. (2-58), as

$$B = \left(\frac{\mu_0}{4\pi} \frac{l \sin \theta}{r^2}\right) I \qquad (2\text{-}68)$$

That is, the magnetic field caused by a current I in any circuit is directly proportional to the current. All of the other factors in Eq. (2-68) depend only upon the geometry of the circuit. Furthermore, the magnetic flux encompassed by the circuit also depends upon the geometry of the circuit, so that Eq. (2-68) may be written

$$N = LI \qquad (2\text{-}69)$$

where N is the magnetic flux intercepted by the circuit loop caused by the current I in the same circuit. The constant L, called the *inductance*, depends primarily upon the geometric shape of the circuit, although the magnetic permeability of nearby materials is also a factor.

Introducing Eq. (2-69) into Faraday's law, the result is

$$V = -L \frac{dI}{dt} \tag{2-70}$$

According to Eq. (2-70), whenever the current in any circuit changes with time an emf is induced in the circuit. The magnitude of the emf depends on the rate of change of current and also upon the geometry as determined by the inductance of the circuit. The minus sign in Eq. (2-70) means that the polarity of the emf is such that it opposes the change of current. That is, if the current is increasing with time the induced emf acts to reduce the current.

The inductance of simple circuits is small enough so that the induced emf may usually be ignored. This is true except at the very highest frequencies of interest in electronic circuits, where the rate of change of current is great. Circuits used at such frequencies are kept as small as possible to minimize inductive effects. By contrast, it is possible to produce electric components which have appreciable inductance, and these are very useful in ac circuits.

2-10 Inductors

Electric components with appreciable inductance are called *inductors* or *inductances* and in some applications, *chokes*. They consist of many turns of wire wound adjacent to one another on the same support. In this way every single coil of wire links the magnetic flux density produced by the current in all other coils, and the total flux intercepted by all the coils together can be made large. The unit of inductance, defined using either Eq. (2-69) or Eq. (2-70), is called the *henry* after Joseph Henry, an early American investigator of inductive effects.

High-frequency electronic circuits frequently employ inductances of the order of 10^{-6} henry (*microhenry*, or μh) which may be a helical coil of a few turns on, say, a 1-cm-diameter support. A few tens of turns produce inductance values in the 10^{-3} henry (*millihenry*, or mh) range. Large inductances for use at low frequencies are obtained by winding many hundreds of turns of wire on a core of a ferromagnetic material such as iron. The magnetic properties of these materials are such that the magnetic flux density is increased appreciably. In this fashion inductances of several hundred henrys are attained. Several typical inductors are pictured in Fig. 2-16.

The cores of iron-core inductors are laminated in order to interrupt currents induced in the metal core by the changing magnetic flux. This reduces the I^2R losses of these so-called *eddy currents* in the core. Individual laminations are stacked on top of each other and separated with insulating varnish to make a core of desired size. *Ferrite* cores, made of high-resistivity ferromagnetic

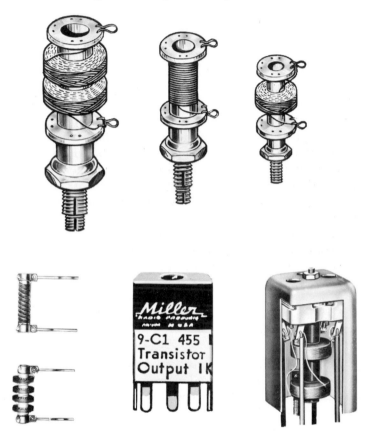

FIGURE 2-16　*Typical inductors used in electronic circuits. (Courtesy J. W. Miller Co.)*

materials, are used at high frequencies, because their high resistance makes eddy currents negligible. Ferrites are not used at low frequencies because the magnetic properties are not as favorable as those of iron. The circuit symbol for an inductor is a helical coil, as shown in Fig. 2-17. Parallel lines along the helix, also illustrated in Fig. 2-17, signify an iron or ferrite core.

Variable inductances can be achieved by moving one portion of the windings relative to the other, but such components are not widely used and most inductors are fixed. In many applications it is necessary to take account of the resistance of the wire in the windings and the capacitance between layers of the winding in determining the effect of a choke in a given ac circuit.

The total flux of inductors in series is equal to the inductance of each inductor times the common current, so according to Eq. (2-69) the total inductance is the sum of the individual inductances. This is the same as found for resistors in series in Chap. 1. Al-

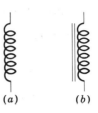

FIGURE 2-17 *Circuit symbols for (a) inductor and (b) iron-core inductor.*

(a)   (b)

though it is not immediately obvious from Eq. (2-70), inductors in parallel also combine as do resistors in parallel. This is discussed in greater detail in the next chapter.

2-11 *RL* filter

The series combination of a resistor and an inductance is a useful ac circuit. When connected to a sinusoidal voltage source (Fig. 2-18) the circuit may be analyzed by the same techniques as em-

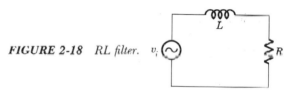

FIGURE 2-18 *RL filter.*

ployed in the case of the *RC* filter. Suppose the input voltage is

$$v_i - V_p \sin \omega t \qquad (2\text{-}71)$$

Then, by Kirchhoff's rules v_i must be equal to the voltage drop across the resistance plus that across the inductance. Thus, using Eq. (2-70),

$$v_i = Ri + L\frac{di}{dt} \qquad (2\text{-}72)$$

The second term on the right-hand side of Eq. (2-72) is positive, because of the meaning of the minus sign in Eq. (2-70). That is, the induced voltage in an inductor opposes the current. There-fore, the polarity of the voltage is the same as the *IR* drop across a resistor. Using Eqs. (2-71) and (2-72) the circuit equation is

$$L\frac{di}{dt} + Ri = V_p \sin \omega t \qquad (2\text{-}73)$$

In solving this differential equation, it is assumed that the cur-rent is sinusoidal and of the same frequency as v_i,

$$i = I_p \sin(\omega t + \phi) \qquad (2\text{-}74)$$

Substituting Eq. (2-74) and di/dt into Eq. (2-73), the result is

$$\omega L I_p \cos(\omega t + \phi) + R I_p \sin(\omega t + \phi) = V_p \sin \omega t \qquad (2\text{-}75)$$

The first two terms in Eq. (2-75) are expanded using the standard trigonometric identity for sums of angles, so that

$$\omega L(\cos \omega t \cos \phi - \sin \omega t \sin \phi) + R(\sin \omega t \cos \phi$$
$$+ \cos \omega t \sin \phi) = \frac{V_p}{I_p} \sin \omega t \qquad (2\text{-}76)$$

Rearranging

$$(\omega L \cos \phi + R \sin \phi) \cos \omega t$$
$$+ \left(R \cos \phi - \omega L \sin \phi - \frac{V_p}{I_p}\right) \sin \omega t = 0 \qquad (2\text{-}77)$$

Note that at $t = 0$, $\sin \omega t = 0$, so that

$$\omega L \cos \phi + R \sin \phi = 0 \qquad (2\text{-}78)$$

On the other hand, when $\omega t = \pi/2$, $\cos \omega t = 0$ and

$$R \cos \phi - \omega L \sin \phi - \frac{V_p}{I_p} = 0 \qquad (2\text{-}79)$$

In order for Eq. (2-74) to be a solution of the differential equation for all values of t, Eqs. (2-78) and (2-79) must both be true. Solving Eq. (2-78),

$$\frac{\sin \phi}{\cos \phi} = \tan \phi = -\frac{\omega L}{R} \qquad (2\text{-}80)$$

from which

$$\phi = \arctan -\frac{\omega L}{R} \qquad (2\text{-}81)$$

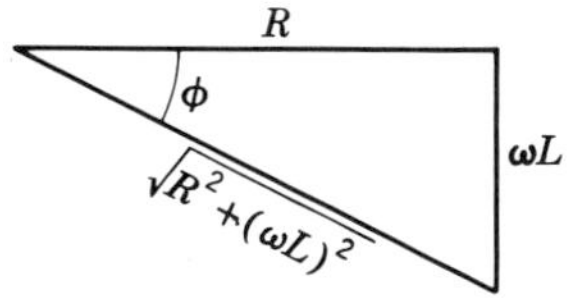

FIGURE 2-19

Equation (2-79) may be solved by substituting for $\sin \phi$ and $\cos \phi$ using the meaning of Eq. (2-81) as illustrated in Fig. 2-19. The result is

$$R \frac{R}{\sqrt{R^2 + (\omega L)^2}} - \omega L \frac{-\omega L}{\sqrt{R^2 + (\omega L)^2}} - \frac{V_p}{I_p} = 0$$
$$\sqrt{R^2 + (\omega L)^2} = \frac{V_p}{I_p} \qquad (2\text{-}82)$$

Therefore, the peak current is

$$I_p = \frac{V_p}{\sqrt{R^2 + (\omega L)^2}} \qquad (2\text{-}83)$$

and the current in the circuit is written

$$i = \frac{V_p}{\sqrt{R^2 + (\omega L)^2}} \sin (\omega t + \phi) \tag{2-84}$$

where

$$\phi = \arctan - \frac{\omega L}{R} \tag{2-85}$$

That Eqs. (2-84) and (2-85) do represent a solution to the circuit differential equation may be verified by substituting directly back into Eq. (2-73).

According to Eq. (2-85) the phase angle is always negative, which means that the current lags the voltage. This is characteristic of an inductive circuit and is the reverse of the situation previously found for a capacitive circuit. Note that at low frequencies $\omega L/R \sim 0$ and the current is in phase with the voltage.

Considering the voltage drop across R to be the output voltage of the circuit, the value of the output voltage is, from Eq. (2-84),

$$V_o = RI_p = \frac{RV_p}{\sqrt{R^2 + (\omega L)^2}} \tag{2-86}$$

The ratio of output to input is therefore

$$\frac{V_o}{V_p} = \frac{1}{\sqrt{1 + (\omega L/R)^2}} \tag{2-87}$$

According to Eq. (2-87) at low frequencies, where $\omega L/R \sim 0$, the output voltage is equal to the input voltage. At high frequencies the output voltage is smaller than the input and the circuit is therefore an inductive low-pass filter. The characteristic half-power frequency is given by

$$\frac{\omega_0 L}{R} = 1 \tag{2-88}$$

The frequency response characteristic for an RL low-pass filter, Eq. (2-87), is identical in shape to the RC low-pass filter (Exercise 2-6), and the circuit used depends upon the particular application and circuit conditions. For example, the RL circuit is common in situations where appreciable direct current is transferred from input to output while ac signals are attenuated. The RL circuit is more efficient because the I^2R losses are a minimum, since there is no appreciable series resistance (compare Figs. 2-12 and 2-18). In this application the inductance, in effect, chokes off the alternating current; this is the origin of the term choke introduced earlier.

TRANSFORMERS

2-12 Mutual inductance

Suppose a changing magnetic flux resulting from current in one circuit is intercepted by another circuit. According to Ampère's law, an emf is induced in the second circuit. The *mutual inductance* between circuit 1 and circuit 2 is defined by analogy with Eq. (2-69) as

$$N_2 = M_{1,2}I_1 \qquad (2\text{-}89)$$

where N_2 is the magnetic flux in circuit 2 produced by the current I_1 in circuit 1. A very important application of mutual inductance is the *transformer*, which has two multiturn coils wound on the same iron core. This makes the mutual inductance between the two coils as large as possible. Schematically, a transformer appears as in Fig. 2-20a, with a *primary* winding which is part of one circuit and a

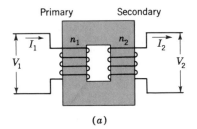

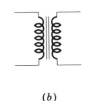

FIGURE 2-20 (a) *Sketch of a transformer and* (b) *circuit symbol.*

(a)

(b)

secondary winding which is part of the second circuit. The symbol for a transformer is shown in Fig. 2-20b.

Consider an ideal transformer, in which all of the magnetic flux from the primary winding is intercepted by the secondary winding. Suppose the secondary winding is open-circuited and the primary is connected to a sinusoidal voltage source. Current in the primary winding is determined by the inductance of the primary. The voltage induced in the primary winding V_1 is proportional to the primary inductance according to Faraday's law, and the inductance is proportional to the number of turns on the primary winding. Since all of the flux is also intercepted by the secondary winding, the voltage V_2 induced in the secondary is proportional to the number of turns on the secondary winding. That is,

$$\frac{V_1}{V_2} = \frac{n_1}{n_2} \qquad (2\text{-}90)$$

Note that it is possible to achieve either a *step-up* transformer or a *step-down* transformer, depending upon whether $n_1 < n_2$ or $n_1 > n_2$, so that the secondary voltage is respectively greater or less than the primary voltage.

Suppose now the secondary is connected to a load such as a

resistor. Current in the secondary circuit results in I^2R losses in the resistor, and this power must come from the primary winding. The way this comes about is as follows. Both the primary current and the secondary current set up magnetic flux in the core. The magnetic flux caused by the secondary current acts to weaken the magnetic flux set up by the primary current in conformity with the minus sign in Faraday's law, Eq. (2-67). The weaker magnetic flux means that the induced primary voltage is correspondingly smaller. Therefore the voltage source connected to the primary winding increases the primary current until the voltages around the primary circuit are zero again as required by Kirchhoff's rules. Thus current in the secondary winding requires current in the primary winding and the peak magnetic flux remains constant at its no-load value.

Note that the total magnetic flux in the core does not change with current, because the magnetic flux from the primary and secondary currents are equal and opposite. This means that, from Eq. (2-69),

$$n_1 I_1 = n_2 I_2 \tag{2-91}$$

where the fact that the inductance is proportional to the number of turns on a winding has again been used. The primary current in Eq. (2-91) really refers only to the additional current accompanying a load on the secondary. The current under no-load conditions is usually so small, however, that it may be neglected.

2-13 Transformer ratio

The ratio of the number of turns on the secondary to that on the primary is called the *transformer ratio*

$$a = \frac{n_2}{n_1} \tag{2-92}$$

The ratio is particularly significant when the resistance connected to the secondary is compared with the apparent resistance in the primary circuit. Consider the situation depicted in Fig. 2-21, where the secondary load is a simple resistance R.

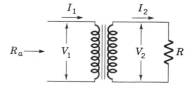

FIGURE 2-21 *Apparent resistance at primary terminals of transformer differs from resistance connected to secondary.*

The magnitude of R determines the secondary current

$$I_2 = \frac{V_2}{R} \tag{2-93}$$

Substituting for I_2 from Eq. (2-91) and for V_2 from Eq. (2-90),

$$\frac{n_1}{n_2} I_1 = \frac{n_2 V_1}{n_1 R}$$

or

$$I_1 = \frac{a^2 V_1}{R} \tag{2-94}$$

Viewed from the primary side, the current I_1 is in an equivalent resistance R_{eq} such that

$$I_1 = \frac{V_1}{R_{eq}} \tag{2-95}$$

Comparing Eqs. (2-94) and (2-95), the secondary load resistance R appears to be a resistance on the primary side given by

$$R_{eq} = \frac{R}{a^2} = \left(\frac{n_1}{n_2}\right)^2 R \tag{2-96}$$

This means that a transformer may be used to match the re- sistances in a circuit to obtain maximum power transfer between a given power source and a fixed load resistance. This very useful property is applied, for example, in coupling the large internal resistance of a vacuum-tube amplifier to the low resistance of a loudspeaker load. Other circuit elements, such as capacitors and inductors, are also transformed by transformer action. Although the corresponding equivalent capacitances and inductances may be determined by a procedure identical to that used above in cal- culating the resistance transformation, it is simpler to delay this calculation until the next chapter.

According to Eq. (2-96) the transformer appears from the pri- mary side as a pure resistance. In particular, the self-inductance of the primary winding is not evident. The reason for this is that the fluxes caused by current in the primary and secondary wind- ings cancel each other. This means that a transformer acts as a device which changes the effective resistance from one circuit to another but which has no inductance of itself. Note also that the primary and secondary circuits in a transformer are not connected electrically and that the two circuits are isolated.

2-14 Transformer construction

Most transformers are constructed in a fashion similar to iron- core chokes described in an earlier section, except, of course, that more than one winding is present on the core. For large trans- former ratios it is common practice to make the low-voltage high- current winding of heavy-gauge wire in order to reduce $I^2 R$ losses in this winding. The other winding is a large number of turns of fine wire since only a small current is present. Laminated cores are ordinarily used to reduce eddy-current losses, but transformers for frequencies in excess of 100,000 cps generally employ high-resistivity ferrite cores.

Transformers with one primary winding and several separate secondary windings are used to supply different voltages to vacuum-tube and transistor devices. Such a *power* transformer may, for example, have a primary winding suitable for connection to a 115-volt 60-cps source with secondaries providing 700, 6.3, and 5.0 volts. Application of such power transformers is studied in a later chapter.

Although for many purposes the inherent inductive effects of the transformer windings may be neglected, in careful work it is necessary to account for the properties of the transformer more exactly. An equivalent circuit of a practical transformer is illustrated in Fig. 2-22. The inductances in the primary and secondary

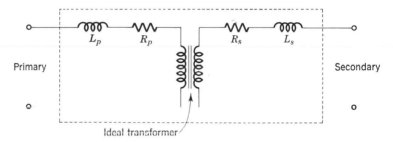

FIGURE 2-22   *Equivalent circuit of practical transformer.*

circuits are caused by leakage magnetic flux which does not link both windings, so that the opposing fluxes do not quite cancel. The resistances are included to account for the resistance of the wire in the windings. With this equivalent circuit the true effect of the transformer in any circuit may be determined.

COMPLEX WAVEFORMS

2-15   Fourier series

Most signals of practical interest are not simple sine waves, but often have more complex waveforms. Nevertheless, the analysis based on sine waves can apply because complex waveforms may be represented by summing sine waves of various amplitudes and frequencies. Consider, for example, the sum of the two sine waves shown in Fig. 2-23, one of which is twice the frequency of the other. The resulting waveform is more complex than either constituent. If this periodic voltage is applied to a circuit, the resulting current may be determined by calculating the current caused by each sinusoidal voltage component separately. In this way the effect of any complex waveshape can be investigated.

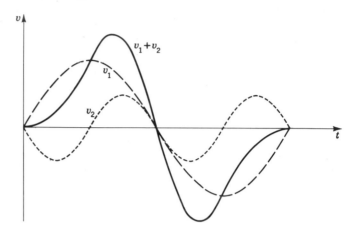

FIGURE 2-23 *Sum of two sine waves is complex waveform.*

Any single-valued periodic waveform may be represented by a *Fourier series* which is a summation of a *fundamental* (or lowest) frequency together with its *harmonics* (integral multiples of the fundamental frequency). The mathematical proof of this representation and the procedure by which the proper series is constructed to represent any given waveshape are not of direct concern here. It is interesting, however, to note the harmonic composition of several waves of practical importance to demonstrate the main features of the series representation.

The Fourier series for a square wave of peak voltage V_p and frequency ω is given by

$$v = \frac{4V_p}{\pi} (\sin \omega t + \tfrac{1}{3} \sin 3\omega t + \tfrac{1}{5} \sin 5\omega t + \tfrac{1}{7} \sin 7\omega t + \cdots)$$

$$(2\text{-}97)$$

The faithfulness of the series representation improves as the number of terms included in Eq. (2-97) is increased, as illustrated graphically in Fig. 2-24. This means that the higher frequencies are necessary in order to reproduce the sharp corners of the square wave. A second example is the sawtooth wave (Fig. 2-25) which is represented by

$$v = \frac{2V_p}{\pi} (\sin \omega t - \tfrac{1}{2} \sin 2\omega t + \tfrac{1}{3} \sin 3\omega t - \tfrac{1}{4} \sin 4\omega t + \cdots)$$

$$(2\text{-}98)$$

Here, again, the high-frequency terms must be included in order to obtain the sharp corner of the sawtooth waveform (Exercise

2-7). The effective value of a complex waveform is defined in exactly the same way as in the case of the sinusoidal wave discussed earlier. The numerical factor relating the rms and peak values depends, of course, upon the exact waveshape. Several waveforms of practical interest are considered in Appendix 2.

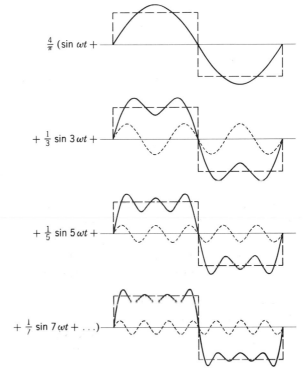

$$\frac{4}{\pi} \left(\sin \omega t + \right.$$

$$+ \tfrac{1}{3} \sin 3 \omega t +$$

FIGURE 2-24 Many frequency components are present in a square wave. Faithfulness of representation improves as number of harmonics is increased.

$$+ \tfrac{1}{5} \sin 5 \omega t +$$

$$+ \tfrac{1}{7} \sin 7 \omega t + \dots)$$

According to Eqs. (2-97) and (2-98), complex waveforms, such as the square wave and the sawtooth wave, are composed of a wide spectrum of frequencies. If the waveform of a given input signal applied to any network is to be preserved at the output, the attenuation of the network must be independent of frequency. For example, a square wave applied to an *RC* high-pass filter can result in a square-wave output signal only if the fundamental frequency of the square wave is greater than the cutoff frequency of the filter. (See Exercises.) It is equally important that the relative phases of the harmonics remain constant in traversing the network if the waveform is to be preserved.

On the other hand, the harmonic composition of a wave is often purposefully altered by a network in order to change one wave-

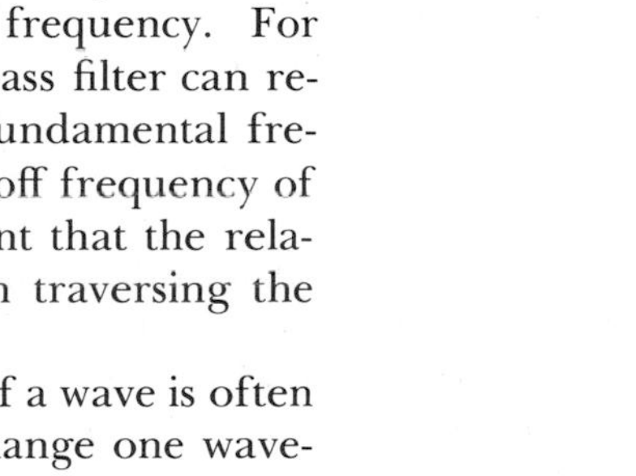

FIGURE 2-25   Sawtooth wave.

form into another. Suppose a square wave is applied to an RC differentiating circuit. The output waveform is a series of alternating positive and negative sharp pulses, as sketched in Fig. 2-26.

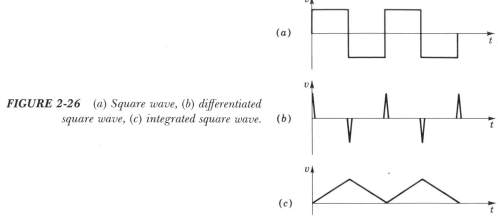

FIGURE 2-26 *(a) Square wave, (b) differentiated square wave, (c) integrated square wave.*

In order for the circuit to differentiate a square wave adequately, it is necessary for the highest frequency term in the Fourier series representation to satisfy the approximation $\omega RC \sim 0$ leading to Eq. (2-54). This is usually easily accomplished in practice, and the simple differentiating circuit is widely used to generate pulses from a square wave.

A second example is the integration of a square wave using a simple RC circuit. The result is a triangular wave (Fig. 2-26). Here the fundamental frequency of the square wave must be large enough that the approximation $\omega RC \to \infty$ leading to Eq. (2-57) is satisfied.

2-16 Oscilloscope

Undoubtedly the most useful instrument for studying complex waveforms is the *cathode-ray oscilloscope,* which is capable of displaying voltage waveforms visually. The heart of the oscilloscope is the cathode-ray tube, in which the position of a thin beam of electrons is electrically controlled to "paint" the waveform on a fluorescent screen. In the cathode-ray tube (CRT) an *electron gun* directs a high-velocity focused beam of electrons onto a glass faceplate covered with fluorescent material that emits light when bombarded by electrons. The beam passes between a pair of horizontal deflecting plates and a pair of vertical deflecting plates on its way to the screen, as sketched in Fig. 2-27. The beam produces a spot of light in the center of the screen when the voltage on the deflection plates is equal to zero. The position of the spot on the screen is easily changed by deflecting the electron beam with voltages applied to either pair of deflecting plates. The beam is deflected as a result of the sidewise force on the electrons caused by the electric field between each pair of deflecting plates. Practical oscilloscopes include a number of auxiliary circuits to increase the versatility of the instrument, as discussed in a subsequent chapter.

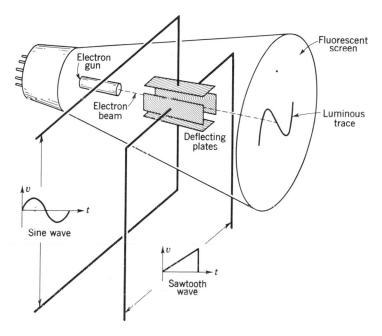

FIGURE 2-27   *Sketch of cathode-ray tube.*

The way in which the oscilloscope displays a waveshape can be understood by referring to Fig. 2-28. Suppose a sine-wave voltage of sufficient amplitude to cause a peak-to-peak deflection of about one-half the screen diameter is applied to the vertical pair of deflection plates. A sawtooth voltage waveform of the same frequency is applied to the horizontal deflecting plates with sufficient amplitude to cause the beam to sweep one-half the screen diameter in this direction. If both waveforms start from zero at the same instant, the spot begins in the center of the screen. The sawtooth wave on the horizontal plates causes the spot to move uniformly to the right while vertical motion depends upon the sine-wave voltage. The result is that the spot traces out a sine-wave pattern on the screen, as the point-by-point plot in Fig. 2-28 illustrates.

When the sawtooth voltage on the horizontal plates drops to zero at the end of the cycle, the spot rapidly returns to the starting point. The same pattern is traced out on subsequent cycles. At most frequencies of interest the spot moves too rapidly to be seen and the pattern on the screen appears to be a stationary sine wave because of the persistence of vision. The sawtooth voltage and the sine wave must start from the beginning at exactly the same instant on each cycle, for otherwise the spot does not trace out the same pattern every time. Therefore, the sawtooth *sweep* voltage is *synchronized* with the signal on the vertical plates by auxiliary circuits associated with the oscilloscope. It is also common practice to turn off the beam during the fast return of the spot to the

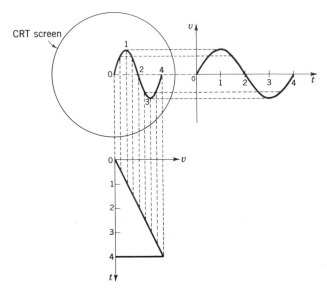

FIGURE 2-28 *Oscilloscope having a sawtooth horizontal deflection voltage displays waveform of voltage applied to vertical plates.*

beginning, in order to eliminate the *retrace* line from the pattern. The sweep voltage may conveniently be made a submultiple of the signal frequency in order to display more than one cycle of the waveform (Exercise 2-14).

The oscilloscope is also useful in measuring the phase angle between sine waves. This is done by applying one sine wave to the vertical plates and the other to the horizontal plates. The pattern which results can be a straight line, a circle, or an ellipse, depending upon the phase angle, as illustrated in Fig. 2-29 for the corresponding phase angles of 0°, 45°, and 90°. The manner in which the phase angle is calculated is as follows. Suppose the horizontal voltage is

$$v_H = V_p \sin \omega t \tag{2-99}$$

and the vertical sine wave is given by

$$v_V = b \sin (\omega t + \phi) \tag{2-100}$$

When $t = 0$, $v_H = 0$, which means the horizontal deflection is zero. The vertical deflection at this point may be labeled a,

$$v_V = b \sin \phi = a \tag{2-101}$$

Solving for ϕ,

$$\phi = \arcsin \frac{a}{b} \qquad (2\text{-}102)$$

The ratio a/b can be determined directly from the dimensions of the pattern on the screen, as shown in Fig. 2-30. Note that the pattern must be centered on the horizontal and vertical reference lines in order for Eq. (2-102) to be valid.

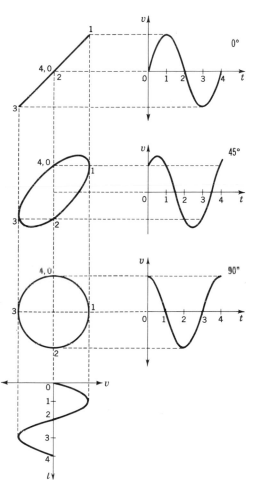

FIGURE 2-29 *Lissajous figures for phase differences of 0°, 45°, and 90° between horizontal and vertical deflection voltages.*

The patterns in Fig. 2-29 are specific examples of so-called *Lissajous figures* which are used to determine the ratio between the frequencies of two sine waves. One sine wave is applied to the vertical deflection plates and the other is applied to the horizontal deflection plates. If the ratio of their frequencies is some integral fraction such as ½, ¼, ⅔, etc., the pattern is stationary. The frequency ratio is determined by the number of loops of the pattern touching a vertical line at the edge of the pattern compared with the number of loops touching a horizontal line at the edge of the pattern. The reason for this is that an integral number of sine waves on the horizontal deflection plates are completed in the same time that an integral number of sine waves are completed on the vertical plates. Some examples of common Lissajous figures are

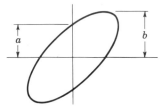

FIGURE 2-30 *Phase angle between sine-wave voltages applied to horizontal and vertical plates is determined from ratio a/b.*

given in Fig. 2-31 for different frequency ratios. These patterns are derived in the same fashion used in connection with Figs. 2-28 and 2-29.

Several different patterns can represent the same frequency ratio, depending upon the interval between the times the two sine

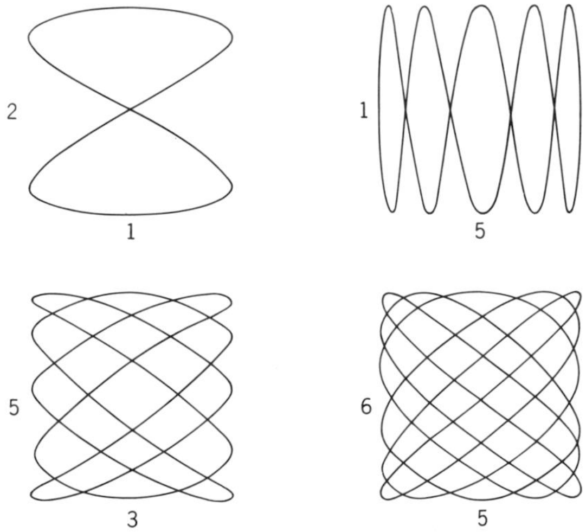

FIGURE 2-31 *Lissajous figures for frequency ratios of 2:1, 1:5, 5:3, and 6:5.*

waves pass through zero. Figure 2-29 is an example of this for a 1:1 frequency ratio. Although in principle Lissajous figures can be used to determine the frequency ratio between nonsinusoidal waveforms, in practice the resulting patterns are confusing and difficult to interpret.

SUGGESTIONS FOR FURTHER READING

R. M. Kirchner and G. F. Corcoran: "Alternating Current Circuits," 4th ed., John Wiley & Sons, Inc., New York, 1960.

Leigh Page and Norman Isley Adams: "Principles of Electricity," D. Van Nostrand Company, Inc., Princeton, N.J., 1931.

"The Radio Amateur's Handbook" (published annually by the American Radio Relay League, West Hartford, Conn.).

EXERCISES

2-1 Compute the capacitance of a parallel-plate capacitor that has a plate area of 4 cm² and a separation between plates of 10^{-3} cm. What separation is needed to achieve a capacitance of 10 μf, as in a typical electrolytic capacitor?

Ans.: 3.54×10^{-10} farad; 3.5×10^{-8} cm

2-2 Three capacitors are connected in series across a 100-volt battery. If the capacitances are 1.0, 0.1, and 0.01 μf, respectively, calculate the potential difference across each capacitor.

Ans.: 0.90 volt, 9.0 volts, 90.1 volts

2-3 Verify that Eq. (2-48) is the solution of the circuit differential equation for a series *RC* circuit, Eq. (2-37), by direct substitution.

2-4 Plot the frequency-response characteristic of an *RC* high-pass filter using Eq. (2-50) for $R = 10^6$ Ω and $C = 0.01$ μf. Cover the frequency interval from two decades below the half-power frequency to two decades above it.

2-5 Develop an expression analogous to Eq. (2-50) for an *RC* low-pass filter (Fig. 2-12). Plot the frequency-response characteristic for $R = 10^6$ Ω and $C = 100$ pf.

2-6 Plot the frequency response characteristic of an *RL* low-pass filter, Eq. (2-87), if $L = 10$ henrys and $R = 100$ Ω. Design an *RC* circuit having the same frequency characteristic.

2-7 Show how the Fourier series representation of a sawtooth wave, Eq. (2-98), approximates the sawtooth more accurately as additional harmonic terms are included by summing two, three, and four terms, as in Fig. 2-24.

2-8 Sketch the output voltage waveform of an *RC* high-pass (differentiating) circuit to which a square-wave signal is applied?

2-9 Repeat Exercise 2-8 for the case of an *RC* low-pass (integrating) circuit.

2-10 Using the Fourier series representation of a square wave, determine the result of integrating a square wave. Do this by integrating Eq. (2-97) term by term and plotting the resulting series. Compare the waveform with the sketch from Exercise 2-9.

2-11 Repeat Exercise 2-10 for a sawtooth waveform, Eq. (2-98). Compare the result with a sketch of the expected waveform.

2-12 Using the Fourier series representation of a square wave, determine the result of differentiating a square wave. Do this by differentiating Eq. (2-97) term by term and plotting the resulting series. Compare the waveform with the sketch from Exercise 2-8.

2-13 Repeat Exercise 2-12 for a sawtooth waveform, Eq. (2-98). Compare the result with a sketch of the expected waveform.

2-14 By a procedure analogous to that used in preparing Fig. 2-28, determine the observed waveform on an oscilloscope screen if the frequency of the horizontal sawtooth is one-half of the vertical sine-wave frequency.

2-15 By a procedure analogous to that used in preparing Fig. 2-29, determine the observed waveform on an oscilloscope screen if a sine wave is applied to both the horizontal and vertical deflection plates and the phase angle between them is 30°. Use the resulting pattern to confirm Eq. (2-102).

2-16 Show that the stored energy in a charged capacitor is equal to $\frac{1}{2}CV^2$ by integrating the expression $dW = V\,dq$. Substitute for dq using Eq. (2-18).

3

AC-CIRCUIT ANALYSIS

The principles of ac circuits treated in Chap. 2 can be used to find the currents in any network. However, solving the differential equation pertaining to each network of most practical circuits is often cumbersome. More powerful techniques of ac-circuit analysis permit solutions for the circuit currents with much less labor. These techniques are, of course, based on the same differential equation of the circuit. The procedures are only slightly more complicated than for dc-circuit analysis, however. Ohm's law and Kirchhoff's rules are used in a modified form. In fact, all of the techniques of dc-network analysis treated in Chap. 1 are applicable.

IMPEDANCE

3-1 Reactance

The rms current in a simple RC circuit is, from Eq. (2-48),

$$I = \frac{V}{\sqrt{R^2 + (1/\omega C)^2}} \tag{3-1}$$

where V is the applied voltage. Similarly, the rms current in a simple RL circuit is, from Eq. (2-84),

$$I = \frac{V}{\sqrt{R^2 + (\omega L)^2}} \tag{3-2}$$

In both cases the second term under the radical appears as important as the resistance in the circuit. As a matter of fact, in the absence of circuit resistance, the current in a capacitance is

$$I = \frac{V}{1/\omega C} \tag{3-3}$$

and the current in an inductance is

$$I = \frac{V}{\omega L} \tag{3-4}$$

which means that the quantity $1/\omega C$ determines the magnitude of the current in purely capacitive circuits, while ωL does so in purely inductive circuits. Clearly both act much the way a resistance does.

The quantity $1/\omega C$ is called the *capacitive reactance*

$$X_C = \frac{1}{\omega C} \tag{3-5}$$

and ωL is called the *inductive reactance*

$$X_L = \omega L \tag{3-6}$$

In ac circuits, the reactance of capacitors and inductors can be treated much like the resistance of resistors. Note, however, that according to Eqs. (3-5) and (3-6) capacitive reactance decreases with frequency, while inductive reactance increases with frequency. In contrast, resistance is a constant. According to Eqs. (3-3) and (3-4), the unit of reactance is a volt per ampere, or an ohm.

The second major difference between reactance and resistance is that the current and voltage in a reactance are not in phase. As found in Chap. 2, the current leads the voltage by a phase angle of 90° in a purely capacitive circuit and lags by 90° in a purely inductive circuit. The phase angle of reactances must always be taken into account in determining their effect upon the current.

3-2 Complex impedance

It is convenient to represent the two elements of reactance, the magnitude and phase angle, in such a way that the result of combining several resistances and reactances can be determined easily. This is done by representing reactance as a complex number.   The real part of the complex number is associated with resistance while the imaginary part stands for reactance. Thus, for example, the series combination of a resistance R and an inductive reactance X_L is written as the complex *impedance* $Z\angle\phi$, so that

$$Z\angle\phi = R + jX_L \tag{3-7}$$

where $j = \sqrt{-1}$.   The symbol j, rather than i, is commonly used to signify $\sqrt{-1}$ in electronic-circuit analysis in order to avoid confusion with the conventional symbol for current.

Note that impedance is a complex number; hence it has both a magnitude and an angle associated with it.   According to the standard graphical representation of a complex number, Fig. 3-1,

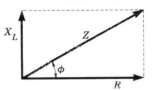

FIGURE 3-1 *Complex impedance is represented graphically by resistive component and reactive component.*

the real part is plotted on the horizontal axis and the imaginary part on the vertical axis.   Therefore, the impedance angle is given by

$$\phi = \arctan \frac{X_L}{R} \tag{3-8}$$

The term impedance comes from the fact that the effect of both reactances and resistances is to impede the current in a circuit. According to Eq. (3-7) the unit of impedance is the ohm.

It is useful to recall some of the properties of complex numbers in order to facilitate their use in circuit analysis.   Two complex numbers are equal only if their real and imaginary parts are equal. Therefore, if it is true that

$$R_1 + jX_1 = R_2 + jX_2 \tag{3-9}$$

then it must be that

$$R_1 = R_2$$

and $\hspace{8cm}$ (3-10)

$$X_1 = X_2$$

From this definition of equality it follows that the addition of two complex numbers is accomplished by separately adding the real and imaginary parts. That is,

$$(R_1 + jX_1) + (R_2 + jX_2) = (R_1 + R_2) + j(X_1 + X_2) \qquad (3\text{-}11)$$

Clearly, the same rule applies to the subtraction of two complex numbers.

Complex numbers are multiplied as follows. According to Fig. 3-1 the complex number $Z\angle\phi$ can be expressed in the form

$$Z\angle\phi = Z(\cos\phi + j\sin\phi) \qquad (3\text{-}12)$$

The product of the numbers $Z_1\angle\phi_1$ and $Z_2\angle\phi_2$ is therefore

$$Z_1\angle\phi_1 Z_2\angle\phi_2 = [Z_1(\cos\phi_1 + j\sin\phi_1)]\,[Z_2(\cos\phi_2 + j\sin\phi_2)]$$

$$= Z_1 Z_2 [(\cos\phi_1\cos\phi_2 - \sin\phi_1\sin\phi_2)$$

$$+ j(\sin\phi_1\cos\phi_2 + \cos\phi_1\sin\phi_2)] \qquad (3\text{-}13)$$

Using the trigonometric identity for the sine and cosine of the sum of angles, Eq. (3-13) becomes

$$Z_1\angle\phi_1 Z_2\angle\phi_2 = Z_1 Z_2 [\cos(\phi_1 + \phi_2) + j\sin(\phi_1 + \phi_2)] \qquad (3\text{-}14)$$

Therefore, the result may be written

$$Z_1\angle\phi_1 Z_2\angle\phi_2 = Z_1 Z_2\angle(\phi_1 + \phi_2) \qquad (3\text{-}15)$$

According to (3-15), the product of two complex numbers is a complex number of magnitude equal to the product of the individual magnitudes and with an angle which is the sum of the individual angles.

Division of complex numbers is achieved by first determining the reciprocal of a complex number. Thus

$$\frac{1}{Z\angle\phi} = \frac{1}{Z(\cos\phi + j\sin\phi)} \qquad (3\text{-}16)$$

This fraction is *rationalized* by multiplying numerator and denominator by the *complex conjugate*, obtained by replacing the imaginary part of the complex number by its negative. Therefore, Eq. (3-16) becomes

$$\frac{1}{Z\angle\phi} = \frac{1}{Z(\cos\phi + j\sin\phi)}\frac{\cos\phi - j\sin\phi}{\cos\phi - j\sin\phi} = \frac{1}{Z}\frac{\cos\phi - j\sin\phi}{\cos^2\phi + \sin^2\phi}$$

$$= \frac{1}{Z}(\cos\phi - j\sin\phi) \qquad (3\text{-}17)$$

Evidently the reciprocal of a complex number is simply a complex number with a magnitude given by the reciprocal of the magnitude of the complex number and an angle which is its negative, or

$$\frac{1}{Z\angle\phi} = \frac{1}{Z}\angle{-\phi} \qquad (3\text{-}18)$$

The ratio of two complex numbers follows immediately from Eq. (3-18), since

$$\frac{Z_1\angle\phi_1}{Z_2\angle\phi_2} = (Z_1\angle\phi_1)\left(\frac{1}{Z_2\angle\phi_2}\right) = (Z_1\angle\phi_1)\left(\frac{1}{Z_2}\angle-\phi_2\right)$$

$$\frac{Z_1\angle\phi_1}{Z_2\angle\phi_2} = \frac{Z_1}{Z_2}\angle(\phi_1-\phi_2) \qquad\qquad (3\text{-}19)$$

Equation (3-19) states that the result of dividing two complex numbers is a complex number whose magnitude is the ratio of the individual magnitudes and whose angle is the difference between the individual angles.

The equivalent forms of representing a complex number

$$Z\angle\phi = Z(\cos\phi + j\sin\phi) = R + jX \qquad\qquad (3\text{-}20)$$

should be noted. Evidently addition and subtraction are easiest in the component form, $R + jX$, while multiplication and division are easiest in the *polar* form, $Z\angle\phi$. Equation (3-20) is used to pass directly from one representation to another as needed. These operations, together with that of rationalization, are useful in computing the equivalent complex impedance of circuits comprising a number of individual impedances, as is illustrated in a later section. Note also that the magnitude of a complex number is equal to the square root of the sum of the squares of the real and imaginary parts.

The complex-impedance concept permits circuit differential equations to be solved directly. Consider, for example, the simple RL circuit in which the current is given by Eq. (2-48)

$$i = \frac{V_p}{\sqrt{R^2 + X_L^2}}\sin(\omega t + \phi) \qquad \phi = \arctan-\frac{X_L}{R} \qquad (3\text{-}21)$$

The quantity $\sqrt{R^2 + X_L^2}$ is the magnitude of the complex impedance $R + jX_L$ and the amplitude of the current is simply the ratio of the applied voltage divided by the magnitude of the impedance. Furthermore, the phase angle ϕ is the negative of the impedance angle. Thus the current can be obtained directly from the *ac form* of Ohm's law,

$$I\angle\theta = \frac{V\angle\phi_1}{Z\angle\phi_2} \qquad\qquad (3\text{-}22)$$

where both the current and voltage are also expressed in complex form. Note that according to Eq. (3-19) the phase angle of the current is $\theta = \phi_1 - \phi_2$. In the case of the RL circuit, where the phase angle of the voltage is taken to be zero as in Chap. 2,

$$I\angle\theta = \frac{V\angle 0}{Z\angle\phi} \qquad\qquad (3\text{-}23)$$

Using Eq. (3-19) for the division of complex numbers,

$$I \angle \theta = \frac{V}{Z} \angle -\phi = \frac{V}{\sqrt{R^2 + X_L^2}} \angle -\phi \tag{3-24}$$

where

$$\phi = \arctan \frac{X_L}{R}$$

This is exactly the result (3-21) found by solving the differential circuit equation. Thus, the magnitude and phase angle of the current are obtained directly from the complex form of Ohm's law after the complex impedance of the circuit has been determined. The corresponding solution for the RC circuit is evidently obtained in an analogous fashion, except that the impedance is $R - j(1/\omega C)$. The minus sign is associated with capacitive reactance, since current lags the voltage in a capacitive circuit (see Exercise 3-1). The validity of Ohm's law for ac circuits rests entirely upon the solution of the circuit differential equations. The complex representation of impedances is simply a very convenient computational device which makes it possible to arrive at the solution with relatively little effort.

Note that in the absence of reactance, Eq. (3-22) reduces to the standard dc form of Ohm's law. This means that series and parallel impedances must combine in the same way as do series and parallel resistances. Thus the equivalent impedance of a series of individual impedances is

$$Z_{eq} \angle \phi = Z_1 \angle \phi_1 + Z_2 \angle \phi_2 + Z_3 \angle \phi_3 + \cdots \tag{3-25}$$

Similarly, the equivalent of parallel impedances is

$$\frac{1}{Z_{eq} \angle \phi} = \frac{1}{Z_1 \angle \phi_1} + \frac{1}{Z_2 \angle \phi_2} + \frac{1}{Z_3 \angle \phi_3} + \cdots \tag{3-26}$$

In applying Eqs. (3-25) and (3-26) due consideration must be given to the complex nature of impedances and the rules pertaining to how complex numbers combine. Several illustrative examples are considered in subsequent sections.

RLC CIRCUITS

3-3 Series resonance

As the first example of ac-circuit analysis using the complex-impedance method, consider the series RLC circuit of Fig. 3-2. According to Kirchhoff's law

$$v = Ri + \frac{q}{C} + L \frac{di}{dt} \tag{3-27}$$

The differential equation of the circuit is, after differentiating with respect to i,

$$L\frac{d^2i}{dt^2} + R\frac{di}{dt} + \frac{1}{C}i = \frac{dv}{dt} \tag{3-28}$$

Note that this is a second-order differential equation. It can be

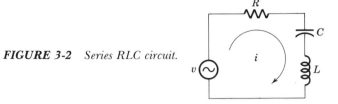

FIGURE 3-2   *Series RLC circuit.*

solved for the steady-state current i by the procedure used in Chap. 2 (see Exercise 3-5). The result is

$$i = \frac{V_p}{\sqrt{R^2 + (1/\omega C - \omega L)^2}} \sin (\omega t + \phi) \tag{3-29}$$

where

$$\phi = \arctan \frac{-(\omega L - 1/\omega C)}{R} \tag{3-30}$$

The complex-impedance technique for the solution of the same circuit proceeds as follows. The total impedance of the series combination is, from Eq. (3-25),

$$Z\angle\phi = R + j\omega L - j\frac{1}{\omega C} = R + j\left(\omega L - \frac{1}{\omega C}\right) \tag{3-31}$$

Using Ohm's law to calculate the current,

$$I\angle\theta = \frac{V\angle 0}{Z\angle\phi} = \frac{V}{R + j(\omega L - 1/\omega C)} \tag{3-32}$$

Equation (3-32) is the final solution, obtained directly in only two simple steps. The voltage V usually is given in terms of its rms value, so that the rms value of I is obtained.

To illustrate more clearly the correspondence between this solution and that given by Eqs. (3-29) and (3-30), Eq. (3-32) is rationalized,

$$I\angle\theta = \frac{V}{R + j(\omega L - 1/\omega C)} \times \frac{R - j(\omega L - 1/\omega C)}{R - j(\omega L - 1/\omega C)}$$

$$= V\frac{R - j(\omega L - 1/\omega C)}{R^2 + (\omega L - 1/\omega C)^2}$$

$$= \frac{V}{\sqrt{R^2 + (\omega L - 1/\omega C)^2}}\left[\frac{R}{\sqrt{R^2 + (\omega L - 1/\omega C)^2}}\right.$$

$$\left. -j\frac{\omega L - 1/\omega C}{\sqrt{R^2 + (\omega L - 1/\omega C)^2}}\right] \tag{3-33}$$

Referring to the complex-impedance diagram of the circuit, Fig. 3-3, Eq. (3-33) may be written

$$I\angle\theta = \frac{V}{\sqrt{R^2 + (\omega L - 1/\omega C)^2}}(\cos\phi - j\sin\phi)$$

$$= \frac{V}{\sqrt{R^2 + (\omega L - 1/\omega C)^2}}\angle-\phi \qquad (3\text{-}34)$$

where

$$\phi = \arctan\frac{\omega L - 1/\omega C}{R} \qquad (3\text{-}35)$$

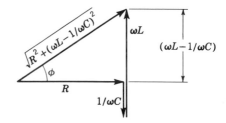

FIGURE 3-3 *Complex impedance diagram of an RLC circuit.*

The exact correspondence between the differential-equation solution, Eq. (3-29), and the result of the complex-impedance approach, Eq. (3-34), is evident. In subsequent sections the latter technique is used exclusively because of its simplicity.

Consider the amplitude of the current in the *RLC* circuit as a function of the frequency of the applied voltage. According to Eq. (3-34), the current is very small at low frequencies ($\omega \to 0$), because the capacitive reactance is great. Similarly, the current is small at high frequencies ($\omega \to \infty$), because the inductive reactance becomes large. Between these two extremes, the current is a maximum when

$$\omega L - \frac{1}{\omega C} = 0 \qquad (3\text{-}36)$$

At this frequency the circuit is said to be in *resonance*, and the current is given by

$$I = \frac{V}{R} \qquad (3\text{-}37)$$

Furthermore, according to Eq. (3-35), the phase angle is zero. The circuit appears as a pure resistance, and the current is in phase with the applied voltage. This is so because the capacitive reactance cancels the inductive reactance at resonance. The *resonant frequency* is, from Eq. (3-36),

$$\omega_0 = 2\pi f_0 = \frac{1}{\sqrt{LC}} \qquad (3\text{-}38)$$

To illustrate the properties of a series resonant circuit, consider the current variation in the specific circuit of Fig. 3-4. After substituting the component values on the diagram into Eq. (3-34) it is

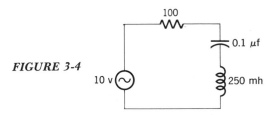

FIGURE 3-4

found that the current in the circuit changes with frequency as illustrated in Fig. 3-5. The current maximum is $I = {}^{10}\!/_{100} = 0.1$ amp at the resonant frequency,

$$f_0 = \frac{1}{2\pi \sqrt{LC}} = \frac{1}{6.28 \sqrt{250 \times 10^{-3} \times 0.1 \times 10^{-6}}} = 1000 \text{ cps} \qquad (3\text{-}39)$$

and the decrease on either side of resonance is clearly evident.

The voltage drops around the circuit at resonance further illus-

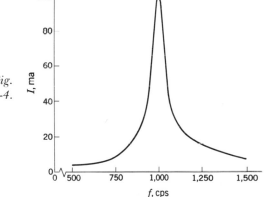

FIGURE 3-5 *Resonance curve of circuit in Fig. 3-4.*

trate an important feature of alternating currents. The drop across the resistor is

$$V_R = RI = 100 \times 0.1 = 10 \text{ volts} \qquad (3\text{-}40)$$

The corresponding voltage drop across the capacitor is the current times the capacitive reactance

$$V_C = I \frac{1}{\omega C} = \frac{0.1}{6.28 \times 10^3 \times 10^{-7}} = 158 \text{ volts} \qquad (3\text{-}41)$$

and, similarly, the voltage across the inductor is

$$V_L = I \omega L = 0.1 \times 6.28 \times 10^3 \times 0.25 = 158 \text{ volts} \qquad (3\text{-}42)$$

It is evident that the rms voltage drops around the circuit do not sum to zero. In fact, the voltages across both reactances rise to large values at resonance. Note, however, that the phase angle of the capacitor voltage is +90° with respect to the current, while the phase angle of the voltage across the inductor is −90°. This means that the instantaneous voltages across the two reactances cancel each other and that the drop across the resistance equals the applied emf, as confirmed by Eq. (3-40). Kirchhoff's voltage rule is valid when the phases of the currents and voltages in ac circuits are accounted for. This matter is considered further in Exercises 3-6 and 3-7.

A voltmeter connected across, say, the capacitor in Fig. 3-4 indicates a voltage corresponding to Eq. (3-41) at resonance. Therefore, the capacitor (and the inductor) must be capable of withstanding high voltages without breakdown, even though the applied voltage is well below the ratings of the components. Resonance is widely used in electronic circuits to increase the current at the resonant frequency.

3-4 Parallel resonance

Resonance also occurs in a parallel circuit, such as the one shown in Fig. 3-6. The current in the circuit is obtained by first comput-

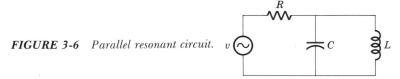

FIGURE 3-6 *Parallel resonant circuit.*

ing the total complex impedance. Since the inductance and capacitance are connected in parallel, their equivalent impedance is found with the aid of Eq. (3-26),

$$\frac{1}{Z_1 \angle \phi_1} = \frac{1}{-j(1/\omega C)} + \frac{1}{j\omega L} = j\omega C + \frac{1}{j\omega L}$$

$$= \frac{-\omega^2 LC + 1}{j\omega L} \tag{3-43}$$

Therefore, the impedance of the LC combination is

$$Z_1 \angle \phi_1 = j \frac{\omega L}{1 - \omega^2 LC} \tag{3-44}$$

According to Eq. (3-44) the impedance is very large, actually infinite, when

$$\omega_0^2 LC = 1$$

or

$$\omega_0 = \frac{1}{\sqrt{LC}} \tag{3-45}$$

This is the same relation found in the case of series resonance, Eq. (3-38). Note, however, that in series resonance the impedance is a minimum, according to Eq. (3-31), while in parallel resonance Eq. (3-44) shows that the impedance is a maximum at the resonant frequency.

The total impedance of the circuit includes the series combination of R with $Z_1 \angle \phi_1$

$$Z \angle \phi = R + j \frac{\omega L}{1 - \omega^2 LC} \tag{3-46}$$

so that the current in the circuit is

$$I \angle \theta = \frac{V}{R + j\omega L/(1 - \omega^2 LC)} \tag{3-47}$$

According to Eq. (3-47) the current is zero at resonance, when the impedance becomes infinite. The voltage V then appears across the LC combination, independent of the value of R. This feature of the parallel resonant circuit is extensively used in practical circuits. The output voltage V_o is simply the current times the impedance Z_1 or

$$V_o \angle \phi_o = I \angle \theta Z_1 \angle \phi_1 = \frac{V}{R + j\omega L/(1 - \omega^2 LC)} \frac{j\omega L}{1 - \omega^2 LC}$$

$$= V \frac{j\omega L}{R(1 - \omega^2 LC) + j\omega L}$$

Rationalizing

$$V_o \angle \phi_o = V \frac{j\omega L}{R(1 - \omega^2 LC) + j\omega L} \times \frac{R(1 - \omega^2 LC) - j\omega L}{R(1 - \omega^2 LC) - j\omega L}$$

$$= V \frac{(\omega L)^2 + j\omega LR(1 - \omega^2 LC)}{(\omega L)^2 + R^2(1 - \omega^2 LC)^2}$$

$$= V \frac{1 + j(R/\omega L)(1 - \omega^2 LC)}{1 + (R/\omega L)^2(1 - \omega^2 LC)^2} \tag{3-48}$$

the magnitude of the output voltage is found by taking the square root of the sum of the squares of the real and imaginary parts. Therefore, the ratio of the output voltage to the input voltage becomes

$$\frac{V_o}{V} = \left\{ \frac{1 + (R/\omega L)^2(1 - \omega^2 LC)^2}{[1 + (R/\omega L)^2(1 - \omega^2 LC)^2]^2} \right\}^{1/2}$$

$$= \frac{1}{[1 + (R/\omega L)^2(1 - \omega^2 LC)^2]^{1/2}} \tag{3-49}$$

The behavior of Eq. (3-49) is illustrated with the specific component values given on the parallel-circuit diagram of Fig. 3-7. The output voltage rises to equal the input voltage at the resonant frequency, as shown in Fig. 3-8. Parallel resonance is commonly used in electronic circuits to achieve a high impedance which develops an appreciable signal voltage at resonance. Resonance is also important in circuits designed to emphasize one single fre-

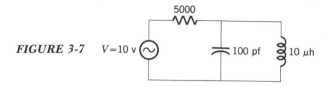

FIGURE 3-7 $V = 10$ v

quency over all others. By adjusting the value of, say, the capacitance, the circuit may be *tuned* to different frequencies. This is the principle used to select different channels in radio and TV receivers.

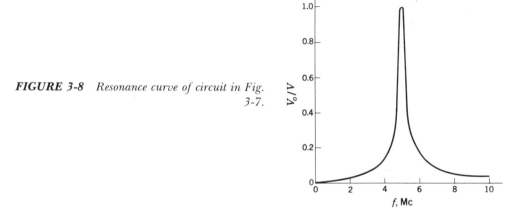

FIGURE 3-8   *Resonance curve of circuit in Fig. 3-7.*

It is interesting to compare the currents in various components of a parallel resonant circuit at resonance. According to Eq. (3-49) the full input voltage is applied across both the capacitor and inductance at resonance, so that the currents are, respectively,

$$I_C = \frac{V}{1/\omega C} \qquad (3\text{-}50)$$

and

$$I_L = \frac{V}{\omega L} \qquad (3\text{-}51)$$

Yet the total current in the circuit is zero, according to Eq. (3-47). This is another situation where the phase angle of the currents must be considered. Since the capacitive reactance equals the inductive reactance at resonance, the magnitudes of the currents in the inductance and capacitance are equal. Their phase angles are such that at, say, the upper branch point in Fig. 3-6 these two currents cancel at every instant and no current is present in the resistor. In this sense a circulating current exists in the parallel *LC* combination at resonance. The validity of Kirchhoff's current rule for ac circuits is explored in greater detail in Exercises 3-10 and 3-11.

3-5 Q factor

The resistance in a resonant circuit is significant in determining the current at frequencies removed from the resonant frequency, as well as at resonance. This is an important consideration since, for example, the resistance of the turns of wire is present in all inductors. The effect is similar in both series and parallel resonance cases, but the former is simpler mathematically and can be used to illustrate all the important features.

Consider the magnitude of the current in a series circuit, Eq. (3-34),

$$I = \frac{V}{[R^2 + (\omega L - 1/\omega C)^2]^{1/2}} \tag{3-52}$$

This can be rearranged as

$$I = \frac{V}{R} \frac{1}{\sqrt{1 + (\omega L/R)^2(1 - 1/\omega^2 LC)^2}} \tag{3-53}$$

The ratio of inductive reactance to resistance is called the *quality factor* or, more usually, the Q of the circuit. For present purposes, it is convenient to consider the Q at resonance,

$$Q_0 = \frac{\omega_0 L}{R} \tag{3-54}$$

Introducing Eq. (3-54) and the resonant frequency from Eq. (3-38) into Eq. (3-53),

$$\frac{I}{I_M} = \frac{1}{\{1 + Q_0^2(\omega/\omega_0)^2[1 - (\omega_0/\omega)^2]^2\}^{1/2}} \tag{3-55}$$

where I_M is the maximum current at resonance. Finally, an alternative form to Eq. (3-55) is, after multiplying the last two quantities under the radical,

$$\frac{I}{I_M} = \left[1 + Q_0^2\left(\frac{\omega}{\omega_0} - \frac{\omega_0}{\omega}\right)^2\right]^{-1/2} \tag{3-56}$$

This expression, plotted in Fig. 3-9 for representative values of Q_0, shows that a large Q_0 (that is, a small value of R) leads to a very sharply resonant circuit. Conversely, low-Q circuits have much broader frequency responses. Values of Q_0 in the range from 10 to 100 are common in electronic circuits and are useful in very selective tuned circuits, as illustrated by the two lower curves of Fig. 3-9. Special resonant components can have Q's as high as several thousand, and these result in very high frequency selectivity indeed. On the other hand, it is sometimes desirable to broaden the frequency response of a resonant circuit so that it is useful over a wide band of frequencies on either side of the resonant fre-

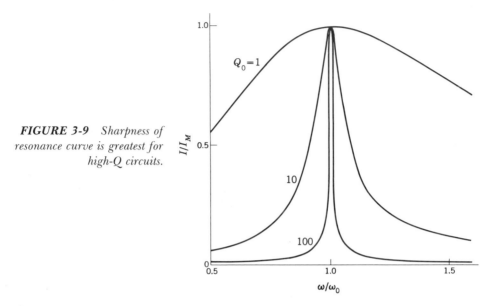

FIGURE 3-9 *Sharpness of resonance curve is greatest for high-Q circuits.*

quency. In this case a resistor is purposely included to yield a lower Q than that of the inductor alone.

BRIDGE CIRCUITS

Figure 3-10 shows the ac analogy of the dc Wheatstone bridge. It has a complex impedance in each arm and uses a sine-wave

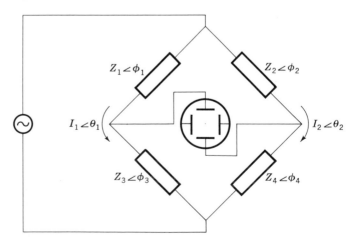

FIGURE 3-10 *The ac Wheatstone bridge uses sine-wave generator and ac detector such as an oscilloscope.*

generator and an ac detector, such as an oscilloscope. Analysis of this circuit proceeds as in the dc case considered in Chap. 1, except that complex impedances and currents are used. Only the balance condition is of interest here, and this is obtained in the following way. At balance, the voltage across the detector is zero, which means that the current in this branch is zero and therefore that the current in $Z_1 \angle \phi_1$ is equal to that in $Z_3 \angle \phi_3$; also, the current in $Z_2 \angle \phi_2$ is equal to that in $Z_4 \angle \phi_4$. Furthermore, since the voltage across the detector is zero, the voltage drops across $Z_1 \angle \phi_1$ and $Z_2 \angle \phi_2$ are equal and so are the voltage drops across $Z_3 \angle \phi_3$ and $Z_4 \angle \phi_4$.

Equating the voltage drops across corresponding arms of the bridge

$$Z_1 \angle \phi_1 I_1 \angle \theta_1 = Z_2 \angle \phi_2 I_2 \angle \theta_2 \tag{3-57}$$

and

$$Z_3 \angle \phi_3 I_1 \angle \theta_1 = Z_4 \angle \phi_4 I_2 \angle \theta_2 \tag{3-58}$$

Dividing Eq. (3-57) by Eq. (3-58), the condition for balance is found to be

$$\frac{Z_1 \angle \phi_1}{Z_3 \angle \phi_3} = \frac{Z_2 \angle \phi_2}{Z_4 \angle \phi_4} \tag{3-59}$$

which should be compared with the condition for balance of the dc Wheatstone bridge, Eq. (1-68).

The balance condition can be rewritten

$$\frac{Z_1 \angle \phi_1}{Z_2 \angle \phi_2} = \frac{Z_3 \angle \phi_3}{Z_4 \angle \phi_4} \tag{3-60}$$

Using Eq. (3-19) to carry out the ratios indicated, the result is

$$\frac{Z_1}{Z_2} \angle (\phi_1 - \phi_2) = \frac{Z_3}{Z_4} \angle (\phi_3 - \phi_4) \tag{3-61}$$

According to Eq. (3-61) the balance condition involves the equality of two complex numbers. This means that both the real and imaginary parts must be equal and implies that two independent balance adjustments are necessary in ac bridge circuits. Specific illustrations of this situation are taken up in the following sections.

3-6 Inductance and capacitance bridge

Bridge circuits in Figs. 3-11 and 3-12 can be used to measure inductance and capacitance in the same way a Wheatstone bridge is used to measure resistance. Consider the inductance bridge, Fig. 3-11, and note the comparison with Fig. 3-10. The impedance $R_u + j\omega L_u$ represents the inductance and resistance of an unknown inductor. The balance condition, Eq. (3-60), means

$$\frac{R_1}{R_2} = \frac{R_3 + j\omega L_3}{R_u + j\omega L_u} \tag{3-62}$$

Cross-multiplying,

$$R_1 R_u + j\omega R_1 L_u = R_2 R_3 + j\omega R_2 L_3 \tag{3-63}$$

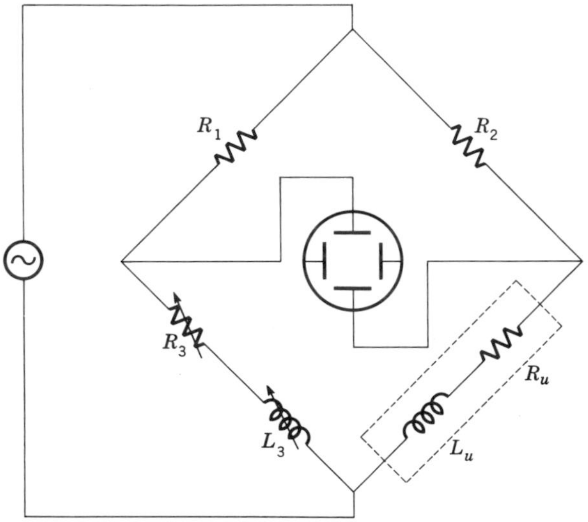

FIGURE 3-11 *Inductance bridge used to measure resistance and inductance of unknown coil.*

After equating real and imaginary parts, the two balance conditions are written as

$$R_1 R_u = R_2 R_3 \qquad \text{and} \qquad R_1 L_u = R_2 L_3 \tag{3-64}$$

The first condition is the same as the Wheatstone bridge condition and may be carried out with dc instruments. The second equation is obtained using ac excitation of the bridge subsequent to obtaining the dc balance.

Rewriting Eqs. (3-64),

$$R_u = \frac{R_2}{R_1} R_3 \qquad \text{and} \qquad L_u = \frac{R_2}{R_1} L_3 \tag{3-65}$$

which illustrates how the ratio R_2/R_1 acts as a multiplying factor on the variable components R_3 and L_3 to yield the unknown resistance and inductance. This suggests that both R_3 and L_3 should be variable, but since variable inductors are difficult to make, the following procedure is more satisfactory. Either R_2 or R_1 is adjusted until balance is obtained with a given value of L_3. Then R_3 is adjusted to satisfy the dc balance condition. In this way the unknown inductance is compared with the standard inductance L_3, and the only variable components needed are resistances.

An interesting feature of the balance conditions, Eqs. (3-65), is that they are independent of frequency, so that the generator frequency may have any convenient value. It is usually best to choose a frequency such that the inductive reactance is approximately equal to the resistances. A similar situation exists in the case of the capacitance bridge, Fig. 3-12, which is analyzed in Exercise 3-13.

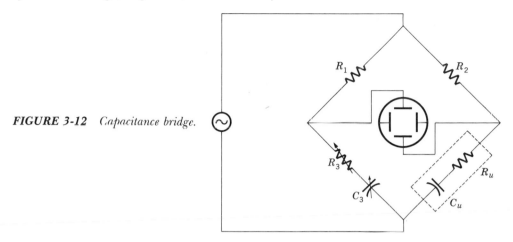

FIGURE 3-12 *Capacitance bridge.*

Since there is no dc path in the lower arms of the capacitance bridge, both balance adjustments are made with ac excitation (this can be done in the inductance bridge case as well). Although calibrated variable capacitors are usually used in this circuit, it is equally possible to employ a fixed standard capacitor together with variable resistors. This is particularly convenient when the same instrument is used as an inductance bridge as well as a capacitance bridge by replacing the standard capacitor C_3 with a standard inductance L_3. Since it is also possible to employ a standard resistor in this position, such an instrument is quite versatile in that it can measure resistance, capacitance, and inductance.

3-7 Wien bridge

A bridge which has a parallel combination in one arm and a series combination in an adjacent arm is known as a *Wien* bridge. A useful example employing only resistors and capacitors, shown in Fig. 3-13, is analyzed by first calculating the impedances $Z_3 \angle \phi_3$ and $Z_4 \angle \phi_4$. Considering the parallel combination first,

$$\frac{1}{Z_3 \angle \phi_3} = j\omega C_3 + \frac{1}{R_3} = \frac{1 + j\omega R_3 C_3}{R_3} \qquad (3\text{-}66)$$

which is rationalized to give

$$Z_3 \angle \phi_3 = \frac{R_3}{1 + (\omega R_3 C_3)^2} (1 - j\omega R_3 C_3) \qquad (3\text{-}67)$$

The series combination is

$$Z_4 \angle \phi_4 = R_4 - j\frac{1}{\omega C_4} \qquad (3\text{-}68)$$

Inserting Eqs. (3-66) and (3-68) into the balance equation (3-60) results in

$$\frac{R_1}{R_2} = \frac{R_3/(1+j\omega R_3 C_3)}{R_4 - j(1/\omega C_4)} \qquad (3\text{-}69)$$

Cross-multiplying,

$$(1+j\omega R_3 C_3)\left(R_4 - \frac{j}{\omega C_4}\right) = \frac{R_2}{R_1} R_3 \qquad (3\text{-}70)$$

$$R_4 + \frac{R_3 C_3}{C_4} + j\left(\omega R_3 R_4 C_3 - \frac{1}{\omega C_4}\right) = \frac{R_2}{R_1} R_3 \qquad (3\text{-}71)$$

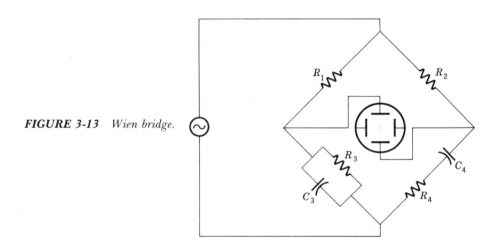

FIGURE 3-13 *Wien bridge.*

Upon equating the real and imaginary parts, the balance conditions are found to be

$$\frac{C_3}{C_4} + \frac{R_4}{R_3} = \frac{R_2}{R_1}$$

and

$$\omega^2 R_3 C_3 R_4 C_4 = 1 \qquad (3\text{-}72)$$

This result differs from those for the inductance and capacitance bridges in that the frequency ω appears in the balance equations. Therefore, it is possible to achieve balance by adjusting the frequency and only one component, say R_1, rather than using two variable impedances. Alternatively, by adjusting two of the components for balance, the bridge is capable of determining the frequency of a sine-wave source.

The Wien bridge is also useful as a frequency-selective network which has properties similar to those of a resonant circuit. Since inductors suitable for use over a wide frequency interval are expensive and difficult to construct, the Wien bridge has considerable advantages in many applications. This is particularly true for low-frequency circuits where inconveniently large inductance values are necessary. Often, the resistors and capacitors in the series and parallel branches are equal, as in Fig. 3-14. This means that the characteristic frequency of the network is, from Eq. (3-72),

$$\omega_0 = \frac{1}{RC} \tag{3-73}$$

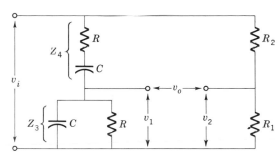

FIGURE 3-14 *Wien bridge used as frequency-selective network.*

The frequency-selective properties of the Wien bridge are illustrated by calculating the output voltage of the network as a function of the frequency of the input voltage. The output voltage is obtained by subtracting the voltages across $Z_3 \angle \phi_3$ and R_1. The drop across $Z_3 \angle \phi_3$ is simply the current in this arm times the impedance,

$$v_1 = \frac{v_i}{Z_3 \angle \phi_3 + Z_4 \angle \phi_4} Z_3 \angle \phi_3 = \frac{v_i}{1 + Z_4 \angle \phi_4 / Z_3 \angle \phi_3} \tag{3-74}$$

where it has been assumed that the current in the output circuit is negligible, even when the bridge is not balanced. This condition is satisfied in practice by connecting a high-impedance load to the output terminals. The impedance ratio in Eq. (3-74) is evaluated from Eqs. (3-67) and (3-68), after making all the R's and C's equal. Also, introducing ω_0,

$$\frac{Z_4 \angle \phi_4}{Z_3 \angle \phi_3} = \frac{R(1 - j\omega_0/\omega)}{R(1 - j\omega/\omega_0)/[1 + (\omega/\omega_0)^2]} = 2 + j \left(\frac{\omega}{\omega_0} - \frac{\omega_0}{\omega} \right) \tag{3-75}$$

Note that according to Eq. (3-75) the reactive term vanishes at the characteristic frequency when $\omega = \omega_0$. This means that the network is resistive at this frequency (and at this frequency only) and that the output voltage is in phase with the input voltage, just as for a resonant circuit.

The drop across R_1 is

$$v_2 = \frac{v_i}{R_1 + R_2} R_1 = \frac{v_i}{1 + R_2/R_1} \tag{3-76}$$

Finally, the output voltage is

$$v_o = v_1 - v_2 = v_i \left[\frac{1}{3 + j(\omega/\omega_0 - \omega_0/\omega)} - \frac{1}{1 + R_2/R_1} \right] \qquad (3\text{-}77)$$

The ratio of the output to the input v_o/v_i can be found after rationalizing. Two plots of Eq. (3-77) are presented in Fig. 3-15 for different values of the ratio R_2/R_1. The output voltage clearly

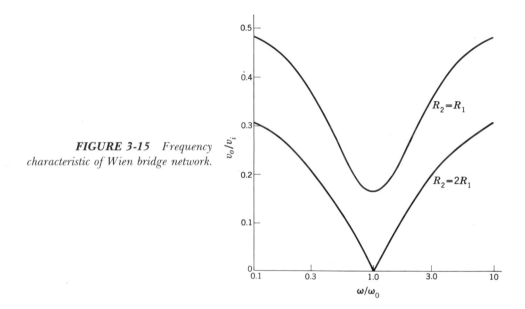

FIGURE 3-15 *Frequency characteristic of Wien bridge network.*

goes through a minimum at $\omega = \omega_0$, very analogous to the situation in series resonance. The minimum is quite sharp and mathematically discontinuous in the case of true balance, $R_2 = 2R_1$. Therefore, the frequency selectivity of the circuit is quite good.

3-8 Bridged-T filter

Although the so-called *bridged-T* filter is not a true bridge circuit, it has properties similar to those of the Wien bridge. In contrast to the Wien bridge, the bridged T, shown in Fig. 3-16, generally

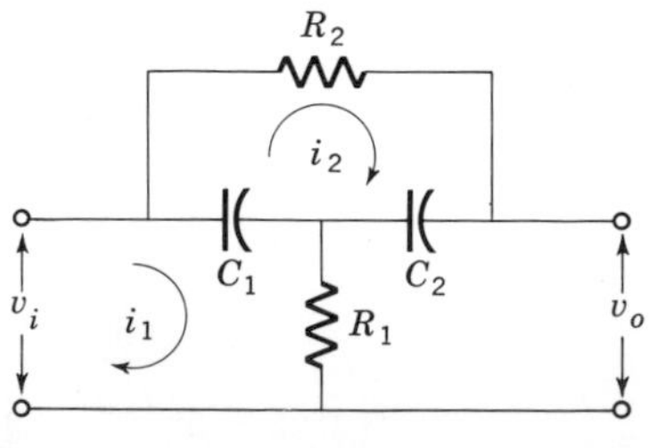

FIGURE 3-16 *Bridged-T filter.*

does not employ equal values of resistance and capacitance in the two positions. To solve for the output voltage, the current in the upper resistor is determined and the output is obtained by subtracting the voltage drop across R_2 from the input voltage.

Kirchhoff's law applied to the i_1 loop in Fig. 3-16 is

$$v_i = i_1 \frac{-j}{\omega C_1} - i_2 \frac{-j}{\omega C_1} + i_1 R_1 \tag{3-78}$$

Adding up the voltages around the second loop,

$$0 = -i_1 \frac{-j}{\omega C_1} + i_2 \frac{-j}{\omega C_1} + i_2 R_2 + i_2 \frac{-j}{\omega C_2} \tag{3-79}$$

After simplification, i_1 is determined from Eq. (3-79),

$$i_1 = \left(1 + \frac{C_1}{C_2} + j\omega R_2 C_1\right) i_2 \tag{3-80}$$

and substituted into Eq. (3-78). The result is solved for i_2 and the output voltage is then given by

$$v_o = v_i - R_2 i_2 = v_i - \frac{v_i \omega R_2 C_2}{\omega C_2 [R_1(1 + C_1/C_2) + R_2] + j(\omega^2 R_1 C_1 R_2 C_2 - 1)} \tag{3-81}$$

The imaginary part vanishes at the critical frequency

$$\omega_0 = \frac{1}{\sqrt{R_1 C_1 R_2 C_2}} \tag{3-82}$$

which should be compared with the corresponding expression for the Wien bridge, Eq. (3-73). After inserting Eq. (3-82) into Eq. (3-81), the complex ratio of output to input voltage may be written

$$\frac{v_o}{v_i} = 1 - \left\{\left[1 + \frac{R_1}{R_2}\left(1 + \frac{C_1}{C_2}\right)\right] + j\sqrt{\frac{R_1 C_1}{R_2 C_2}}\left(\frac{\omega}{\omega_0} - \frac{\omega_0}{\omega}\right)\right\}^{-1} \tag{3-83}$$

The frequency-response characteristic of the bridged-T filter, Eq. (3-83), is similar to that of the Wien bridge, except that the minimum is not as sharp at the characteristic frequency (see Exercises 3-16 and 3-17). Nevertheless, its relative simplicity, and the fact that both input and output terminals have a common connection, make the bridged T a useful frequency-selective network. Specific applications of this circuit are considered in a later chapter.

3-9 Twin-T network

Somewhat more complicated than the bridged T is the *twin-T* filter shown in Fig. 3-17a, which may be analyzed by the technique used in the previous section. The twin T is equivalent in response characteristic to the Wien bridge, which it resembles somewhat

(Fig. 3-17*b*). It also has the advantage of a common input-output terminal. The choice between the Wien bridge, bridged-T, and twin-T network for any given application depends on factors such

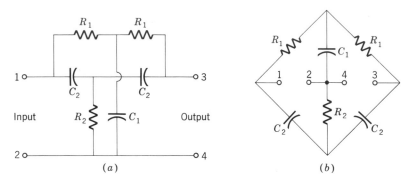

FIGURE 3-17 *(a) Twin-T filter, (b) network redrawn as a bridge.*

as frequency range, desired performance, and complexity; all three circuits are commonly used.

TRANSIENT CURRENTS

3-10   Inductive time constant

The study of ac circuits to this point has implicitly assumed that the rms values of the sinusoidal emfs are constant. Transient effects are associated with sudden changes in the voltages applied to ac networks, as, for example, when an emf is first applied. These transient currents dissipate rapidly, leaving steady-state currents in the network which persist as long as the emf is applied. Although most often the steady-state currents are of primary con-cern, in many cases transient effects are important as well. This is particularly so in determining the response of a network to iso-lated voltage pulses.

Transient currents in ac networks are found by solving the cir-cuit differential equation, taking into account the magnitude of the current at the time the applied voltage is changed. Actually, the sum of the transient current and the steady-state current is the complete solution of the circuit differential equation. It is gener-ally satisfactory to consider the two aspects of ac-circuit analysis separately because the response of circuits is most often of interest in connection either with steady emfs alone or with transient effects alone.

It is convenient to investigate first the transient currents in a simple *LR* series circuit incorporating a battery and a two-position switch, as shown in Fig. 3-18.　Suppose the switch is suddenly connected to terminal 1.　The circuit differential equation is, from Kirchhoff's rule,

$$V = Ri + L\frac{di}{dt} \tag{3-84}$$

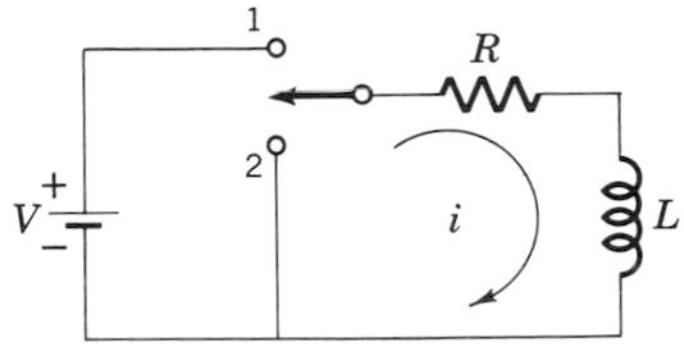

FIGURE 3-18

This equation is solved by first rewriting it as

$$\frac{L}{R}\frac{di}{dt} = \frac{V}{R} - i$$

and then

$$\frac{di}{V/R - i} = \frac{R}{L}\,dt \tag{3-85}$$

Both the left side and the right side of Eq (3-85) are standard integrals, so that upon integrating,

$$-\ln\left(\frac{V}{R} - i\right) = \frac{R}{L}t + K \tag{3-86}$$

where K is a constant to be evaluated later.　Another way of writing Eq. (3-86) is

$$\frac{V}{R} - i = \exp\left(\frac{-t}{L/R} - K\right) = Ae^{-t/(L/R)} \tag{3-87}$$

where the constant A replaces $\exp -K$ for simplicity.　In order to evaluate A, note that the current is zero at the time the switch is closed at $t = 0$.　Therefore

$$\frac{V}{R} - 0 = Ae^0 = A$$

and the final solution for the current is, after substituting for A in Eq. (3-87),

$$i = \frac{V}{R}\left(1 - e^{-t/(L/R)}\right) \tag{3-88}$$

The quantity L/R, which has the dimensions of seconds, is called the *time constant*

$$\tau = \frac{L}{R} \tag{3-89}$$

The growth of current in an inductive circuit according to Eq. (3-88) is shown in Fig. 3-19.　Note that the current starts rapidly from zero and approaches a steady-state value given by the dc current V/R. After a time equal to one time constant the current is equal to $1 - e^{-1} = 1 - 0.368 = 63\%$ of its final value. The actual

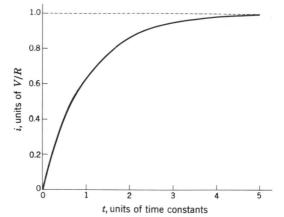

FIGURE 3-19   *Exponential growth of current in an inductive circuit.*

time at which this current is attained depends upon the magnitude of the inductance and resistance. A long time is achieved for large values of L and small values of R, and vice versa, according to Eq. (3-89).

Suppose now the switch in Fig. 3-18 is suddenly connected to terminal 2. This removes the emf from the circuit, and the circuit differential equation becomes

$$L \frac{di}{dt} + Ri = 0 \qquad (3\text{-}90)$$

This may be rewritten as

$$\frac{di}{i} = -\frac{R}{L} dt \qquad (3\text{-}91)$$

Integrating both sides

$$\ln i = -\frac{R}{L} t + K'$$

where K' is a constant. This result may be put in the form

$$i = Be^{-t/\tau}$$

where $B = \exp K'$ and $\tau = L/R$. Since $i = V/R$ at $t = 0$, the final solution is

$$i = \frac{V}{R} e^{-t/\tau} \qquad (3\text{-}92)$$

Evidently, the current decays exponentially to zero from the dc value at a rate governed by the circuit time constant. The growth and decay of current in an inductive circuit are symmetrical, as can be seen by comparing Figs. 3-19 and 3-20.

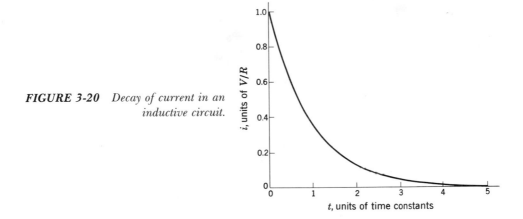

FIGURE 3-20 *Decay of current in an inductive circuit.*

3-11   Capacitive time constant

The simple RC circuit is analogous to the inductive case, as may be illustrated by considering the circuit in Fig. 3-21.   The circuit equation with the switch in position 1 is

$$V = Ri + \frac{q}{C} \qquad\qquad (3\text{-}93)$$

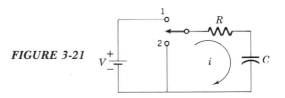

FIGURE 3-21

Differentiating with respect to t,

$$0 = R\frac{di}{dt} + \frac{i}{C} \qquad\qquad (3\text{-}94)$$

or

$$\frac{di}{i} = -\frac{1}{RC}\,dt$$

By analogy with Eq. (3-91), the solution is

$$i = Ae^{-t/RC} \qquad\qquad (3\text{-}95)$$

Evidently the time constant of the RC circuit is given by

$$\tau = RC \qquad\qquad (3\text{-}96)$$

The constant A is evaluated by noting that at $t = 0$ the charge on the capacitor is zero, so that the voltage across C is also zero. The initial current is simply V/R, according to Eq. (3-93). Therefore, the current is

$$i = \frac{V}{R} e^{-t/RC} \tag{3-97}$$

The capacitive charging current starts at a high value and falls exponentially to zero as the capacitor becomes charged, Fig. 3-22.

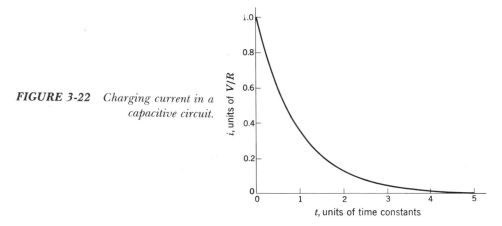

FIGURE 3-22 *Charging current in a capacitive circuit.*

According to Eq. (3-96) large values of resistance and capacitance result in long characteristic time constants.

The decay of current upon closing the switch to position 2 is identical with that given by Eq. (3-97). This can be seen by writing the circuit voltage equation for this case

$$\frac{q}{C} + Ri = 0$$

Differentiating with respect to t, the circuit differential equation is

$$\frac{i}{C} + R \frac{di}{dt} = 0 \tag{3-98}$$

which is identical to Eq. (3-94). Furthermore, the potential across the capacitor is equal to V when the capacitor is fully charged. This means that the initial discharge current is V/R, just as in the charging-current case.

The voltage across the capacitor at any time may be determined by calculating the charge on the capacitor using the solution (3-97). The variation of the capacitor voltage with time is analogous to Figs. 3-19 and 3-20, except that the steady-state asymptote upon charging is equal to V (see Exercise 3-18).

Transient currents also accompany the turning on of ac voltage sources. For example, consider the circuit in Fig. 3-23, for which the circuit differential equation is

$$R \frac{di}{dt} + \frac{1}{C} i = \frac{dv}{dt} \qquad (3\text{-}99)$$

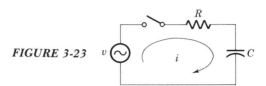

FIGURE 3-23

It is convenient to express the applied voltage as

$$v = V_p \sin (\omega t + \theta) \qquad (3\text{-}100)$$

where the phase angle θ is introduced in order to choose the instantaneous input voltage amplitude at $t = 0$. Since the full solution of Eq. (3-99) involves a transient current and a steady-state
current of frequency ω, the total current is

$$i = i_1 + i_2 \qquad (3\text{-}101)$$

where i_1 is the transient current and i_2 is the steady-state current.
Substituting Eq. (3-101) into the differential equation (3-99)
and rearranging, the result is

$$\left(R \frac{di_1}{dt} + \frac{1}{C} i_1 \right) + \left(R \frac{di_2}{dt} + \frac{1}{C} i_2 - \frac{dv}{dt} \right) = 0 \qquad (3\text{-}102)$$

This equation is solved if both parentheses are equal to zero. The
first one is just Eq. (3-94), for which the solution previously found
is Eq. (3-95). Similarly, the second parenthesis is just Eq. (2-36),
and the solution is Eq. (2-48). Using these expressions, the total
current is written

$$i = A e^{-t/\tau} + \frac{V_p}{\sqrt{R^2 + (1/\omega C)^2}} \sin (\omega t + \theta + \phi) \qquad (3\text{-}103)$$

where

$$\tau = RC$$

$$\phi = \arctan R\omega C$$

and the constant A is determined from the voltage of the source
at the time the switch is closed. Note that Eq. (3-103) consists of
a transient part together with a steady-state term, as discussed
above.

Suppose the applied voltage is at its peak, that is, $v = V_p$, when
the switch is closed at $t = 0$. This means we choose $\theta = \pi/2$, according to Eq. (3-100), and the initial current is V_p/R. Thus, Eq.
(3-103) for $t = 0$ becomes

$$\frac{V_p}{R} = A + \frac{V_p}{\sqrt{R^2 + (1/\omega C)^2}} \sin \left(\frac{\pi}{2} + \phi \right) \qquad (3\text{-}104)$$

This is solved for the constant A, which is then substituted into Eq. (3-103). The result is the final solution

$$i = \frac{V_p}{R} \frac{1}{1 + (\omega RC)^2} e^{-t/\tau} + \frac{V_p}{\sqrt{R^2 + (1/\omega C)^2}} \sin\left(\omega t + \frac{\pi}{2} + \phi\right) \quad (3\text{-}105)$$

In order for the transient term of Eq. (3-105) to have an appreciable magnitude compared with the steady-state term, the denominator of its coefficient must not be too large. This means that

$$(\omega RC)^2 < 1$$

or

$$\tau < \frac{1}{\omega} \qquad\qquad (3\text{-}106)$$

According to this expression, the time constant of the transient current is smaller than one period of the sine-wave current. Therefore, any transient current is negligible after only a fraction of a cycle of the ac wave, and the transient may therefore be ignored. If, on the other hand, the time constant is much greater than one period, the transient persists over many cycles, but, according to Eq. (3-105), the amplitude is small. This reasoning demonstrates why the steady-state solution alone is sufficiently accurate for most purposes.

3-12 Ringing

Sudden changes of voltage in a resonant circuit may produce *ringing*, in which a current is generated at the resonant frequency of the circuit. The amplitude of the resonant current dies away exponentially as in nonresonant circuits. For example, after the switch is closed in the circuit of Fig. 3-24, the current may oscillate as sketched in Fig. 3-25 before decaying away. The phenomenon is obviously analogous to striking a bell a sharp mechanical blow as with a hammer, whence the origin of the term ringing.

Actually, the resistance in the circuit must be small in order for ringing to occur. If the resistance is larger than a certain critical value, the current transient decays uniformly to zero much like in the simple RC circuit discussed previously. The reason for this is that I^2R losses in the resistor damp out the oscillating current.

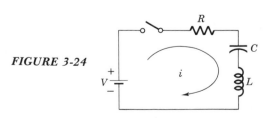

FIGURE 3-24

Thus, in most cases oscillating transient effects in resonant circuits may be ignored unless the circuit is specifically designed to
emphasize ringing.

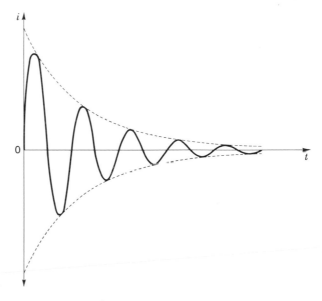

FIGURE 3-25 *Transient current in a
resonant circuit can be decaying
sinusoidal oscillation.*

3-13 Square-wave response

It is useful to investigate the response of reactive circuits to
square-wave voltages by the transient methods of the previous section. This is possible since a square wave can be considered to be
a dc voltage which is switched on and off at the frequency of the
wave. Transient-current analysis complements the Fourier-series
method discussed in the previous chapter and is often simpler.
The transient technique yields the output waveform directly and
makes it unnecessary to determine the response of the circuit to
each of the harmonics.

Consider first the high-pass RC filter of Fig. 3-26 to which is applied the square wave of period T as indicated on the diagram.
According to Eq. (3-97) the transient current accompanying each
half-cycle of the square wave has the form

$$i = Ae^{-t/\tau} \qquad\qquad (3\text{-}107)$$

where the constant A depends upon the current in the circuit resulting from the previous transient. For example, if $\tau = T/2$, the
current has decayed 63 percent of the way at the time the square-
wave voltage reverses. This means that the voltage across the
capacitor causes a transient current in the reverse direction, and

so forth. The output voltage ($= Ri$) is a succession of exponential transients, as shown in Fig. 3-27. These waveforms correspond to different values of the RC time constant compared with the period of the square wave.

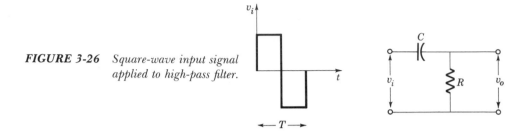

FIGURE 3-26   *Square-wave input signal applied to high-pass filter.*

Note that when the circuit time constant is very small compared with the period of the square wave, the output waveform approaches the differential of the square wave. This is an alternative approach to the study of differentiating circuits discussed in Chap. 2.

The low-pass filter circuit, Fig. 3-28, may be analyzed in the same fashion. The voltage across the capacitor is an exponential, as discussed earlier, and the output waveform, Fig. 3-29, again depends upon the relative magnitude of the circuit time constant compared with the period. In particular, note that when the circuit time constant is large the capacitor voltage rise is essentially

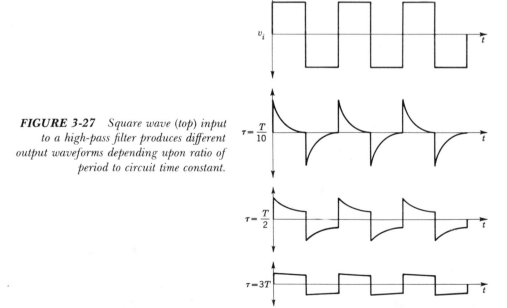

FIGURE 3-27   *Square wave (top) input to a high-pass filter produces different output waveforms depending upon ratio of period to circuit time constant.*

linear during the pulse time. The output voltage is thus just the integral of the input signal, again in conformity with the harmonic-circuit analysis presented in Chap. 2.

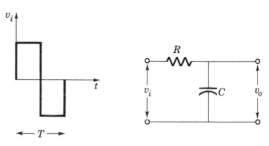

FIGURE 3-28 *Square-wave input signal applied to a low-pass filter.*

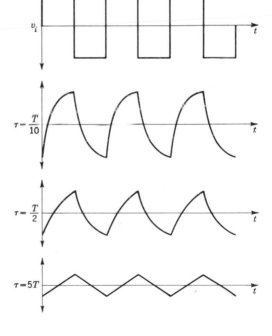

FIGURE 3-29 *Square-wave input to low-pass filter produces different output waveforms depending upon ratio of period to circuit time constant.*

SUGGESTIONS FOR FURTHER READING

A. M. P. Brookes: "Basic Electric Circuits," The Macmillan Company, New York, 1963.

S. Fich and J. L. Potter: "Theory of AC Circuits," Prentice-Hall, Inc., Englewood Cliffs, N.J., 1959.

"The Radio Amateur's Handbook" (published annually by the American Radio Relay League, West Hartford, Conn.).

EXERCISES

3-1 Determine the current in a series RC circuit using the ac form of Ohm's law and show that the result is identical with the differential-equation solution in Chap. 2.

3-2 Calculate the equivalent impedance of the network shown in Fig. 3-30. Is the reactive term capacitive or inductive?

Ans.: Capacitive

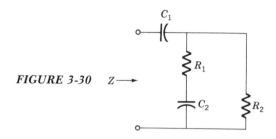

FIGURE 3-30 $Z \longrightarrow$

3-3 Determine the rms current in the 1000-Ω resistor of the circuit in Fig. 3-31. Is the current inductive or capacitive?

Ans.: 6.5 ma; capacitive

FIGURE 3-31

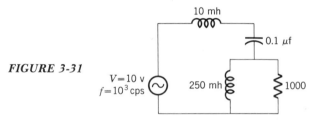

3-4 Calculate the equivalent impedance of the circuit in Fig. 3-32 at a frequency of 100 cps. Repeat for 1000 cps.

Ans.: $0.198 + j2.63 \times 10^6 \ \Omega$; $384 + j2.47 \times 10^9 \ \Omega$

FIGURE 3-32 $Z \longrightarrow$

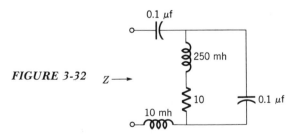

3-5 Solve the series RLC circuit by the differential-equation technique to arrive at Eq. (3-29).

3-6 Determine the current and the rms voltages across each component in the circuit of Fig. 3-4 at a frequency of 900 cps. Show that, considering the phase angles of the voltages, Kirchhoff's rule concerning the sum of the voltages around a loop is valid.

Ans.: $2.86 \times 10^{-2} \angle 88.4°$ amp; $0.286 \angle 88.4°$ volts; $50.6 \angle -1.6°$ volts;
$40.6 \angle 178.4°$ volts

3-7 Repeat Exercise 3-6 at a frequency of 1100 cps.

Ans.: $3.57 \times 10^{-2}\angle{-88°}$ amp; $0.357\angle{-88°}$ volt; $51.7\angle{-178}$ volts; $61.8\angle{2°}$ volts

3-8 Is the equivalent impedance of a parallel resonant circuit inductive or reactive below resonance? Above resonance? *Hint:* Use Eq. (3-44). Compare with a series resonant circuit.

Ans.: Inductive; capacitive

3-9 The impedance at resonance of a parallel resonant circuit is limited by the resistance of the windings of the inductor. Derive an expression for the impedance of the circuit of Fig. 3-33 and calculate the value at resonance appropriate to the components given on the circuit diagram. *Ans.:* $2 \times 10^5 - j447$ Ω

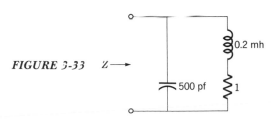

FIGURE 3-33 $Z \longrightarrow$

0.2 mh

500 pf

1

3-10 Compute the currents in the components of the circuit of Fig. 3-7 at resonance. Repeat for a frequency $\omega = \omega_0/2$. In both cases show that, considering the phase angles of the currents, Kirchhoff's current rule is valid.

Ans.: 0 amp, $3.16 \times 10^{-3}\angle{-90°}$ amp, $3.16 \times 10^{-3}\angle{+90°}$ amp; $2 \times 10^{-3}\angle{-2.4°}$ amp, $2.67 \times 10^{-3}\angle{-2.4°}$ amp, $6.67 \times 10^{-4}\angle{177.6°}$ amp

3-11 Repeat Exercise 3-10 for a frequency of $\omega = 2\omega_0$.

Ans.: $2\angle{2.4°}$ ma, $0.67\angle{-177.6°}$ ma, $2.67\angle{2.4°}$ ma

3-12 Using Eq. (3-56) determine the upper and lower half-power frequencies for $Q_0 = 1$, 10, and 100. Express the bandwidth in terms of a percentage of the center (resonant) frequency.

Ans.: $1.61\omega_0$, $0.67\omega_0$, 94%; $1.05\omega_0$, $0.95\omega_0$, 10%; $1.005\omega_0$, $0.995\omega_0$, 1%

3-13 Determine the balance conditions for the capacitance bridge, Fig. 3-12. *Ans.:* $R_2R_3 = R_1R_u$, $R_1/R_2 = C_u/C_3$

3-14 Describe how you might use a simple inductance and capacitance bridge together with an unknown inductor and capacitor to determine the frequency of the generator supplying the bridge.

3-15 Plot the phase angle of the output voltage as a function of frequency for the Wien bridge of Fig. 3-14 with $R_1 = R_2 = R = 1$ MΩ and $C = 100$ pf. Contrast the results with those of a resonant circuit, Exercise 3-8.

3-16 In the bridged-T network of Fig. 3-16, plot v_o/v_i as a function of ω/ω_0 if $R_1 = R_2$ and $C_1 = C_2$.

3-17 Repeat Exercise 3-16 if $R_2 = 100 R_1$ and $C_2 = C_1$. Compare with the results of Exercise 3-16.

3-18 Derive expressions for the growth and decay of the voltage across the capacitor in Fig. 3-21 accompanying closing of the switch. Do this by solving the circuit differential equations (3-93) and (3-98) for the charge on the capacitor at any time.

3-19 Determine the constant A in Eq. (3-103) if the switch in Fig. 3-23 is closed as the source voltage is passing through zero. Compare with Eq. (3-105). *Ans.*: $-V_p \omega C / [1 + (\omega RC)^2]$

3-20 Show that the condition for an RC high-pass filter to differentiate a square wave, which is that the time constant be small compared with the period of the wave, is equivalent to the condition on the half-power frequency derived in Chap. 2.

4
DIODES

Resistors, capacitors, and inductors are called linear components, because
the current increases in direct proportion to the applied voltage,
in accordance with Ohm's law. Components for which this
proportionality does not hold are termed nonlinear devices; they
are widely used in practical electronic circuits. This chapter
examines the properties of an important nonlinear device, the
diode rectifier. The term "diode" comes from the fact that
rectifiers have two active terminals, or electrodes.

A rectifier is nonlinear in that it passes a greater current for one polarity
of applied voltage than for the other. In fact, an ideal rectifier
has zero resistance in the forward direction and infinite
resistance in the reverse direction, as the current-voltage
characteristic, Fig. 4-1, indicates. If a rectifier is included in an
ac circuit, the current is zero whenever the polarity of the voltage
across the rectifier is in the reverse direction. Therefore, only a
unidirectional current exists and the alternating current is said to
have been rectified.

A major application of rectifiers is in power-supply circuits which convert
conventional 115-volt 60-cps ac line voltages to dc potentials
suitable for use with vacuum tubes and transistors. Two types of
rectifiers, the vacuum diode and the semiconductor junction diode,
are commonly used in power supplies. Because of its superior
properties, the junction diode is rapidly supplanting the vacuum
diode.

PRACTICAL RECTIFIERS

4-1   The vacuum diode

The vacuum diode comprises a hot *cathode* surrounded by a metal *anode* inside an evacuated enclosure, usually glass, as sketched in Fig. 4-2. At sufficiently high temperatures electrons are emitted from the cathode and are attracted to the positive anode. Electrons moving from the cathode to the anode constitute a current; they do so when the anode is positive with respect

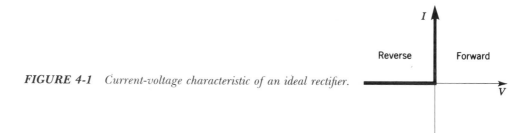

FIGURE 4-1   *Current-voltage characteristic of an ideal rectifier.*

to the cathode. When the anode is negative with respect to the cathode, electrons are repelled by the anode and the reverse current is zero. The space between the anode and cathode is evacuated, so that electrons may move between the electrodes unimpeded by collisions with gas molecules.

Cathodes in vacuum diodes take several different forms. The free electrons in any conductor, given sufficient energy by heating, will escape from the solid. Some materials are much more satisfactory in this respect than others, however, either because it is relatively easy for electrons to escape, or because the material can safely withstand high temperatures. Tungsten, for example, is a useful cathode material, because it retains its mechanical strength at extreme temperatures. A thin layer of thorium on the surface of a tungsten cathode filament increases electron emission, and appreciable current is attained at temperatures of about 1900°K. This form of cathode is directly heated by an electric current the way the filament in an incandescent lamp is. It is used in vacuum diodes suitable for high-voltage applications. The conventional symbol for a vacuum diode of this type is shown in Fig. 4-3*a*.

The modern oxide-coated cathode, which consists of a metal sleeve coated with a mixture of barium and strontium oxides, is the most efficient electron emitter developed to date. Copious electron emission is obtained at temperatures near 1000°K, which means that the power required is much less than for tungsten.

Usually the oxide cathode is indirectly heated by a separate heater located inside the metal sleeve, as in Fig. 4-2. This isolates the heater current electrically from the cathode connection, which is a considerable advantage in electronic circuits. Also, an ac heater

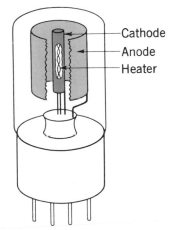

Cathode
Anode
Heater

FIGURE 4-2   *Sketch of vacuum diode.*

current may be used without introducing undesirable temperature variations in the cathode at the frequency of the heater current. Oxide cathodes are employed in the great majority of vacuum tubes. The heater is often omitted in the conventional circuit symbol, Fig. 4-3b, since it is not directly an active part of the rectifier.

When the anode is negative with respect to the cathode, the electron current is zero and the reverse characteristic is essentially that of an ideal diode. The forward characteristic is determined by the motion of electrons in the space between the cathode and the anode when the anode has a positive potential. For simplicity, consider a plane cathode and a plane parallel anode separated by a distance d, as in Fig. 4-4. Assume that the potential difference between anode and cathode is V_b and that electrons are emitted from the cathode with zero velocity, which is very nearly true in practice.

If one electron is present in the cathode-anode space, it experiences a force caused by the electric field V_b/d and is uniformly accelerated to the anode. The total current is not just the sum of the currents due to many individual electrons, however. The

FIGURE 4-3   *Circuit symbols for vacuum diodes of (a) filamentary-cathode and (b) heated-cathode types.*

(a)   (b)

number of electrons emitted from the cathode is so great that the electric fields due to the electron charges drastically alter the uniform field V_b/d set up by the applied voltage. Therefore, the ef-

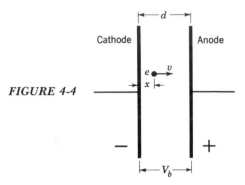

FIGURE 4-4

fect of all the electrons must be considered simultaneously. This is done by applying *Poisson's equation,* which is basically a reformulation of Coulomb's law relating electric field to charge distribution. The solution of Poisson's equation gives the potential V at any point in a region containing a volume density of charge ne. Here, n is the number of electrons per unit volume, and e is the charge on each electron. In one dimension, suitable for Fig. 4-4, Poisson's equation is written

$$\frac{d^2V}{dx^2} = -\frac{ne}{\epsilon_0} \qquad (4\text{-}1)$$

where ϵ_0 is the permittivity of free space.

The current density between cathode and anode is, from Eq. (1-13),

$$J = -nev \qquad (4\text{-}2)$$

where v is the velocity of the electrons and the minus sign accounts for the negative charge of the electrons. According to the definition of potential (work per unit charge), the kinetic energy of an electron at any point is related to the potential at that point by

$$\tfrac{1}{2}mv^2 = eV \qquad (4\text{-}3)$$

where m is the electronic mass. Introducing the current density from Eq. (4-2) and v from Eq. (4-3), Poisson's equation becomes

$$\frac{d^2V}{dx^2} = \frac{J}{\epsilon_0 v} = \frac{J}{\epsilon_0}\left(\frac{m}{2eV}\right)^{1/2} \qquad (4\text{-}4)$$

The solution to this differential equation for V is

$$V^{3/4} = \frac{3}{2}\left(\frac{J}{\epsilon_0}\sqrt{\frac{m}{2e}}\right)^{1/2} x \qquad (4\text{-}5)$$

which can be verified by direct substitution. In arriving at Eq. (4-5) it has been assumed that the cathode is at zero potential and that the electric field at the cathode is zero. These approximations are quite accurate in practical diodes.

Since we are interested in the current between cathode and anode, put $x = d$ and $V = V_b$ in Eq. (4-5) and solve for the current density. The result is

$$J = \frac{4\epsilon_0}{9d^2} \left(\frac{2e}{m}\right)^{1/2} V_b^{3/2} \tag{4-6}$$

This equation, known as *Child's law*, shows that the current varies as the $3/2$ power of the voltage, rather than as the first power, as in Ohm's law. The current-voltage characteristic of a vacuum

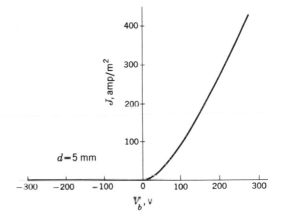

FIGURE 4-5 *Current-voltage characteristic of vacuum diode according to Child's law. Anode-cathode distance is chosen to be 5 mm.*

diode is therefore a horizontal line in the reverse direction and Eq. (4-6) in the forward direction, as shown in Fig. 4-5.

Actually the forward characteristics of practical vacuum diodes depart somewhat from Eq. (4-6) because the electrodes are normally cylindrical rather than planar and because of the simplifications introduced in deriving Child's law. For this reason the forward characteristics of practical diodes are determined experimentally. These characteristic current-voltage curves are presented graphically in manufacturer's compilations known as *tube manuals*.

According to Child's law, the current density in a vacuum diode depends upon the separation d between anode and cathode as well as upon the anode voltage. In addition, the total current of any diode varies directly with the area of the cathode. Thus it is possible to obtain different current-voltage characteristics by altering the geometric shape of the anode and cathode. Two examples of practical diode characteristics are given in Fig. 4-6. The type 5U4 diode is a medium-power rectifier; the type 1V2 diode is designed for high-voltage low-current power supplies. The anode-cathode separation is considerable in the 1V2 in order to minimize the possibility of a discharge passing between anode and cathode on the reverse portion of the voltage cycle. Consequently, the current in the forward direction is much smaller than in the case for the 5U4, in conformity with Child's law. The 5U4 is designed for use at lower voltages, so the separation between anode and cathode is smaller. The forward current is correspondingly greater at the same forward voltage.

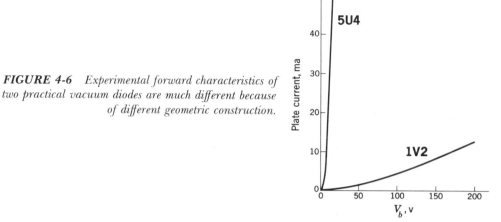

FIGURE 4-6 *Experimental forward characteristics of two practical vacuum diodes are much different because of different geometric construction.*

In any practical vacuum diode the reverse current is not truly zero, because of leakage currents on the surfaces of the glass insulators and similar secondary effects. Typically, the reverse resistance is of the order of 10 MΩ. Since the forward resistance may be of the order of 100 Ω at a suitable operating potential, the ratio of the reverse resistance to the forward resistance, or the *rectification ratio*, is appreciable. The interelectrode capacitance between the cathode and anode limits the maximum frequency at which a vacuum diode is useful. The cathode-anode capacitive reactance is effectively in parallel with the electron current and tends to short out the reverse resistance at high frequencies (see Exercise 4-2).

4-2 The junction diode

As will be shown in Chap. 6, the addition of certain foreign atoms to otherwise pure semiconductor materials such as germanium or silicon produces free electrons which carry electric current. A semiconductor crystal containing such foreign atoms is called an *n-type* crystal because of the negative charge of the current carrying electrons. Similarly, by incorporating certain other kinds of foreign atoms, the semiconductor appears to conduct current by positive current carriers. Such a crystal is called a *p-type* conductor because the current carriers have a positive charge. It is possible to change from *n*-type to *p*-type conductivity in the same crystal by introducing an abrupt change from one impurity type to the other across a given region of the semiconductor. The junction between an n-type region and a p-type region in a semiconductor crystal, called a *pn junction*, is a very good rectifier. The rectifying characteristics of a *junction diode* can be described in the following way.

Electrons in the n-type region tend to diffuse into the p-type region at the junction. In equilibrium, this is compensated by an equal flow of electrons in the reverse direction, for there is a minor, though important, concentration of electrons in the p region. Since the concentration of electrons is much larger in the n-type material than in the p-type, the electron current from the n region would dominate if it were not for the presence of a potential rise at the junction which reduces the current flow in this direction. The polarity and magnitude of this internal potential difference are such as to make the two currents equal. A similar argument applies to the positive carriers crossing the junction between the n and p regions.

When the pn junction is in equilibrium the internal potential barrier V_0 exists between the n and p regions, as indicated schematically in Fig. 4-7a. The current I_1 resulting from electrons diffusing from the n side is equal to the current I_2 which arises from electrons leaving the p side. Suppose now an external potential is applied to the junction so as to increase the internal barrier, as in Fig. 4-7b. The number of electrons diffusing across the junction from the n region is much reduced since very few electrons have sufficient energy to surmount the larger potential barrier. On the other hand, the number moving from the p to the n side is not affected because these electrons encounter no barrier. Thus a net current exists, but it is limited by the small number of electrons in the p region. If the polarity of the external potential is reversed, Fig. 4-7c, the internal barrier is reduced and I_1 is large because the number of electrons in the n region is so great. Again, the electron current I_2 from p-type to n-type remains unaffected. The net current in this case is large and corresponds to the forward direction. The reverse polarity increases the potential barrier and results in only a small current.

In determining the current-voltage characteristic of the junction diode, the same considerations apply to the current carried by the positive carriers as to that carried by electrons, and the total current is the sum of the two. Focusing attention on the electrons first, the current from the p region to the n region is proportional to the electron concentration in the p region n_p, so that

$$I_2 = -C_1 n_p \qquad (4\text{-}7)$$

where C_1 is a constant involving the junction area and properties of the semiconductor crystal which are not of direct interest here. The minus sign in Eq. (4-7) accounts for the negative charge on the electron. According to the preceding discussion, I_2 is independent of the applied potential V. The current I_1, from the n side to the p side, is proportional to the number of electrons in the n region with sufficient energy to surmount the barrier. This

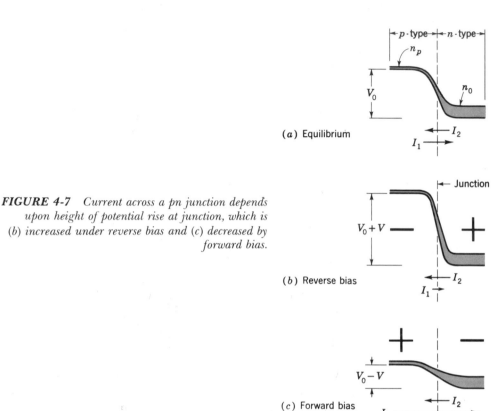

(a) Equilibrium

Junction

FIGURE 4-7 Current across a pn junction depends upon height of potential rise at junction, which is (b) increased under reverse bias and (c) decreased by forward bias.

(b) Reverse bias

(c) Forward bias

number may be determined from the Boltzmann distribution, which relates the concentrations in two regions having different potential energies. That is,

$$I_1 = -C_1 n_0 e^{-e(V_0 - V)/kT} \tag{4-8}$$

where n_0 is the concentration of electrons in the n region, and the exponential represents the Boltzmann relation. When the applied potential is zero, $I_1 = I_2$. From Eqs. (4-7) and (4-8)

$$n_p = n_0 e^{-eV_0/kT} \tag{4-9}$$

The net electron current is therefore

$$I_n = I_2 - I_1$$

$$= C_1 n_0 (e^{eV/kT} - 1) e^{-eV_0/kT}$$

$$= C_1 n_p (e^{eV/kT} - 1) \tag{4-10}$$

An identical expression can be derived for the positive carrier current. The result is

$$I_p = C_2 p_n (e^{eV/kT} - 1) \qquad (4\text{-}11)$$

where p_n is the concentration of positive carriers in the n region and C_2 is a constant analogous to C_1. The total current is the sum of Eqs. (4-10) and (4-11),

$$I = I_n + I_p$$
$$= (C_1 n_p + C_2 p_n)(e^{eV/kT} - 1) \qquad (4\text{-}12)$$
$$I = I_0 (e^{eV/kT} - 1) \qquad (4\text{-}13)$$

where I_0 is called the *saturation current*. Equation (4-13) is known as the *rectifier equation*.

The polarity of the applied potential is such that the p region is positive for forward bias. According to Eq. (4-13) the current increases exponentially in the forward direction. In contrast, the reverse current is essentially equal to I_0, independent of reverse potentials greater than a few volts. A plot of the rectifier equation for small values of applied voltage is shown in Fig. 4-8. It

FIGURE 4-8   *Current-voltage characteristic of pn junction according to rectifier equation.*

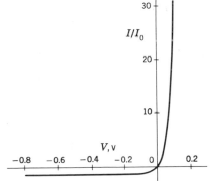

turns out that experimental current-voltage characteristics of practical junction diodes are in good agreement with the rectifier equation.

The junction diode is very nearly an ideal rectifier for the voltages commonly encountered in practical applications. This can be illustrated by comparing the current-voltage characteristics of a typical silicon junction diode with the type 5U4 vacuum diode, Fig. 4-9. Note that the voltage drop in the forward direction is much less for the junction diode. The size of this junction is only about 2 mm², so the junction diode is physically very much smaller than the vacuum diode. A third major advantage of the semiconductor device is that a hot cathode is not required. This means that heater power is not wasted and also that no warmup time is necessary after applying power to the circuit.

The reverse current of a *pn* junction is somewhat greater than that of the vacuum diode, although it is still small enough to be negligible. Of greater concern is the fact that the reverse satura-

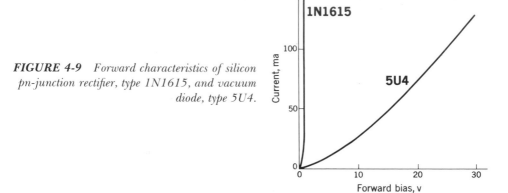

FIGURE 4-9 *Forward characteristics of silicon pn-junction rectifier, type 1N1615, and vacuum diode, type 5U4.*

tion current increases rapidly with temperature. According to Eq. (4-13)

$$I_0 = C_1 n_p + C_2 p_n \tag{4-14}$$

Substituting from Eq. (4-9) and its equivalent for the positive carrier current

$$I_0 = (C_1 n_0 + C_2 p_0) e^{-eV_0/kT} \tag{4-15}$$

According to Eq. (4-15), the reverse current of a junction diode increases exponentially as the temperature increases. Even though I_0 is of the order of only 10 μa at room temperature for a typical silicon diode, the rapid increase means that only a modest temperature rise can be tolerated. Silicon junction diodes, for example, are inoperative above about 200°C. Junction diodes used in circuits at power levels above a few watts or so are cooled in order to dissipate joule heat caused by the current in the device. It is common practice to attach junction diodes firmly to metal heat sinks having radiator fins to conduct the heat away from the diode.

In spite of their temperature sensitivity, a characteristic common to most semiconductor devices, junction diodes are extremely good rectifiers and enjoy wide application. Commercial junction diodes are made of either silicon or germanium by processes similar to those described in Chap. 6. Practical devices are completely encapsulated to protect the semiconductor surface from contamination. This is accomplished by placing the diode in a small metal can filled with an inert atmosphere or by encasing the diode in plastic. Because of their superior electrical characteristics, silicon and germanium junction diodes have largely supplanted older forms of semiconductor rectifiers made of selenium or copper oxide. It is interesting to note that the latter rectifiers were the first commercially useful semiconductor devices. The circuit symbol for all semiconductor diodes, given in Fig. 4-10, has an arrow to indicate the direction of conventional forward current in the device.

FIGURE 4-10 *Circuit symbol for semiconductor diode.*

The excellent forward conductivity of a *pn* junction means that practical diodes can be quite small. Therefore the stray capacitive reactances are correspondingly small and junction diodes are useful at high frequencies. This feature is enhanced in *point-contact* diodes, in which a metal probe is placed in contact with a semiconductor crystal. During processing a minute *pn* junction is formed immediately under the point. Such tiny devices can operate at frequencies corresponding to millimeter wavelengths and are used, for example, in radar and high-speed computer circuits. A typical point-contact diode is shown in Fig. 4-11.

FIGURE 4-11 *Point-contact gold-bonded diode. (Courtesy Ohmite Manufacturing Company.)*

RECTIFIER CIRCUITS

4-3 Half-wave rectifier

An elementary rectifier circuit, Fig. 4-12, has a vacuum diode in series with an ac source and a resistive load. When the polarity of the source makes the anode positive with respect to the cathode, the diode conducts and produces a current in the load. On the reverse half-cycle the diode does not conduct and the current is zero. The output current is therefore a succession of half-sine waves, as indicated in Fig. 4-12, and the circuit is called a *half-wave* rectifier. The average value of the half-sine waves is clearly not zero, so that the output current has a dc component. That is, the input sine wave has been rectified.

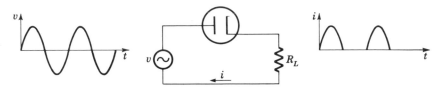

FIGURE 4-12   *Elementary half-wave rectifier circuit.*

The current in the circuit is determined from the voltage equation

$$v = iR_L + v_b \tag{4-16}$$

where v_b is the voltage across the diode. Solving for i,

$$i = \frac{v - v_b}{R_L} \tag{4-17}$$

This equation and Child's law, Eq. (4-6), must be solved to determine the current which satisfies both equations. Actually, the solution is carried out graphically, because the current-voltage characteristic of a practical vacuum diode is determined experimentally. Starting with a given instantaneous value of the input voltage v_1

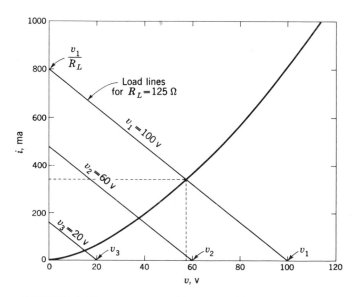

FIGURE 4-13   *Intersection of load line with diode characteristic gives current in circuit.*

Eq. (4-17) is plotted together with the characteristic curve of the diode. The plot of Eq. (4-17) is a straight line, as shown in Fig. 4-13, with a slope $-1/R_L$ and intercepts at $v = v_1$ and at $i = v/R_L$. The intersection of this so-called *load line* with the diode characteristic gives the current at the time the instantaneous input voltage is v_1. As the input voltage swings through the positive half of the cycle the current at every instant can be determined from a similar load line having a voltage intercept corresponding to the instantaneous voltage of the source.

A plot of the current as a function of applied voltage, Fig. 4-14, is called the *dynamic characteristic* of the circuit. The *static character-*

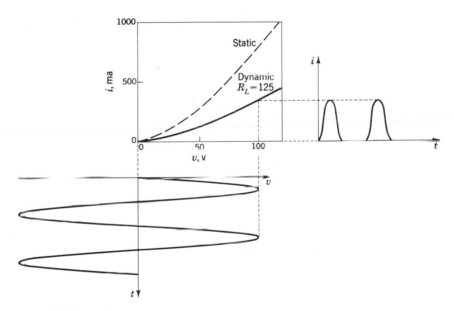

FIGURE 4-14   *Current waveform is nonsinusoidal because of curvature in rectifier dynamic characteristic.*

istic, which is simply the current-voltage curve of the diode, and the dynamic characteristic differ because of the voltage drop across the load resistance. The voltage drop reduces the anode-cathode potential for a given input voltage.

The dynamic characteristic can be used to plot the current waveform resulting from any input voltage waveform, as illustrated in Fig. 4-14. In particular, if the input voltage is sinusoidal, the output current is not truly a half-sine wave because of curvature of the diode characteristic. For many purposes, however, this curvature may be ignored and the forward characteristic replaced by a straight line approximating the true curve. In this case the diode is represented by a fixed resistance R_p in the forward direction. The approximate current in the circuit may then be found immediately from Eq. (4-16) after replacing v_b by iR_p.

4-4 Full-wave rectifier

The half-wave rectifier is inactive during one-half of the input cycle and is therefore less efficient than is possible. By arranging two diodes as in Fig. 4-15 so that each diode conducts on alternate

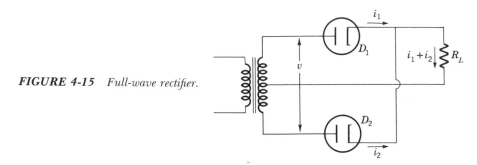

FIGURE 4-15 *Full-wave rectifier.*

half-cycles, *full-wave* rectification results. This is accomplished by using a center-tapped transformer winding. Then, the anode of diode D_1 is positive with respect to the center tap (and hence its cathode) when the anode of diode D_2 is negative with respect to the center tap. On the alternate half-cycle, the conditions are reversed so that the output-current waveform, Fig. 4-16, has only momentary zero values, in contrast to the half-wave circuit.

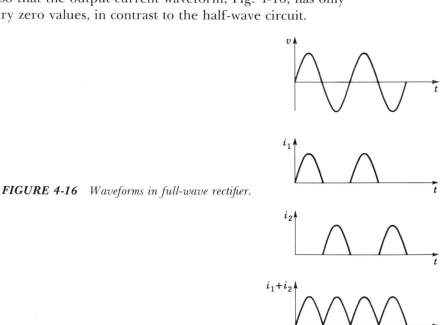

FIGURE 4-16 *Waveforms in full-wave rectifier.*

The full-wave rectifier, a widely used circuit, can be analyzed exactly as in the case of the half-wave rectifier. Note that each diode in the diagram of Fig. 4-15 must withstand the full end-to-end voltage of the transformer winding. Therefore the *peak inverse voltage* rating of the diodes must be at least twice the peak output voltage. This is usually not a serious drawback except for circuits designed to operate at highest voltages. Comparing the output waveforms of half-wave and full-wave rectifiers, Figs. 4-12 and 4-16, reveals that the fundamental frequency equals the supply voltage in the half-wave rectifier but is twice the supply frequency in the case of the full-wave circuit. This is an important consideration in power-supply circuits, as will be demonstrated in a later section. The center-tapped transformer in the full-wave circuit supplies current on both half-cycles of the input voltage, which permits a more efficient transformer design than is possible in the case of the half-wave circuit. Note, however, that the output voltage is only one-half the total voltage of the transformer secondary.

4-5   Bridge rectifier

Full-wave rectification without a center-tapped transformer is possible with the *bridge rectifier,* Fig. 4-17. The operation of this circuit may be described by tracing the current on alternate half-

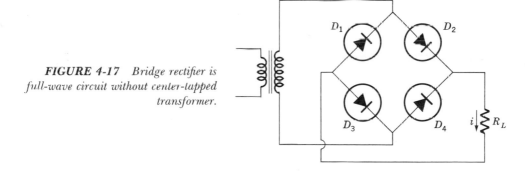

FIGURE 4-17   *Bridge rectifier is full-wave circuit without center-tapped transformer.*

cycles of the input voltage. Suppose, for example, the upper terminal of the transformer is positive. This means that diode D_2 conducts, as does diode D_3, and current is present in the load resistor. On the alternate half-cycle diodes D_4 and D_1 conduct and the current direction in the load resistance is the same as before. The voltage across R_L corresponds to full-wave rectification and the peak voltage is equal to the transformer voltage less the potential drops across the diodes.

Note that if vacuum diodes are used in a bridge rectifier circuit, the heater currents must be supplied from separate sources, since the diode cathodes are not at the same potential. For this reason it is common to employ junction diodes in this circuit. Since two diodes are in series with the load, the output voltage is reduced by twice the diode drop. On the other hand, the peak inverse voltage rating of the diodes need only be equal to the transformer voltage, in contrast to the previous full-wave circuit.

4-6 Voltage doubler

Consider the circuit of Fig. 4-18, in which two diodes are connected to the same voltage source but in the opposite sense. On
the half-cycle during which the upper terminal of the source is

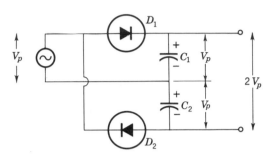

FIGURE 4-18 *Voltage-doubler rectifier
yields dc output voltage equal to twice peak
input voltage.*

positive, diode D_1 conducts and capacitor C_1 charges to the peak
value of the input voltage. On the reverse half-cycle D_2 conducts
and C_2 also charges to the full input voltage. Meanwhile, the
charge on C_1 is retained, since the potential across D_1 is in the reverse direction. Thus both C_1 and C_2 charge to the peak supply
voltage and the dc output voltage is equal to twice the peak input
voltage. Accordingly, this circuit is called a *voltage doubler*.

The above analysis applies to the case when no current is delivered to the load. When a load resistance is connected, current
is supplied by the discharge of the capacitors. On alternate half-
cycles the capacitors are subsequently recharged. This implies,
however, that the output voltage under load is no longer dc, but
has an ac component. It is necessary to make the capacitance of
C_1 and C_2 large enough to minimize this variation in output voltage, taking into account the current drain and the supply frequency. The filtering action of the capacitors in this circuit is
treated in greater detail in the next section.

FILTERS

It is usually desirable to reduce the alternating component of
the rectified waveform so that the output is primarily a dc voltage.
This is accomplished by means of *filters* which are composed of
suitably connected capacitors and inductances. A power-supply
filter is a low-pass filter which reduces the amplitudes of all alternating components in the rectified waveform and passes the dc
component. A measure of the effectiveness of a filter is given by
the *ripple factor r*, which is defined as the ratio of the rms value of
the ac component to the dc or average value. That is,

$$r = \frac{V_{\text{rms}}}{V_{\text{dc}}} \tag{4-18}$$

According to this definition it is desirable to make the ripple factor as small as possible. Although rectified waveforms contain many harmonics of the input voltage frequency, it is generally satisfactory to determine the ripple factor at the fundamental frequency only. This is so because the fundamental frequency is predominant and also because higher harmonics are attenuated more than the fundamental by the low-pass filter characteristic.

4-7 Capacitor filter

The simplest filter circuit consists of a capacitor connected in parallel with the load resistance, as in the typical low-voltage bridge-rectifier power supply shown in Fig. 4-19. If the reactance

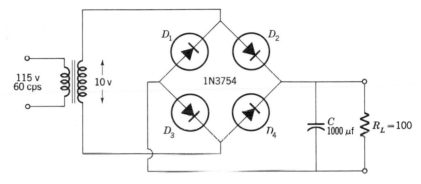

FIGURE 4-19 *Practical low-voltage power supply using capacitor filter.*

of the capacitor at the power-line frequency is small compared with the load resistance R_L, the ac component is shorted out and only dc current remains in the load resistor.

Characteristics of the *capacitor filter* are determined by examining waveforms in the circuit, Fig. 4-20. The capacitor is charged to the peak value of the rectified voltage V_p and begins to discharge

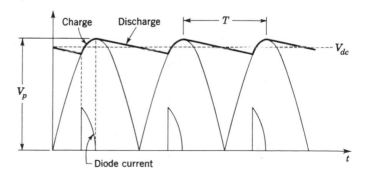

FIGURE 4-20 *Output voltage of capacitor filter is dc voltage and small triangular ripple voltage.*

through R_L after the rectified voltage decreases from the peak value. The decrease in capacitor voltage between charging pulses depends upon the relative values of the RC time constant and the period of the input voltage. A small time constant means the decrease is large and the ripple voltage is also large. On the other hand, a large time constant results in a small ripple component. The diodes conduct only during the portion of the cycle that the capacitor is charging, because only during this interval is the sum of the supply voltage and the capacitor voltage such that the potential across the diodes is in the forward direction.

The ripple voltage is approximately a triangular wave if the RC time constant is long compared with the period, $R_L C \gg T$. In this case the exponential decrease of capacitor voltage during one period is given approximately by $V_p \times T/R_L C$. The dc output voltage is the peak capacitor voltage minus the average ripple component, or

$$V_{dc} = V_p - \frac{V_p T}{2R_L C} = V_p \left(1 - \frac{1}{2fR_L C}\right) \tag{4-19}$$

where f is the main frequency of the rectified waveform. The effective voltage of a triangular wave is calculated in Appendix 2. In present notation

$$V_{rms} = \frac{1}{2\sqrt{3}} \frac{V_p T}{R_L C} \tag{4-20}$$

Therefore, using Eq. (4-18), the ripple factor becomes

$$r = \frac{1}{2\sqrt{3}} \frac{1}{fR_L C} \tag{4-21}$$

where the approximation $R_L C \gg T$ has been used again.

This result shows that ripple is reduced by increasing the value of the filter capacitor. When the load current is equal to zero ($R_L \to \infty$), the ripple factor becomes zero, which means that the output voltage is pure dc. As the load current is increased (smaller values of R_L), the ripple factor increases. Inserting component values given on the circuit diagram of Fig. 4-19, the ripple factor is found to be 0.05. Thus the ripple voltage is about 5 percent of the dc output. Note that the ripple voltage of a full-wave rectifier is approximately one-half that of the half-wave circuit, because the frequency of the rectified component is twice as great.

The dc output voltage may be written, using Eq. (4-19), as

$$V_{dc} = V_p - \frac{1}{2fC} I_{dc} \tag{4-22}$$

where the approximation $I_{dc} \approx V_p/R_L$ has been used. According to Eq. (4-22), the dc output voltage decreases linearly as the dc current drawn by the load increases. The constancy in output voltage with current is called the *regulation* of the power supply; Eq. (4-22) shows that a large value of filter capacitance improves the regulation. It should be noted that the decrease in output voltage given by this equation refers only to the change accompanying the increase in the ac ripple component. The *IR* drops associated with diode resistances and the resistance of the transformer winding further reduce the output voltage as the load current increases.

The simple capacitor filter provides very good filtering action at low currents and is often used in high-voltage low-current power supplies. Because of its simplicity, the circuit also is found in those higher current supplies where ripple is relatively less important. The dc output voltage is high, equal to the peak value of the supply voltage. The disadvantages of the capacitor filter are poor regulation and increased ripple at large loads.

4-8   L-section filter

It is useful to add a series inductor to the capacitance filter, as in the circuit of Fig. 4-21. The series inductance in this *L-section* or *choke-input* filter opposes rapid variations in the current and so

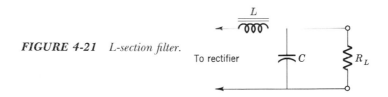

FIGURE 4-21   *L-section filter.*

contributes to the filtering action. The ripple factor may be determined by noting that the ac voltage components of the rectified waveform divide between the inductance and the impedance Z of the resistor-capacitor combination. Therefore

$$r = \left(\frac{V_{\text{rms}}}{V_{\text{dc}}}\right)_f = \frac{(V_{\text{rms}})_r [Z/(Z + X_L)]}{(V_{\text{dc}})_r} \tag{4-23}$$

where the subscript f refers to the voltage ratio at the output of the filter and the subscript r refers to the rectified waveform. Equation (4-23) may be put in a more instructive form by calculating the magnitude of the impedance and rearranging,

$$r = \left(\frac{V_{\text{rms}}}{V_{\text{dc}}}\right)_r \frac{1}{1 + X_L/Z} = \left(\frac{V_{\text{rms}}}{V_{\text{dc}}}\right)_r \frac{1}{1 + \omega L \sqrt{(1/R_L)^2 + (\omega C)^2}} \tag{4-24}$$

$$r = \left(\frac{V_{\text{rms}}}{V_{\text{dc}}}\right)_r \frac{1}{1 + \omega^2 LC \sqrt{1 + (1/\omega R_L C)^2}} \tag{4-25}$$

Note that the dependence upon R_L, that is, upon the load current, is much smaller than is the case for the capacitor filter. In fact, if $\omega R_L C > 1$, as is done in practice, the ripple factor is independent of the load. Inserting the rms/dc ratio appropriate for a full-wave rectifier (Appendix 2), Eq. (4-25) becomes

$$r = \frac{\sqrt{2}}{3}\frac{1}{\omega^2 LC} \qquad\qquad (4\text{-}26)$$

According to Eq. (4-26) large values of L and large values of C improve the filtering action.

The inductance chokes off alternating components of the rectified waveform and the dc output voltage is simply the average, or dc, value of the rectified wave. For a series of half-sinusoids this means that the dc output voltage is (Appendix 2)

$$V_{dc} = \frac{2}{\pi}V_p \cong 0.9V \qquad\qquad (4\text{-}27)$$

where V_p is the peak and V is the rms value of the transformer voltage. Therefore, the output voltage of the choke-input filter is considerably less than that of the capacitor filter.

According to Eq. (4-26) the ripple is independent of the load current. This means that there is no decrease in output voltage due to a decrease in filtering action at high currents, such as in Eq. (4-22) for the capacitor filter. Therefore, the output voltage is independent of the load, except for IR drops in the diodes and transformer windings. For this reason the L-section filter is used in applications where wide variations in the load current are expected. The advantage of good regulation must be balanced against the comparatively low output voltage in considering any given application.

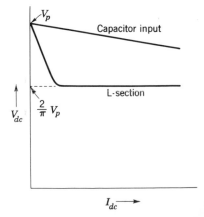

FIGURE 4-22   *Voltage-regulation characteristics of capacitor-input filter and L-section filter.*

The effectiveness of the inductance is reduced at low currents, so at very light loads the L-section filter acts like a simple capacitance filter. Therefore the output voltage rises to the peak value of the input voltage. In order to prevent this, it is common practice to include a resistance across the capacitor. This resistor draws sufficient current to make the inductance effective even when the load current drops to zero. Such a *bleeder* resistor is also useful in draining the charge from the filter capacitor after the power supply is turned off, which reduces the injury hazard. A comparison of the voltage-regulation curves of a capacitor filter and a choke-input filter, Fig. 4-22, shows the poor regulation but high output of the former and the good regulation but lower voltage of the latter. The minimum current necessary to ensure good filtering action in the case of the L-section filter is clearly evident.

4-9 π-section filter

The combination of a capacitor-input filter with an L-section filter, as shown in the power-supply diagram of Fig. 4-23, is a very popular circuit. The output voltage of this *π-section filter* is nearly that of the capacitor-input filter, and the regulation characteristics are about the same. The ripple is very much reduced by the double filtering action, however. In fact, the overall ripple factor

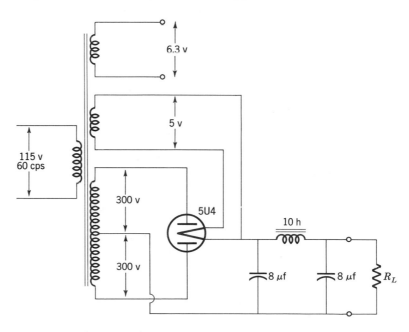

FIGURE 4-23   *A practical 300-volt power supply.*

is essentially the product of the ripple factor of the capacitor filter times the impedance ratio of the L-section filter. Therefore, using Eq. (4-21) and the impedance ratio developed for (4-26),

$$r = \frac{\pi}{\sqrt{3}} \frac{1}{\omega R_L C_1} \frac{1}{\omega^2 L C_2}$$

$$= \frac{\pi}{\sqrt{3}} \frac{X_{C_1} X_{C_2}}{X_L R_L} \tag{4-28}$$

According to Eq. (4-28), if the reactances of both capacitors are small at the ripple frequency, and that of the inductance is large, the ripple factor is small. Note that the ripple increases with load as R_L is made smaller. In spite of the poor regulation properties of the π-section filter, it is widely used, because of its excellent filtering action.

The practical power-supply diagram of Fig. 4-23 has several other features of note. Both rectifiers are enclosed in the same glass envelope of the type 5U4 diode to simplify full-wave recti-fication. The 5-volt heater-cathode (the oxide emitter is coated directly on the heater) is heated by a separate secondary winding on the power transformer. Finally, a 6.3-volt winding is also pro-vided to supply the heaters of other vacuum tubes in the associated circuitry. A circuit similar to Fig. 4-23 is very common in elec-tronic devices.

Other combinations of filter types are also used. Two L-section filters, Fig. 4-24a for example, provide the good regulation of the choke-input filter together with very low ripple. The ripple factor of any filter design is calculated by considering each simple filter separately, as in the case of the π-section filter described above.

A useful variant of the π-section filter particularly suitable for low-current circuits replaces the inductance with a resistor, Fig. 4-24b; the ripple factor is simply Eq. (4-28) with X_L replaced by the value of the series resistor R. This circuit is useful only if the current is low enough so that the IR drop across the resistor is not excessive and if regulation is of secondary concern. Within these restrictions, the circuit provides better filtering action than a simple capacitance filter.

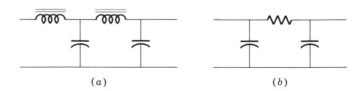

(a)   (b)

FIGURE 4-24   (a) *Double L-section filter,* *and (b) π-section RC filter.*

VOLTAGE REGULATORS

It is often desirable that the voltage of a power supply remain fixed independent of the load current. Although the regulation of the choke-input filter is very good, the output voltage decreases with increasing current even in this circuit, because of the *IR* drops across the transformer winding resistance and the rectifier diodes. Other variables, such as changes in the line voltage and component aging, may also contribute to variations in the power-supply voltage. In order to maintain the output voltage constant, *voltage regulator* devices are made part of the power supply. These are fairly elaborate electronic circuits if very precise regulation is necessary, as discussed in a later chapter. In other cases, special components that maintain modest voltage stability are used.

4-10 Zener diodes

At some particular reverse-bias voltage the reverse current in a *pn* junction increases very rapidly. This happens when electrons are accelerated to high velocities by the field at the junction and produce other free electrons by ionization collisions with atoms. These electrons are similarly accelerated by the field and in turn cause other ionizations. This avalanche process leads to very large current and the junction is said to have suffered breakdown. The breakdown is not destructive, however, unless the power dissipation is allowed to increase the temperature to the point where local melting destroys the semiconductor. The voltage across the junction remains quite constant over a wide current range in the breakdown region. This effect can be used to maintain the output of a power supply at the breakdown voltage.

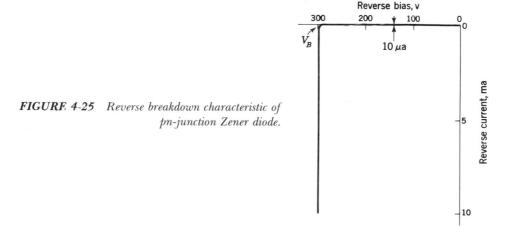

FIGURE 4-25 *Reverse breakdown characteristic of pn-junction Zener diode.*

These *pn* junctions are called *Zener diodes*, because Clarence Zener first suggested an explanation for the rapid current increase at breakdown. The current-voltage curve of a Zener diode, Fig. 4-25, has a sharp transition potential and a flat current plateau above breakdown. Zener diodes may be obtained with breakdown voltages ranging from about two volts to several hundred volts and with current ratings of a few milliamperes to many amperes.

The way in which a Zener diode is used to regulate the output voltage of a power supply is illustrated in Fig. 4-26. The un-regulated output voltage of the supply V must be greater than the

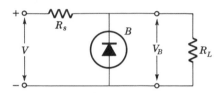

FIGURE 4-26   *Zener diode used as voltage regulator.*

Zener breakdown voltage of the diode. Then the voltage drop across R_S caused by the diode current plus the diode breakdown potential adds up to the power-supply potential. As the load current increases, the diode current decreases, so the drop across R_S always is the difference between the breakdown potential and the power-supply voltage. Even if the power-supply voltage varies under load, the regulated output voltage remains constant.

The minimum value of the series resistor R_S is determined by the maximum permissible diode current I_M.

$$R_S = \frac{V}{I_M} \tag{4-29}$$

If it is known that the load current never falls below a certain minimum value, the series resistance can profitably be increased above that given by Eq. (4-29). This minimizes the power lost in the series resistor.

4-11   VR tubes

An older form of voltage regulator, the *VR tube*, is based on the properties of an electric glow discharge in a low-pressure inert gas between two unheated electrodes. If the potential between the electrodes is high enough, electrons are accelerated sufficiently to ionize gas atoms by collision and a current avalanche results. As in the case of the Zener diode, the electrode potential is nearly independent of the current in the discharge, so the device can be used as a voltage regulator in a power supply. It turns out that the electrode potential required to initiate the gas discharge is about 10 percent greater than the sustaining potential, so that the un-regulated power-supply voltage must be correspondingly greater.

VR tubes are available with 75-, 90-, 105-, and 150-volt ratings and with a nominal current range of 5 to 40 ma. It is therefore possible to exert control over load-current variations covering this same range. Different regulated voltages can be obtained by using two or more VR tubes in series (Fig. 4-27). This can also be done

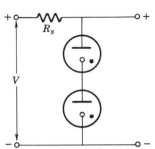

FIGURE 4-27   *Two voltage-regulator tubes may be placed in series to regulate dc voltage equal to sum of individual breakdown voltages.*

with Zener diodes, if necessary, although the wider selection of voltage ratings available usually makes this unnecessary. Parallel connection of regulators to increase the current range is not feasible, for one of the parallel-connected units unavoidably has a slightly lower operating potential and therefore carries all of the current. The circuit symbol for the VR tube, shown in Fig. 4-27, has an open circle symbolizing the cold cathode. The solid dot indicates a gas-filled tube.

Both VR tubes and Zener diodes also provide filtering action since they tend to maintain the output voltage constant against changes in the power-supply voltage, including ripple. For this reason it is often possible to employ only rudimentary, inductance-capacitance filtering in conjunction with voltage regulators.

4-12   Controlled rectifiers

It is often necessary to control the power delivered to some load, such as an electric motor or the heating element of a furnace. Series resistances or potentiometers waste power, a serious drawback in high-power circuits. *Controlled rectifiers* have been developed which are capable of adjusting the transmitted power with little waste.

The most satisfactory unit of this kind is the *silicon controlled rectifier*, or *SCR*. This semiconductor device contains four parallel *pn* junctions; it is described in detail in Chap. 6. For present purposes it is sufficient to note that it is similar to a junction rectifier in which forward conduction is controlled by the current in a control electrode, called the *gate*. The inclusion of the gate electrode is shown on the SCR symbol (Fig. 4-28).

The current-voltage characteristic of a typical SCR, Fig. 4-29, is identical to a junction rectifier in the reverse direction. The forward direction has both an ON state, which is equivalent to normal

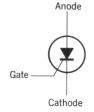

Anode

Gate

Cathode

FIGURE 4-28 *Circuit symbol for silicon controlled rectifier.*

forward conduction in a junction rectifier, and a low-current OFF state. So long as the forward anode-cathode potential remains below a certain critical value (actually it is the corresponding current which is critical), the forward current is small. Above this

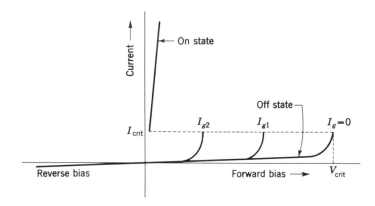

FIGURE 4-29 *Current-voltage characteristic of SCR.· Unit can be triggered into ON state by gate current. Here $I_{g2} > I_{g1} > 0$.*

critical value the SCR is in the high-current low-voltage ON condition. The critical current may be supplied by the gate electrode, which means that the SCR may be triggered into the ON position by a small current (as low as 100 μa) supplied to the gate terminal. It is not necessary to maintain the gate current, for once the SCR is triggered into the high-conduction state it remains in this condition until the anode potential is reduced to zero.

Consider the simple SCR circuit of Fig. 4-30, in which the motor speed is controlled by the power delivered to it. The peak value of the transformer voltage V_p is less than the critical value, so that, unless the SCR is triggered by a gate current, the load current is zero. Suppose the gate is supplied with a current pulse each cycle that lags the transformer voltage by a phase angle α, as illustrated in Fig. 4-31. Forward conduction is delayed until this point in each cycle and the rectified output waveform is similar to that of a half-wave rectifier, except that the first part of each cycle is missing. The average, or dc, value of the current in the motor is found by integrating the output current over a complete cycle, or

$$I_{dc} = I_p \int_\alpha^\pi \sin \omega t \, d\omega t \qquad (4\text{-}30)$$

where I_p is the peak value of the current. Integrating,

$$I_{dc} = \frac{I_p}{2\pi} (1 + \cos \alpha) \qquad (4\text{-}31)$$

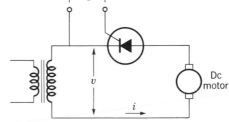

FIGURE 4-30 *Simple SCR circuit to control speed of dc motor.*

According to Eq. (4-31) the motor current can be adjusted from a maximum ($\alpha = 0$) to zero ($\alpha = \pi$) simply by changing the phase angle of the gate pulses. Simple circuits are available to generate such pulses, as described in a later chapter.

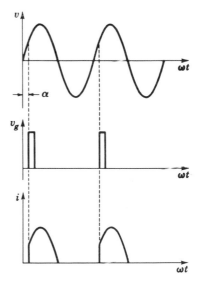

FIGURE 4-31 *Output current waveform depends upon phase angle between transformer voltage and gate current pulse.*

It is not necessary to use pulses in the gate circuit, so long as care is taken to limit the power dissipated by the control electrode below that which might damage the SCR. Consider the *phase-shift control* circuit of Fig. 4-32, in which the gate current is shifted in phase with respect to the anode voltage. Since the gate voltage is the sum of the secondary voltage v_1 and the drop across R, the gate voltage is

$$v_g \angle \phi_g = v_1 - Ri \angle \phi \tag{4-32}$$

This is easily solved for the phase angle between the gate voltage and the anode voltage, which has the same phase as v_1. The result

$$\phi_g = \arctan \frac{2R\omega C}{(R\omega C)^2 - 1} \tag{4-33}$$

shows that the gate voltage may be put in phase with the anode potential ($R = 0$) or nearly 180° out of phase ($R = \infty$).

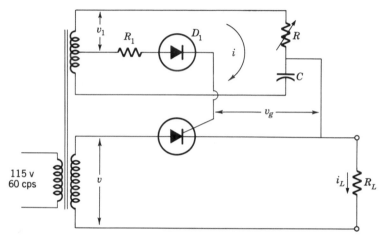

FIGURE 4-32   *Phase-shift control of SCR.*

The waveforms of Fig. 4-33 show how variation of ϕ_g alters the time at which the diode conducts on each forward cycle as the gate voltage becomes larger than the critical value. Note that the gate signal remains *on* during part of the reverse half-cycle as well, but this has no effect upon the reverse characteristic. The purpose of resistor R_1 and diode D_1 in the circuit (Fig. 4-32) is to limit the gate current to a safe value and to prevent reverse gate current, both of which are deleterious to the SCR.

Characteristics similar to those of the SCR are also obtained in hot-cathode gas tubes provided with a control electrode, called the *grid*. The circuit symbol of such a so-called *thyratron* is shown in Fig. 4-34. Proper operation of these tubes is based on a gas discharge similar to that in the VR tube, except that a heated cathode is used and the grid determines the extent to which the current avalanche can proceed at a given anode potential. Electron emission from the heated cathode greatly increases the current-carrying ability of the discharge. The anode-to-cathode potential necessary to maintain the discharge is quite low. In fact, hot-cathode gas-filled diodes are used as rectifiers in many applications.

The control electrode initiates the discharge, but the anode potential must maintain it. Thus, the action is quite similar to that of the gate electrode in an SCR. Many different kinds of thyra-

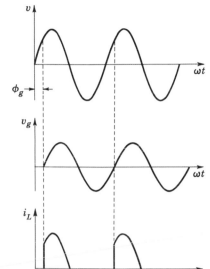

FIGURE 4-33   *Waveforms in phase-shift control SCR circuit.*

trons have been developed, some of which require a positive grid potential with respect to the cathode whereas others employ a negative grid potential. The former do not conduct unless the

FIGURE 4-34   *Circuit symbol for thyratron.*

control grid is made momentarily positive to initiate the discharge. The negative control type starts conduction whenever the anode voltage is high enough for a given negative grid potential. In either type the discharge is maintained independent of the grid potential until the anode voltage is removed.

Thyratrons are used in circuits similar to those appropriate for semiconductor controlled rectifiers. Actually SCRs are gradually replacing thyratrons in many applications, because of their small size, savings in heater power, smaller internal voltage drop, and faster switching speed. In applications involving high ambient temperatures, or extreme operating conditions, thyratrons and other gas-filled devices are unsurpassed, however.

DIODE CIRCUITS

Diodes prove to be useful in circuits other than power supplies. A major application is in circuits designed to operate with square-

wave pulses, as will be discussed in a later chapter. The rectification characteristics of diodes are also put to work in circuits dealing
with sine-wave signals. In these applications the nonlinear diode
modifies the sine-wave signals in a specified manner.

4-13 Clippers

Consider the diode *clipper* circuit, Fig. 4-35, in which two diodes
are connected in parallel with an ac voltage source. Batteries V_1
and V_2 bias each diode in the reverse direction. Whenever the

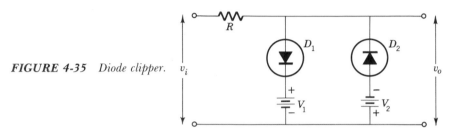

FIGURE 4-35 *Diode clipper.*

input voltage signal is greater than V_1, diode D_1 conducts and
causes a voltage drop across the series resistor R. Similarly, every
time the input voltage becomes more negative than V_2, diode D_2
conducts. Thus, the output waveform is *clipped* or *limited* to the
voltages set by the reverse biases V_1 and V_2. The clipping action
is most efficient when the series resistance is much greater than the
load impedance.

Clipper circuits produce square waves from a sine-wave generator, as illustrated by the waveforms in Fig. 4-36. If $V_1 = V_2$ and

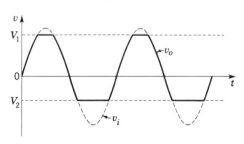

FIGURE 4-36 *Maximum amplitudes in output
waveform of diode clipper are limited to values
of bias voltages.*

the amplitude of the input signal is considerably greater than the
bias voltages, the output waveform is very nearly a square wave.
Note that if, say, $V_2 = 0$, the output can never swing negative, so the
waveform is a train of positive-going square pulses. The clipping
action operates on any input waveform; it can be adjusted by
altering the reverse-bias voltages V_1 and V_2.

The clipper circuit is also a useful protective device which limits
input voltages to a safe value set by the bias voltage. In radio-
receiver circuits limiters are often used to reduce the effect of
strong noise pulses by limiting their amplitude to that of the

desired signal. The signal waveform is transmitted undistorted
so long as the instantaneous amplitude remains smaller than the
bias voltages.

4-14 Clamps

The diode *clamp* circuit is shown in Fig. 4-37. Consider first the
situation in which the bias voltage V is set equal to zero. The diode
conducts on each negative cycle of input voltage and charges the

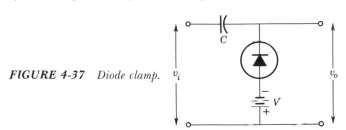

FIGURE 4-37 *Diode clamp.*

capacitor to a voltage equal to the negative peak value of the input
signal. If the load current is zero, the capacitor retains its charge
on the positive half-cycle, since the diode voltage is in the reverse
direction. Thus, the output voltage is

$$v_o = v_i + V_p \qquad (4\text{-}34)$$

where V_p is the negative peak value of the input voltage. According to Eq. (4-34) the output voltage waveform replicates the input
signal except that it is shifted by an amount equal to the dc voltage
across the capacitor.

The output waveform corresponding to a sinusoidal input, Fig.
4-38, has the negative peaks of the sine wave *clamped* at zero volt-

FIGURE 4-38 *Negative peak of output waveform is clamped
at zero when $V = 0$ in diode clamp circuit of Fig. 4-37.*

age. This is always the case, independent of the amplitude of
the input voltage. Furthermore, the negative peaks are always
clamped at zero volts no matter what form the input waveshape
takes. When the terminals of the diode are interchanged, the
same circuit analysis applies; the positive peaks of the output wave
are clamped at zero.

If the bias voltage V in Fig. 4-37 is set at a potential other than
zero, the capacitor charges to a voltage equal to $V_p + V$. Therefore, the negative peaks are clamped at the voltage V (see Exercise
4-16). Similarly, when the bias is $-V$, the negative peaks are

clamped at this potential. Reversing the diode polarity makes it possible to clamp the positive peaks of the input wave at the voltage equal to the bias potential.

The diode clamp is used in circuits which require that the voltages at certain points have fixed peak values. This is important, for example, if the waveform is subsequently clipped at a given voltage level. In most diode clamp circuits it is useful to connect a large resistance across the output terminals so that the charge on the capacitor can eventually drain away. This makes it possible for the circuit to adjust to changes in amplitude of the input voltage.

4-15 Ac voltmeters

The rectifying action of diodes makes it possible to measure ac voltages with a dc voltmeter, such as the d'Arsonval meter discussed in the first chapter. Two ways in which this is accomplished in VOM meters are illustrated in Fig. 4-39. In Fig. 4-39a diode

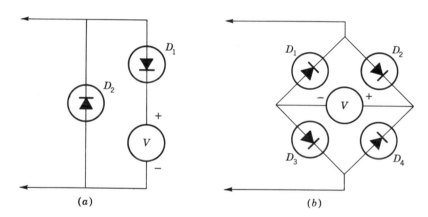

FIGURE 4-39 (a) Half-wave and (b) full-wave ac voltmeters.

D_1 is a half-wave rectifier and the dc component of the rectified waveform registers on the dc voltmeter. Diode D_2 is included to rectify the negative cycle of the input waveform. Although no meter current results from the action of diode D_2, it is included so that both halves of the ac voltage are rectified. This ensures that the voltmeter loads the circuit equally on both half-cycles and avoids possible waveform distortion. The bridge circuit, Fig. 4-39b, has greater sensitivity than the half-wave circuit because it is a full-wave rectifier.

The deflection of a d'Arsonval meter is proportional to the average current, so that the voltmeters of Fig. 4-39 measure the average value of the ac voltage. The meter scale is commonly calibrated in terms of rms readings, however, in order to facilitate comparison with dc readings. This calibration assumes that the ac waveform is sinusoidal, and, if this is not the case, the meter readings must be interpreted in terms of the actual waveform measured. Series resistor multipliers are used with ac voltmeters to increase the range, just as in the case of dc meters.

The half-wave rectifier, Fig. 4-40, makes a useful *peak-reading* voltmeter if the current drain through the meter circuit is small. In this case the capacitor charges to the positive peak value of the

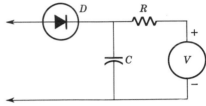

FIGURE 4-40   *Peak-reading ac voltmeter.*

input waveform on each half-cycle, and the dc meter deflection corresponds to this value. Here again, it is common practice to calibrate the meter scale in terms of rms readings, assuming that the unknown voltage is sinusoidal. This is accomplished by designing the scale to indicate the peak value divided by $\sqrt{2}$. In case the unknown voltage is not sinusoidal, the peak value is obtained by multiplying the scale reading by $\sqrt{2}$. A difficulty with this circuit is that the system being measured must contain a dc path. If this is not so and a series capacitor is present, the voltage across C depends upon the relative values of the two capacitors, since they are effectively in series during the forward cycle. This results in erroneous voltage readings.

The diode clamp is a peak-reading circuit which does not have this difficulty. It is customary to include an RC filter, Fig. 4-41, to

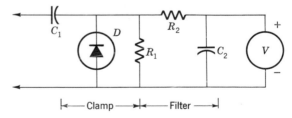

FIGURE 4-41   *Diode clamp used as peak-reading voltmeter.*

remove the ac component of the clamped wave. Referring to the waveform in Fig. 4-38, the average value is equal to the negative peak of the input voltage, so the dc meter reading corresponds to the negative peak voltage. Note that a series capacitor in the circuit to be measured in effect becomes part of the clamping action and does not result in a false meter indication. If the filter in Fig. 4-41 is replaced with a diode peak rectifier, Fig. 4-40, the combination reads the peak-to-peak value of the input wave (Exercise

4-17). Although usually calibrated in terms of rms readings for a sine wave, a peak-to-peak voltmeter is very useful in measuring complex waveforms.

4-16 Detectors

Nonlinear diode properties are useful in other ways than those corresponding to actual rectification. Suppose that the amplitude of the ac voltages applied is very small, so the diode current-voltage characteristic, Eq. (4-6) or (4-13), can be represented by the expression

$$i = a_1 v + a_2 v^2 \qquad (4\text{-}35)$$

where a_1 and a_2 are constants. An expression of this form is a satisfactory approximation to the diode characteristic for sufficiently small values of applied voltage. According to Eq. (4-35), one part of the current is proportional to the square of the input voltage.

Consider the circuit shown in Fig. 4-42, in which two sinusoidal

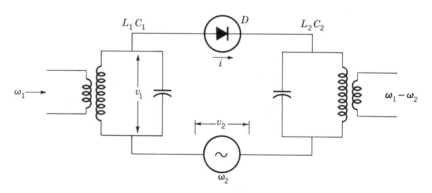

FIGURE 4-42 *Diode mixer uses nonlinear properties of diode.*

signals of somewhat different frequencies, ω_1 and ω_2, are supplied to a diode. The total diode voltage is the sum of the individual waves,

$$v = V_1 \sin \omega_1 t + V_2 \sin \omega_2 t \qquad (4\text{-}36)$$

where V_1 and V_2 are the peak amplitudes. The current is found by substituting Eq. (4-36) into Eq. (4-35), assuming for the moment that the diode impedance is greater than other impedances in the circuit,

$$i = a_1 V_1 \sin \omega_1 t + a_1 V_2 \sin \omega_2 t + a_2 V_1{}^2 \sin^2 \omega_1 t$$

$$+ a_2 V_2{}^2 \sin^2 \omega_2 t + 2a_2 V_1 V_2 \sin \omega_1 t \sin \omega_2 t \qquad (4\text{-}37)$$

Rearranging terms and introducing trigonometric substitutions for $\sin^2$ and $\sin \omega_1 t \sin \omega_2 t$,

$$i = \frac{a_2}{2} (V_1{}^2 + V_2{}^2) + a_1 (V_1 \sin \omega_1 t + V_2 \sin \omega_2 t)$$

$$- \frac{a_2}{2} (V_1{}^2 \cos 2\omega_1 t + V_2{}^2 \cos 2\omega_2 t)$$

$$+ a_2 V_1 V_2 \cos (\omega_1 - \omega_2)t - a_2 V_1 V_2 \cos (\omega_1 + \omega_2)t \qquad (4\text{-}38)$$

The first term in Eq. (4-38) is a direct current, while the second corresponds to the input voltages. The last two terms are at frequencies not present in the original inputs. Suppose ω_1 and ω_2 are not too different; then the term involving $\omega_1 - \omega_2$ is a comparatively low frequency.

In the *diode mixer* circuit of Fig. 4-42 the output circuit $L_2 C_2$ is tuned to the frequency $\omega_1 - \omega_2$, so only this component has an appreciable amplitude at the output terminals. In effect, an input signal of frequency ω_1 is mixed with a constant-amplitude sine wave at ω_2 and is converted to an output frequency $\omega_1 - \omega_2$. This is called *heterodyning* and is of considerable importance in, for example, radio receivers. The incoming high-frequency signal is converted into a lower-frequency signal which is easier to amplify. Furthermore, changing the frequency ω_2 means that the receiver is tuned to a different ω_1, such that $\omega_1 - \omega_2$ is a constant. This is important because the amplification of the $\omega_1 - \omega_2$ signal is accomplished by fixed tuned circuits that are inexpensive and easy to keep in adjustment, yet the receiver may be tuned to different input frequencies. In this application Fig. 4-42 is called a *first detector* because the signal frequency is modified in the first stages of the receiver.

This circuit has another important use, which may be illustrated by rearranging Eq. (4-38). Using the trigonometric substitution,

$$2 \sin a \sin b = \cos (a - b) - \cos (a + b) \qquad (4\text{-}39)$$

Equation (4-38) may be put in the form

$$i = \frac{a_2}{2} (V_1{}^2 + V_2{}^2) + a_1 V_2 \sin \omega_2 t - \frac{1}{2}(V_1{}^2 \cos 2\omega_1 t + V_2{}^2 \cos 2\omega_2 t)$$

$$+ a_1 V_1 \sin \omega_1 t + 2a_2 V_1 (V_2 \sin \omega_2 t) \sin \omega_1 t \qquad (4\text{-}40)$$

Suppose ω_2 is much smaller than ω_1 and that the output circuit $L_2 C_2$ is tuned to the frequency ω_1. Then only the last two terms in Eq. (4-40) have an appreciable output amplitude. The first of these is simply the current resulting from the input voltage at the frequency ω_1. Careful inspection of the last term in Eq. (4-40) shows that it is a sinusoidal waveform at a frequency ω_1 but with an amplitude that varies sinusoidally at a frequency corresponding to ω_2.

The waveform of the last term in Eq. (4-40), illustrated in Fig. 4-43, shows how the amplitude varies. The frequency ω_1 is said to be modulated at the frequency of ω_2. This is the basis for radio

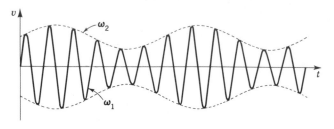

FIGURE 4-43   *Modulated waveform.*

and television communication wherein a high-frequency *carrier* ω_1 is modulated in accordance with a low-frequency signal ω_2 corresponding to the sound or picture to be transmitted. The high-frequency voltage is radiated from the sending station to a receiver where the waveform of the signal is recovered.

The signal is recovered by *demodulating* the modulated waveform with a diode peak rectifier, Fig. 4-44. Since the output of the peak

FIGURE 4-44   *Diode peak rectifier used to demodulate modulated waveform.*

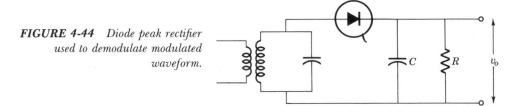

rectifier is equal to the peak value of the input voltage, the waveform across the output capacitor corresponds to that of the modulating signal, as in Fig. 4-45. In this application the peak

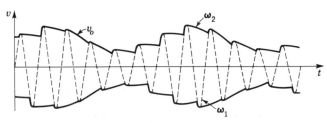

FIGURE 4-45   *Modulating waveform recovered at output of second detector.*

rectifier is called a second detector, because the waveform is changed for the second time in the receiver circuit. The second detector circuit, Fig. 4-44, is widely used in radio and television receivers.

SUGGESTIONS FOR FURTHER READING

Paul M. Chirlian and Armen H. Zemanian: "Electronics," McGraw-Hill Book Company, New York, 1961.

W. Ryland Hill: "Electronics in Engineering," McGraw-Hill Book Company, New York, 1961.

Jacob Millman and Samuel Seely: "Electronics," McGraw-Hill Book Company, New York, 1951.

EXERCISES

4-1 Calculate the forward resistance of a 5U4 vacuum diode at a voltage of 50 volts. Assuming the reverse resistance is 10 MΩ, what is the reverse to forward resistance ratio?   *Ans.*: 115 Ω; 8.6×10^4

4-2 Assuming the interelectrode capacitance of a 5U4 diode is 4 pf and the reverse resistance is 10 MΩ, what is the approximate upper limit to the frequency at which the diode is useful?

Ans.: 4.0×10^3 cps

4-3 By differentiating the rectifier equation for a junction diode, Eq. (4-13), determine an expression for the junction resistance $R = (dI/dV)^{-1}$. Given that $e/kT = 38$ volts^{-1} at room temperature, calculate the rectification ratio at a potential of 1 volt.   *Ans.*: 10^{33}

4-4 Approximate the forward characteristic of a 5U4 diode with a straight line, using Fig. 4-6, and determine the peak rectified current in a half-wave circuit with a 5000-Ω load and an input voltage of 100 volts rms. Determine the direct current by averaging the rectified half-sine wave over a full cycle and compare with the peak current.   *Ans.*: 27.5 ma; 8.7 ma

4-5 Repeat Exercise 4-4 for a full-wave circuit in which the transformer secondary voltage is 200 volts rms center-tapped. Note that the direct current is found by averaging a rectified half-sine wave over one-half a cycle.   *Ans.*: 27.5 ma; 17.5 ma

4-6 In the voltage-doubler circuit, Fig. 4-18, the input voltage is 115 volts rms at a frequency of 60 cps. If the load resistance is 10,000 Ω, what is the minimum value of the capacitors necessary to be sure the voltage drop between charging pulses is less than 10 percent of the output voltage?   *Ans.*: 8.3×10^{-6} farad

4-7 Calculate the output voltage and ripple factor of the circuit of Fig. 4-19 after diodes D_1 and D_4 are removed.   *Ans.*: 11.8 volts; 0.096

4-8 Plot the dc output and the ripple voltage of the rectifier circuit of Fig. 4-19 as a function of load current up to a current of 1 amp. Repeat for the circuit of Exercise 4-7.

4-9 Plot the dc output and the ripple voltage of the full-wave rectifier circuit given in Fig. 4-23 up to a current of 200 ma.

4-10 Determine the ripple factor of an L-section filter comprising a 10-henry choke and a 8-μf capacitor used with a full-wave rectifier. Compare with a simple 8-μf capacitor filter at a load current of 50 ma and also 150 ma, assuming an output of 50 volts.

Ans.: 0.042; 0.604; 1.82

4-11 What are the ripple factor and ripple voltage of the full-wave circuit of Fig. 4-23 if the load resistance is 2000 Ω? Repeat, assuming the output capacitor is defective and is open-circuited.

Ans.: 0.026; 11 volts

4-12 In the Zener-diode voltage regulator of Fig. 4-26 determine the range of load resistances over which the circuit is useful if $R_S = 1500$ Ω and the supply voltage $V = 150$ volts; the diode breakdown voltage is 100 volts and maximum rated current is 100 ma. For a fixed $R_L = 10,000$ Ω, over what range of input voltages does the circuit regulate?   *Ans.*: Greater than 3 kΩ; 115 to 265 volts

4-13 In Exercise 4-12, what is the proper value of R_S if the maximum diode current is 10 ma?   *Ans.*: 15 kΩ

4-14 The power-supply voltage in Fig. 4-27 is 350 volts, the series resistor is 2500 Ω, and the VR tubes are rated at 105 volts. If the load current is 20 ma at 210 volts, what is the maximum current possible in a second load resistor connected to the point between the tubes so that this output voltage is 105 volts?   *Ans.*: 36 ma

4-15 Using the phase-shift controlled rectifier circuit, Fig. 4-32, plot the dc load current as a function of control resistance R if the transformer secondary voltage is 100 volts rms, the load resistance is 10 Ω, and $C = 0.1$ μf. Assume the SCR turns on whenever the gate voltage is positive with respect to the cathode.

4-16 Sketch the waveforms of the sinusoidal input voltage, the diode voltage, and the output voltage for the diode clamp, Fig. 4-37, with a positive bias voltage V. Repeat for $-V$.

4-17 Analyze the peak-to-peak voltmeter circuit, Fig. 4-46, by sketching

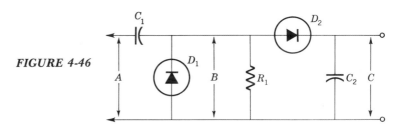

FIGURE 4-46

the voltage waveforms at points A, B, and C, assuming the input voltage A is sinusoidal. Note that the circuit is a diode clamp followed by a peak rectifier.

4-18 Can you suggest a power-supply use for the circuit of Exercise 4-17? What advantage does it have over the one discussed in the text? Are there any disadvantages? (*Hint:* Consider the voltages across the diodes and capacitors in both circuits.)

4-19 Determine the expression corresponding to Eq. (4-35) for the rectifier equation (4-13).   *Ans.*: $(e/kT)v + \frac{1}{2}(e/kT)^2 v^2$

4-20 Select suitable values of R and C for the diode second-detector circuit, Fig. 4-44, if f_1 is equal to 1 Mc and f_2 is 1000 cps. Note that the value of R should be reasonably large to minimize loading the resonant circuit.   *Ans.*: 10^5 Ω, 100 pf

5

VACUUM
TUBE
CIRCUITS

The advent of electronics can be reckoned from the discovery that the current in a vacuum diode can be controlled by including a third electrode, the grid, in the space between the anode and cathode. Variations of the grid potential change the anode current even though the anode potential may remain constant. Very little power is consumed by the grid in controlling the anode current, which makes the triode vacuum tube an exceedingly efficient amplifier. Triodes are widely used, for example, to increase the strength of feeble electric signals. The device is termed a triode, since it has three active electrodes: cathode, grid, and anode.

The triode, a nonlinear device, must necessarily be treated graphically, as with vacuum diodes. It is possible, however, to develop a useful equivalent circuit representation which is most satisfactory for circuit analysis. A very large number of different vacuum-tube circuits have been developed to perform a multitude of functions. The versatility of the vacuum tube is further enhanced by the availability of many different types, including multigrid tubes which outperform triodes in certain applications.

TRIODES

5-1 The grid

The grid in a vacuum triode usually consists of a wire helix surrounding the cathode, as sketched in Fig. 5-1. If the grid potential is always negative, electrons are repelled and the grid cur-

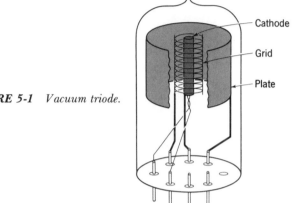

Cathode

Grid

Plate

FIGURE 5-1 *Vacuum triode.*

rent is negligible. This means that the power expended in the grid circuit to control the anode current is very small. It is desirable to minimize the area of the grid, so the number of electrons intercepted on their way to the anode is negligible. On the other hand, if the wires are spaced too widely, the grid's ability to control the anode current is reduced. Practical triodes are designed to strike a useful compromise between these conflicting requirements. The anode in vacuum tubes is commonly termed the *plate*, because of its shape in early tube designs. The conventional circuit symbol for a triode is shown in Fig. 5-2.

FIGURE 5-2 *Triode circuit symbol.*

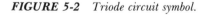

The grid potential alters the electric-field configuration in the space between the cathode and plate from that corresponding to the vacuum diode discussed in the previous chapter. The manner in which this happens can be described in the following way. According to the derivation of Child's law, the plate voltage sets the current so that the electric field near the cathode is very small. The grid potential has a similar effect. Under the combined influence of the grid potential and the plate potential, the tube current is such that the electric field at the cathode remains small.

Since the grid is much closer to the cathode, its potential is relatively more effective in controlling the current than is the plate voltage. Therefore, using Child's law, the current in the tube may be written [1]

$$I_b = A(\mu V_c + V_b)^{3/2} \tag{5-1}$$

where A is a constant involving the tube geometry, V_c is the grid voltage, V_b is the plate voltage, and μ is a constant called the *amplification factor*. The amplification factor accounts for the greater effect of the grid voltage compared with the plate voltage. This equation agrees reasonably well with experimental current-voltage characteristics of practical triodes. It is difficult to evaluate A from first principles, however, and the exponent is often not exactly $3/2$. Therefore, it is common practice to display the characteristics of practical tubes graphically, rather than attempt an accurate mathematical representation.

The action of V_c in Eq. (5-1) opposes that of the plate voltage V_b since the grid potential is negative. An expression for the amplification factor is obtained by noting that these opposing actions cancel out if the electric charge induced on the cathode by the grid potential is equal and opposite to the charge produced by the plate voltage, or

$$-C_{gk}V_c + C_{pk}V_b = 0 \tag{5-2}$$

where C_{gk} is the capacitance between the grid and cathode. Solving for the amplification factor

$$\mu = \frac{V_b}{V_c} = \frac{C_{gk}}{C_{pk}} \tag{5-3}$$

According to Eq. (5-3) the amplification factor is increased if the grid is close to the cathode since the grid-cathode capacitance is increased. The plate is further away, and is shielded from the cathode by the grid, so that μ is always greater than unity. Actually, triodes with amplification factors ranging from 10 to 100 are commercially available.

5-2 Plate characteristics

Of the several graphical ways to represent the current-voltage characteristics of a triode, the most useful is a plot of the plate current as a function of plate voltage for fixed values of grid voltage. The curves for several grid potentials are called the *plate characteristics* of the tube. A typical set of plate characteristics, as provided by the tube manufacturer, is illustrated in Fig. 5-3. Note

[1] It has become commonly accepted to associate the subscripts p and b with the plate circuit and g and c with the grid circuit of a vacuum tube. Similarly, the subscript k refers to the cathode.

that each curve is similar to the current-voltage curve of a vacuum diode. Furthermore, the current at a given plate voltage is reduced as the grid is made increasingly negative. The plate cur-

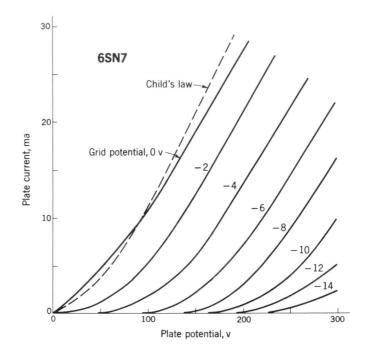

FIGURE 5-3 *Plate characteristics of type 6SN7 triode. Curve for zero grid voltage is in approximate agreement with Child's law.*

rent-voltage curves are displaced to the right with little change in shape for each negative increment in grid potential, in conformity with Eq. (5-1). Comparing Eq. (5-1) with the experimental curves shows why it is necessary to use graphical data: although Child's law represents the general behavior of the plate characteristics, it is not sufficiently accurate to yield satisfactory quantitative results (see Exercise 5-1).

According to Fig. 5-3, the plate current is essentially zero at sufficiently large negative grid potentials. The negative grid voltage necessary to put the tube in this *cutoff* condition depends upon the plate voltage. In effect, the tube is an open circuit when cut off. If the grid is at a positive potential, there is appreciable grid current. Then the grid is the anode of a diode biased in the forward direction and represents a much lower resistance than is the case for a negative grid voltage. In most circuits this effect prevents the grid from ever becoming positive. Therefore, at zero grid voltage the tube is said to be *saturated* since it is in its maximum conducting condition. The range between cutoff and saturation is the normal grid voltage range.

The plate characteristics for any triode are obtained experimentally with the aid of the circuit in Fig. 5-4, including suitable meters to measure the actual plate current and voltage. This cir-

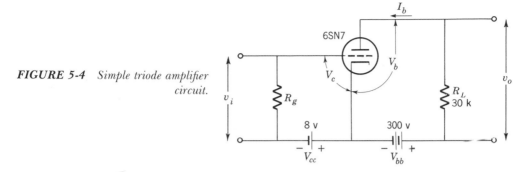

FIGURE 5-4 *Simple triode amplifier circuit.*

cuit also illustrates how a triode is used as a simple amplifier. First it is necessary to plot the load line corresponding to the load resistance R_L on the plate characteristics. This is done just as for the vacuum diode considered in Chap. 4, by noting that the current is given by

$$I_b = \frac{V_{bb} - V_b}{R_L} \tag{5-4}$$

As explained previously, this is the equation of a straight line with slope $-1/R_L$ with intercepts at $(V_b = 0; I_b = V_{bb}/R_L)$ and $(V_b = V_{bb}; I_b = 0)$, Fig. 5-5. The intersection of the load line with each curve of the plate characteristic gives the plate current for the given grid voltage.

The plate current and voltage corresponding to the dc grid bias V_{cc}, found by this procedure, is called the *operating point*. As the grid voltage varies in accordance with an applied ac input signal v_i, the plate-current excursions move back and forth along the load line, so Eq. (5-4) is satisfied at every instant. The corresponding changes in plate current give rise to an output signal across the load resistor. Suppose, for example, that the input signal is sinusoidal, as in Fig. 5-5. The output voltage is then also nearly sinusoidal but of much greater amplitude, indicating that the circuit amplifies the input signal.

Note that the input power is very small, because the grid current is negligible. In contrast, the output power, which is equal to the square of the ac plate current times the load resistance, may be appreciable. This power is derived from the plate voltage supply V_{bb} and is controlled by the valvelike action of the grid. The output voltage waveform is not an exact amplified replica of the input signal, because of curvature of the plate characteristics. This *distortion* is minimized by proper circuit design and by suitable choice of the operating point. Note also in Fig. 5-5 that as the grid voltage increases, the output voltage is reduced. This means that the triode amplifier introduces a 180° phase shift between the input and output signals. It is often convenient to account for this phase shift by writing the amplification factor as $-\mu$. The minus sign signifies that the output signal lags the input by a phase difference of 180°.

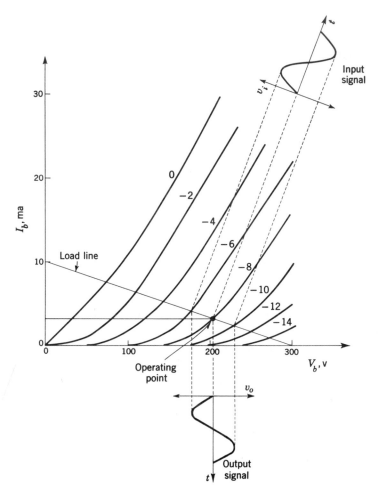

FIGURE 5-5 *Analysis of triode amplifier of Fig. 5-4 using load line. Note 4-volt peak-to-peak input signal results in a 40-volt peak-to-peak output signal.*

It is easier to determine the output waveform corresponding to a given input signal by using the *transfer characteristics* of a triode. These are curves of plate current as a function of grid voltage for fixed values of plate voltage, Fig. 5-6. Careful comparison of Figs. 5-5 and 5-6 reveals that the transfer characteristics contain the same basic information as the plate characteristics, so that one set of curves may be determined from the other. Actually, the dynamic transfer characteristic must be used to study the input-

output properties because of the voltage drop across the load resistance. This is found by the same procedure developed for the
vacuum diode in the previous chapter (see Exercises 5-2 and 5-3).

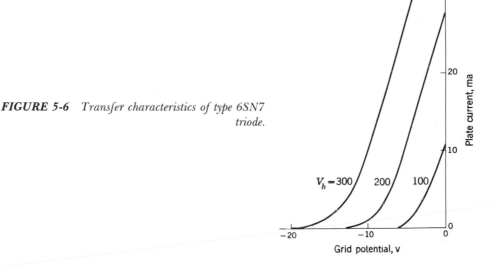

FIGURE 5-6 *Transfer characteristics of type 6SN7 triode.*

5-3 Small signal parameters

Very frequently the signal amplitudes applied to a vacuum tube
are small compared with the full range of voltages covered by the
plate characteristics. In this situation graphical analysis of tube
performance is inaccurate because the plate characteristics are
not given with sufficient precision. It is possible to represent the
tube characteristics using an approximation to Child's law which
is quite accurate for small signals. Once the operating point is
established graphically, small departures about the operating point
caused by small ac signals are treated by assuming the triode is
linear. This approach may be illustrated in the following way.
According to Child's law, Eq. (5-1), the plate current is a function
of two variables, the plate voltage and the grid voltage,

$$I_b = f(V_c, V_b)$$

The change in plate current resulting from changes in grid voltage may be determined from the Taylor expansion of this equation about the operating point. Retaining only the first two terms,
the change in plate current ΔI_b is written

$$\Delta I_b = \left(\frac{\partial I_b}{\partial V_c}\right)\Delta V_c + \left(\frac{\partial I_b}{\partial V_b}\right)\Delta V_b \tag{5-5}$$

The first partial derivative in Eq. (5-5) is the slope of the transfer
characteristic, Fig. 5-6, at the operating point and is called the
mutual transconductance g_m. The meaning of this terminology is

that g_m has the dimensions of conductance but relates the mutual changes between current in one circuit and voltage changes in another circuit. The second partial derivative in Eq. (5-5) is the slope of the plate characteristics, Fig. 5-3, at the operating point. The reciprocal of this slope is called the *plate resistance* r_p, since it represents the change in voltage associated with a change in current in the plate circuit. Introducing these definitions

$$g_m = \frac{\partial I_b}{\partial V_c}$$

and

$$\frac{1}{r_p} = \frac{\partial I_b}{\partial V_b} \tag{5-6}$$

Eq. (5-5) may be written

$$\Delta I_b = g_m \, \Delta V_c + \frac{1}{r_p} \Delta V_b \tag{5-7}$$

A useful relation between r_p and g_m is obtained by noting that if the net change in plate current is zero, Eq. (5-7) becomes

$$0 = g_m \, \Delta V_c + \frac{1}{r_p} \Delta V_b$$

or

$$g_m r_p = -\frac{\Delta V_b}{\Delta V_c} \tag{5-8}$$

The ratio $-\Delta V_b/\Delta V_c$ is just the definition of ·the amplification factor. The minus sign signifies that the plate voltage decreases when the grid potential increases, as discussed previously. Therefore, Eq. (5-8) is written

$$\mu = r_p g_m \tag{5-9}$$

This relation is useful in obtaining one of the three parameters if the other two are known.

If the variations ΔV_c and ΔV_b in Eq. (5-5) are sufficiently small, the partial derivatives may be regarded as constants and higher terms in the expansion safely ignored. The magnitudes of these *small signal parameters*, μ, r_p, and g_m, can be derived from the slopes of the characteristic curves at the operating point, as described above. So long as the quiescent operating point remains constant, the operation of the tube for small voltage signals around the operating point is adequately described by Eq. (5-7). Typical values of the small signal parameters for several triodes are given in Table 5-1.

The magnitudes of the small signal parameters depend upon the quiescent operating point. For this reason it is usually necessary

TABLE 5-1

TRIODE SMALL SIGNAL PARAMETERS

Type	μ	r_p, 10^3 Ω	g_m, 10^{-3} mho
6C4	20	6.3	3.1
6CW4	68	5.4	12.5
6SL7	70	44	1.6
12AT7	55	5.5	10
12AU7	17	7.7	2.2
12AX7	100	62	1.6
7895	74	7.3	10.9

to evaluate μ, r_p, and g_m graphically at the point determined by the dc potentials and tube characteristics. To a first approximation, the amplification factor is independent of the operating point, since it depends only upon the ratio of the interelectrode capacitances, Eq. (5-3). The plate resistance depends upon the plate current, as may be shown with the aid of Child's law. Differentiating Eq. (5-1) with respect to V_b

$$\frac{1}{r_p} = \frac{\partial I_b}{\partial V_b} = \frac{3}{2}A(\mu V_c + V_b)^{1/2} \tag{5-10}$$

Substituting for the quantity in parentheses from Eq. (5-1),

$$\frac{1}{r_p} = \frac{3}{2}A\left(\frac{I_b}{A}\right)^{1/3} = \frac{3}{2}A^{2/3}I_b^{1/3} \tag{5-11}$$

$$r_p = \frac{2}{3}A^{-2/3}I_b^{-1/3} \tag{5-12}$$

According to Eq. (5-12), the plate resistance decreases slowly as the plate current increases. The variation of the mutual transconductance is also determined by differentiating Child's law with respect to V_c or, more simply, by using Eq. (5-9). Inserting Eq. (5-12) into Eq. (5-9) and solving for g_m,

$$g_m = \frac{3}{2}A^{2/3}\mu I_b^{1/3} \tag{5-13}$$

which indicates that the mutual transconductance increases with plate current.

Since Child's law is not useful as a quantitative description of triode behavior, it is not expected that Eqs. (5-12) and (5-13) exactly represent the variation of the small signal parameters with tube current. Nevertheless, experimental data for a practical triode, Fig. 5-7, are in surprisingly good agreement with the analytical results. Note that the amplification factor is sensibly constant, except at the smallest plate currents, while g_m and r_p respectively increase and decrease with increasing plate current. According to Fig. 5-7, it is possible to obtain considerable variation in the small signal parameters by selecting different operating points. This is important in the design of vacuum-tube circuits for specific applications.

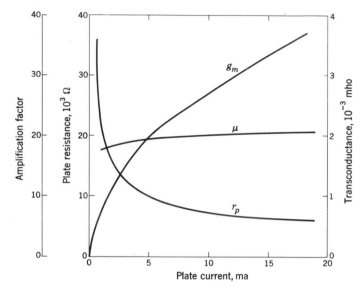

FIGURE 5-7   *Variation of triode small signal parameters with plate current.*

5-4   Triode equivalent circuit

The small signal parameters of a triode are used to calculate the performance of the tube in any circuit, so long as the signal voltages and currents are small compared with the quiescent dc values. According to Eq. (5-7), the ac component of the plate current is a function of the ac grid potential and the ac plate voltage so that

$$i_p = g_m v_g + \frac{1}{r_p} v_p \tag{5-14}$$

Henceforth the subscripts g and p signify the ac components of the grid and plate voltages (and currents), respectively. It must be kept in mind that the total electrode current or voltage has, in addition, a dc component corresponding to the operating point. After multiplying Eq. (5-14) by r_p and using Eq. (5-9), the ac plate voltage is given by

$$v_p = -\mu v_g + i_p r_p \tag{5-15}$$

Equation (5-15) may be interpreted as the series combination of a generator $-\mu v_g$ in series with a resistor r_p, as shown in Fig. 5-8. This configuration is reminiscent of the Thévenin equivalent circuit discussed in Chap. 1. Its validity in representing the performance of a triode rests on the concept of small signal parameters for a vacuum tube. Since Eq. (5-14) refers only to the ac components of the tube currents and voltages, Fig. 5-8 is called the *triode ac equivalent circuit.*

FIGURE 5-8 *Triode ac equivalent circuit.*

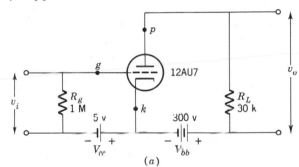

Consider the simple triode amplifier illustrated in Fig. 5-9a. According to Fig. 5-8, the equivalent circuit of the amplifier is obtained by replacing the triode with a generator and a resistor, as in Fig. 5-9b. Note that the dc battery supplies are omitted since the

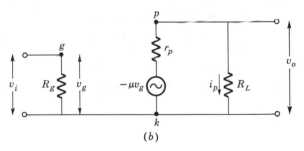

FIGURE 5-9 (a) Triode amplifier and (b) its ac equivalent circuit.

equivalent circuit refers only to ac quantities and the ac impedance of a battery is negligible. All other circuit components are included, however. According to Fig. 5-9b, there is no direct electrical connection between the input circuit and the output circuit. This illustrates the valve action of the grid in controlling the plate current with essentially zero power expenditure. Note that the minus sign associated with the generator accounts for the 180° phase difference between the grid voltage and the plate voltage.

The output voltage of the amplifier circuit is calculated immediately from the equivalent circuit, Fig. 5-9b. The result is

$$v_o = i_p R_L = \frac{-\mu v_g}{r_p + R_L} R_L = \frac{-\mu v_g}{1 + r_p/R_L} \qquad (5\text{-}16)$$

The ratio of the output signal to the input signal is called the *gain* of the amplifier. Suppressing the minus sign, since it represents only a 180° phase shift, and noticing that $v_g = v_i$, the gain of the amplifier is

$$a = \frac{v_o}{v_i} = \frac{\mu}{1 + r_p/R_L} \tag{5-17}$$

According to Eq. (5-17), the maximum gain of the circuit is equal to the amplification factor of the triode. This value is achieved when the load resistance is much greater than the plate resistance.

It is not always desirable to make the load resistance much larger than the triode plate resistance in a practical amplifier. A large load resistance introduces considerable dc power loss and requires a large plate supply voltage V_{bb} to put the tube at its optimum operating point. The amplification factor of most tubes is sufficiently large to yield appreciable gains with lower values of load resistance. It is also possible to use a transformer in the plate circuit. The impedance-matching properties of a trans-former reflect a large ac impedance from the secondary, as ex-plained in Chap. 2. In this case the dc resistance corresponds to the primary-winding resistance, which may be quite small. The expense and limited frequency range of transformers restrict their use to rather special applications.

The magnitude of the grid resistor R_g in this circuit is limited only by the voltage drop caused by residual grid current. The corresponding IR drop across R_g can change the grid bias from the value set by the grid bias battery V_{cc}. Since grid current is normally an uncontrolled quantity and varies considerably even between tubes of the same type, this is an undesirable condition. Grid resistances in the 0.5- to 10-MΩ range are satisfactory for most triodes. These values are large enough that the loading effect of the grid resistor on the input voltage source may be safely ignored in most applications.

PENTODES

5-5   Screen and suppressor grids

The capacitance between the grid and plate in a vacuum triode introduces serious difficulties when the tube is used as an amplifier at high frequencies. The ac plate signal introduced into the grid circuit through the grid-plate capacitance interferes with the proper operation of the circuit. Another grid is interposed in the space between the grid and plate to circumvent this difficulty. This *screen grid* is an effective electrostatic shield that reduces the grid-plate capacitance by a factor of 1000 or more. The screen grid is at a positive potential with respect to the cathode, and the current of electrons from cathode to plate is maintained. The helical grid winding is much more open than is the case for the control grid, so that the screen current is smaller than the plate current.

Two-grid four-electrode tubes called *tetrodes* are virtually obsolete except for certain special-purpose types. The reason for this is that electrons striking the plate dislodge other electrons. These may be attracted to the screen, particularly when the screen voltage is greater than the instantaneous plate potential. This introduces serious irregularities in the plate characteristics at low plate voltages. A *suppressor grid* is introduced between the screen and plate to eliminate this effect. The suppressor is held at cathode potential and effectively prevents all electrons dislodged from the plate from reaching the screen. The pitch of the suppressor grid helix is even larger than that of the screen grid. Therefore, the suppressor does not interfere with electrons passing from cathode to plate.

A tube with three grids is called a *pentode* because there are a total of five active electrodes. The conventional circuit symbol of a pentode is shown in Fig. 5-10. In normal operation the screen and

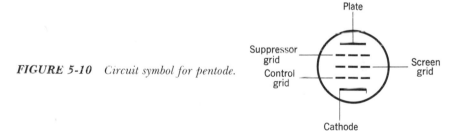

FIGURE 5-10 *Circuit symbol for pentode.*

suppressor grids are maintained at fixed dc potentials. Therefore the same small signal parameters used to describe the operation of a triode are suitable for pentodes as well. Addition of the screen and suppressor grids introduces major changes in the current-voltage characteristics, however, which are reflected in the magnitudes of the small signal parameters.

The influence of the plate potential on the electric field near the cathode is practically zero in pentodes, because of the shielding action of the screen and suppressor. This means that plate-voltage changes cause little or no change in the plate current, and, according to Eq. (5-6), the plate resistance is very large. Since the plate current is almost independent of the plate voltage, the plate characteristics are nearly straight lines parallel to the voltage axis. The action of the control grid is essentially the same as in a triode, however, so that their mutual transconductances are comparable. Therefore the amplification factor of a pentode is very large, according to Eq. (5-9). Typical values of plate resistance lie in the range 0.1 to 2 MΩ. Since g_m is of the order of 500 to 10,000 μmhos, the amplification factor may be as high as 10,000.

Typical plate characteristics of a pentode for a given positive screen potential and for the suppressor connected to the cathode are illustrated in Fig. 5-11. Note that the plate current is rela-

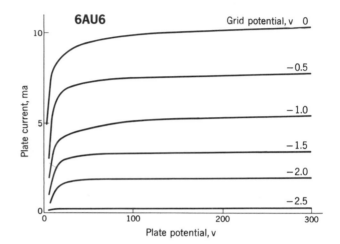

FIGURE 5-11 *Plate characteristics of type 6AU6 pentode.*

tively independent of plate voltage, as anticipated above. The plate characteristics can be used to determine the operating point and circuit performance, much as in the case of a triode. Actually, however, the plate characteristics also depend upon the fixed screen potential. Higher screen voltages shift the curves in Fig. 5-11 upward to higher current values with little change in shape. It is common practice to specify pentode characteristics at two or three specific values of screen potential.

The screen voltage is maintained below the plate potential in most circuits. It turns out that the screen current is about 0.2 to 0.4 of the plate current at the recommended operating point. As mentioned above, it is almost universal to connect the suppressor grid to the cathode; in many tubes this connection is made internally.

The pentode is extensively used in amplifier circuits because of its very high amplification factor. It surpasses the triode as a high-frequency amplifier where small grid-plate capacitance is important. Plate-voltage excursions can be nearly as large as the plate supply voltage without introducing excessive distortion, so high-power operation is possible. Finally, the pentode is a useful constant-current source, because the plate current is essentially independent of the plate voltage.

5-6 Norton equivalent circuit

Pentodes may be represented by the same equivalent circuit as triodes so long as appropriate values of the small signal parameters are used. These parameters depend upon the operating point and therefore vary with the screen and suppressor potentials, in addition to the grid bias and plate voltage. Because of the high plate resistance and constant-current properties of pentodes, it is generally most useful to use the Norton representation in preference to the Thévenin circuit. According to Eq. (1-85), the equivalent current generator is given by the ratio of the Thévenin equivalent voltage generator divided by the equivalent internal resistance. Therefore, using Fig. 5-8,

$$I_{eq} = \frac{-\mu v_g}{r_p} = -g_m v_g \tag{5-18}$$

The Norton equivalent circuit for a pentode is shown in Fig. 5-12.

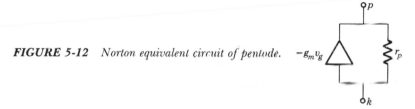

FIGURE 5-12   *Norton equivalent circuit of pentode.*

A pentode amplifier stage, Fig. 5-13*a*, is represented by the equivalent circuit shown in Fig. 5-13*b*. The output voltage is simply the constant-current source times the parallel combination of the plate resistance and load resistance,

$$v_o = -g_m v_i \frac{r_p R_L}{r_p + R_L} \tag{5-19}$$

Neglecting the minus sign, the gain is

$$a = \frac{v_o}{v_i} = g_m \frac{R_L}{1 + R_L/r_p} \tag{5-20}$$

In most cases, the plate resistance is much greater than the load resistance so that a satisfactory approximation to Eq. (5-20) is just

$$a = g_m R_L \tag{5-21}$$

Plate load resistors much in excess of 0.1 MΩ or so are inconvenient, because the excessive dc-voltage drop caused by the plate current requires a very large plate-voltage source. Nevertheless, amplifications as great as $(10{,}000 \times 10^{-6}) \times (0.1 \times 10^6) = 1000$ are obtainable from a single pentode amplifier stage.

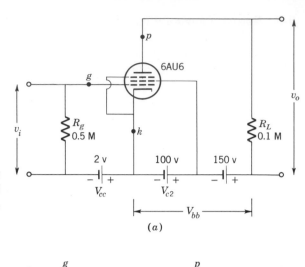

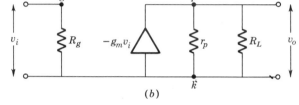

FIGURE 5-13 (a) Elementary pentode amplifier, (b) its ac equivalent circuit.

5-7 Other multigrid tubes

Many other vacuum-tube designs suitable for special circuit applications have been developed. A pentode having a control grid wound with a helix of varying pitch has an amplification factor that depends markedly upon the grid bias. This is so because electrons are controlled best in the region of the grid where the spacing is small. At sufficiently large values of negative grid bias the electron stream is cut off at this portion of the grid. Therefore, the amplification factor of the tube corresponds to that of a vacuum tube whose grid wires are widely spaced. At less negative biases the amplification factor is that of a tube with narrow grid spacing and the amplification factor is larger. These *variable-μ* tubes are used in automatic volume-control circuits where the amplification of the tube is automatically adjusted by controlling the grid bias. The bias is adjusted to maintain the output signal constant against variations in input signal. These designs are also called *remote-cutoff tubes*, since a very large negative grid voltage is required to reduce the plate current to a small value.

More than one electrode structure may be included within a single envelope when two tube types are often used together in circuits. An example of this is the dual vacuum diode for full-wave rectifier circuits discussed in the previous chapter. Other common structures are the dual triode and the dual diode-triode.

Many other combinations are possible and have been constructed. The symbol for a dual triode is indicated in Fig. 5-14a. This symbol also illustrates the method commonly employed to indi-

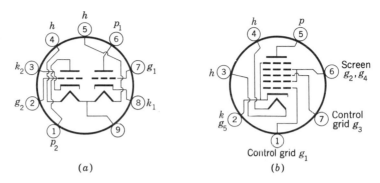

FIGURE 5-14   (a) *Base diagram of 12AX7 dual triode,* (b) *base diagram of 6BE6 pentagrid converter.*

cate the tube base pin connections to various electrodes. The base pins are numbered clockwise when viewed from the bottom. This convention facilitates identification of the various electrodes when the tube socket is examined in an actual circuit.

Vacuum tubes with more than three grids have been designed for special purposes. An example is the *pentagrid converter*, Fig. 5-14b. This tube has two control grids, g_1 and g_3, shielded from each other by two screen grids, g_2 and g_4. The fifth grid is the suppressor, g_5. This tube is used in frequency-converter circuits where two signals of different frequencies are applied to the two control grids. Nonlinearities of the tube characteristics result in sum and difference frequencies analogous to the diode first detector described in Chap. 4. Actually, the pentagrid converter can be used also to generate one of the signals within the tube itself, so only the input signal need be supplied externally.

In certain *beam power tubes*, most notably the type 6L6, the screen-grid wires are aligned with wires of the control grid. This forms the electron stream into sheets and reduces the screen current by a factor of five or so below that of conventional pentodes. There is no suppressor grid as such, but beam-forming plates at cathode potential further shape the electron stream. This specific electrode design causes the electron charges in the beam to produce an effective suppressor action. The result is that the plate characteristics are straight nearer to the $V_b = 0$ axis than is the case for a standard pentode. Accordingly, the beam power tube is useful as a power amplifier since the allowable plate-voltage range is nearly as large as the plate supply voltage. In addition, such tubes are often constructed with sturdy cathodes and anodes, so high-current operation is possible.

GRID BIAS

5-8 Cathode bias

A grid-bias battery is economically impractical in most circuits. Instead, negative grid bias is obtained by inserting a resistor in series with the cathode, Fig. 5-15. The *IR* drop across this re-

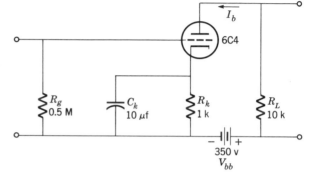

FIGURE 5-15 *Circuit diagram of a practical triode amplifier using cathode bias.*

sistor is $I_b \times R_k$, and the polarity makes the grid negative with respect to the cathode. The quiescent operating point may be found by first drawing the load line corresponding to

$$I_b = \frac{V_{bb} - V_b}{R_L + R_k} \tag{5-22}$$

According to Eq. (5-22) the intercepts of the load line are at V_{bb} and at $V_{bb}/(R_L + R_k)$, Fig. 5-16. By definition, the operating point must be located somewhere along the load line. Since the

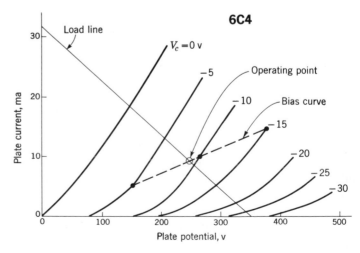

FIGURE 5-16 *Determination of operating point for 6C4 amplifier in Fig. 5-15.*

grid bias depends upon the plate current, it is necessary to draw a second line connecting the points $I_b = -V_c/R_k$ on every plate-characteristic curve. The intersection of this curve with the load line is the operating point.

Capacitor C_k shunting the cathode-bias resistor R_k in Fig. 5-15 prevents ac signals caused by the ac plate current in the cathode resistor from appearing in the grid circuit. This is illustrated

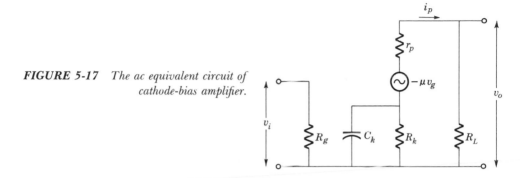

FIGURE 5-17 *The ac equivalent circuit of cathode-bias amplifier.*

with the aid of the ac equivalent circuit, Fig. 5-17. The impedance of R_k and C_k in parallel is

$$Z_k = \frac{R_k}{1 + jR_k\omega C_k} \qquad (5\text{-}23)$$

The ac signal current is given by

$$i_p = \frac{-\mu v_g}{r_p + R_L + Z_k} \qquad (5\text{-}24)$$

According to Fig. 5-15, the grid-cathode voltage is equal to the input voltage plus the ac voltage across Z_k, or

$$v_g = v_i + i_p Z_k \qquad (5\text{-}25)$$

Inserting Eq. (5-25) into Eq. (5-24) and calculating the gain of the amplifier,

$$a = \mu \frac{R_L}{r_p + R_L + (1 + \mu)Z_k} \qquad (5\text{-}26)$$

Suppose now the capacitor is omitted, so $Z_k = R_k$. Comparing Eq. (5-26) with Eq. (5-17) shows that the gain is reduced, because of the factor $(1 + \mu)R_k$ in the denominator. If, on the other hand, the capacitor is large enough that $(1 + \mu)Z_k$ is small compared with the plate resistance plus load resistance, the gain is restored to its original value. In effect the capacitor provides an ac path around R_k and, accordingly, it is called a *cathode bypass* capacitor. A convenient rule of thumb states that the capacitive reactance of the bypass capacitor should equal $\frac{1}{5}$ of R_k at the lowest frequency of interest.

Determining the operating point for cathode-biased pentodes is slightly more involved than for triodes because the bias voltage depends upon the screen current as well as the plate current. It is usually satisfactory to assume the screen current is a fixed fraction of the plate current and proceed as in the case of the triode. The correct fraction to choose depends somewhat upon the tube type in question and may be estimated from the tube's screen-current characteristics. For most pentodes the total cathode current is approximately $1.3I_b$ at the operating point. This approximation usually yields a sufficiently accurate determination of the quiescent condition.

In many cases it is simpler to resort to the following "cut-and try" procedure for determining the operating point. Choose a point on the load line corresponding to an arbitrary grid-bias voltage and plate current. The screen current is then determined from the screen characteristics for these values of V_c and V_b. The product $-(I_b + I_s)R_k$ is compared with the chosen value of V_c. If these two values are equal, the original choice is satisfactory. If they are not, the process is repeated until the desired accuracy is obtained.

5-9 Screen bias

It is advantageous to eliminate the screen-grid-bias battery by deriving the screen potential from the plate supply voltage. This can be accomplished by means of a resistive voltage divider across the plate supply voltage. A simple series dropping resistor, Fig. 5-18, is even more convenient, however. The value of R_s is

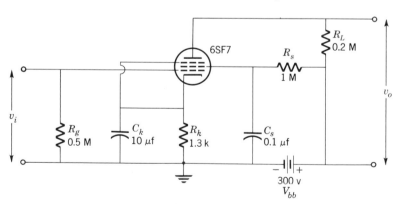

FIGURE 5-18 *Practical pentode amplifier circuit.*

selected to yield the desired screen voltage at the given screen current and plate supply potential. Values in the range from 0.05 to 1.0 MΩ are typical.

The screen resistor is bypassed with capacitor C_s to maintain the screen voltage constant independent of variations caused by signal voltages. This means that the reactance of C_s must be small compared with R_s at the lowest frequency of interest. Modest values of capacitance are sufficient because of the relatively large resistance of the screen dropping resistor.

Aside from the obvious economy achieved by providing grid, plate, and screen potentials from one voltage source, these bias techniques also result in more stable quiescent operation than does fixed bias. Suppose, for example, that the plate current tends to increase because of tube aging. This increases the negative grid bias and this, in turn, tends to lower the plate current. The net change in operating point is much less than is the case for fixed bias. The same situation exists with regard to the screen voltage.

It is inconvenient to measure electrode voltages with respect to the cathode in circuits employing a cathode-bias resistor. This is particularly true when more than one tube is used in a circuit. The usual practice is to refer all potentials to a common point called the *ground*. The ground point is considered to be electrically neutral so that, for example, the ground points of two different circuits may be connected with no influence upon the operation of either circuit. A typical use of the ground symbol, Fig. 5-19, is illustrated

FIGURE 5-19   *Ground symbol.*

in the pentode-amplifier diagram of Fig. 5-18. Practical electronic circuits are often constructed on a metal base, or *chassis*, which serves as the ground.

SPECIAL CIRCUITS

Many different vacuum-tube circuits are considered in subsequent chapters, but it is useful to analyze a few special circuits at this point. These circuits have important applications and the analysis illustrates the equivalent-circuit approach.

5-10   Cathode follower

The cathode is common to the input and output terminals in the simple amplifier circuit, insofar as ac signals are concerned. This configuration is used most often and is sometimes referred to as the *grounded-cathode connection*. Another configuration is the *grounded-plate* amplifier, Fig. 5-20. The plate resistor is omitted, and the output signal is developed across the cathode resistor.

Note that in this circuit the plate is common to both input and output terminals and is at ground potential so far as ac signals are concerned. It is maintained at a high dc potential, however. The

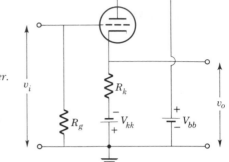

FIGURE 5-20 *Elementary cathode-follower amplifier.*

battery V_{kk} in the cathode lead counteracts the large dc voltage across R_k caused by the quiescent tube current. The difference between the cathode potential and the grid potential results in the proper grid-bias value. This circuit is commonly called a *cathode follower* because the cathode potential follows that of the grid.

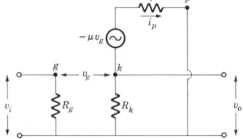

FIGURE 5-21 *Equivalent circuit of a cathode follower.*

The equivalent circuit of the cathode follower is given in Fig. 5-21. We proceed to find the output signal by first calculating the current

$$i_p = \frac{-\mu v_g}{r_p + R_k} \tag{5-27}$$

The grid-cathode voltage is equal to the input voltage plus the voltage across the cathode resistor, or

$$v_g = v_i + i_p R_k \tag{5-28}$$

Inserting Eq. (5-28) into Eq. (5-27), the current in the circuit is

$$i_p = \frac{-\mu v_i}{(1 + \mu)R_k + r_p} \tag{5-29}$$

The drop across R_k caused by this current represents the output voltage. Note, however, that the output voltage is the negative of

$i_p R_k$, because current always enters the positive terminal of a load. Therefore

$$v_o = \frac{\mu v_i R_k}{(1 + \mu)R_k + r_p} \tag{5-30}$$

The gain of the amplifier,

$$a = \frac{v_o}{v_i} = \frac{\mu}{(1 + \mu) + r_p/R_k} \tag{5-31}$$

is always less than unity. In fact, if $R_k > r_p$, which is usually the case,

$$a = \frac{\mu}{\mu + 1} \approx 1 \tag{5-32}$$

The voltage gain of the cathode-follower circuit is essentially equal to unity, and, according to Eq. (5-30), the output voltage is in phase with the input signal. Therefore, the cathode voltage follows the input voltage very closely.

The virtue of the cathode follower is that the cathode voltage replicates the input signal in a much lower impedance circuit. Therefore, the internal impedance of the circuit as a power source is very low. This means the tube can deliver appreciable power to low impedance loads. The equivalent internal impedance is determined using Thévenin's theorem. The theorem cannot be applied directly to Fig. 5-21, because the generator voltage $-\mu v_g$ depends upon the load current through R_k, according to Eq. (5-28). To find a more suitable circuit, Eq. (5-29) is put in the form

$$i_p = \frac{-v_i \mu/(1 + \mu)}{R_k + r_p/(1 + \mu)} \tag{5-33}$$

This expression is the ratio of an emf, $-v_i \mu/(1 + \mu)$, divided by a resistance, $R_k + r_p/(1 + \mu)$, which can be represented by the diagram of Fig. 5-22. Applying Thévenin's theorem to this circuit,

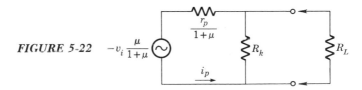

FIGURE 5-22 $-v_i \dfrac{\mu}{1+\mu}$

the equivalent internal impedance is the parallel combination of R_k and $r_p/(1 + \mu)$,

$$R_o = \frac{R_k r_p/(1 + \mu)}{R_k + r_p/(1 + \mu)} = \frac{R_k r_p}{(1 + \mu)R_k + r_p} \tag{5-34}$$

The *output impedance* of any circuit is the ratio of the output voltage divided by the output current when the input signal is zero. This is simply the internal impedance in the Thévenin equivalent representation. According to Eq. (5-34), the output impedance of the cathode follower is

$$R_o = \frac{r_p}{(1+\mu) + r_p/R_k} \approx \frac{r_p}{1+\mu} \approx \frac{r_p}{\mu} \qquad (5\text{-}35)$$

This means that the output impedance is small. Note that the circuit results in an output impedance much smaller than R_k, since $R_k \gg r_p/\mu$.

It is inconvenient to employ two bias-voltage sources, so that a different bias arrangement, Fig. 5-23, is commonly used. The size

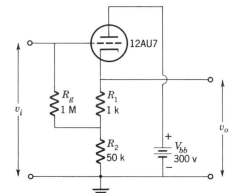

FIGURE 5-23 *Practical cathode-follower circuit.*

of R_1 is selected to yield the proper grid bias at the quiescent current, and the magnitude of R_2 is then determined by the desired value of $R_k = R_1 + R_2$. The operating point is determined by the same procedure used for the cathode-bias circuit, Fig. 5-16.

This circuit, Fig. 5-23, illustrates the second significant feature of the cathode follower: its large input impedance. The input impedance is the ratio of the input voltage to the current in the input circuit

$$R_i = \frac{v_i}{i_i} \qquad (5\text{-}36)$$

Applying Kirchhoff's voltage rule to the input circuit, the input current is

$$i_i = \frac{v_i + i_p R_2}{R_g + R_2} \qquad (5\text{-}37)$$

The current i_p is given by Eq. (5-29) with R_k replaced by $R_1 + R_2$. Substituting into Eq. (5-37),

$$i_i = \frac{v_i}{R_g + R_2}\left[1 - \frac{\mu R_2}{(1+\mu)(R_1+R_2)+r_p}\right]$$

$$= \frac{v_i}{R_g + R_2}\left[1 - \frac{\mu}{(1+\mu)(1+R_1/R_2)+r_p/R_2}\right] \qquad (5\text{-}38)$$

Most often, $R_2 \gg R_1$ and $R_2 \gg r_p$, so that

$$i_i = \frac{v_i}{R_g + R_2}\left(1 - \frac{\mu}{1 + \mu}\right) = \frac{v_i}{R_g + R_2}\frac{1}{1 + \mu} \tag{5-39}$$

Comparing Eq. (5-39) with Eq. (5-36), the input impedance is

$$R_i = (1 + \mu)(R_g + R_2) \tag{5-40}$$

which is quite large. This is an advantage since the cathode follower presents a very light load to preceding circuits. The reason for the high input impedance is, of course, the opposing voltage introduced into the grid circuit from the cathode resistor.

The cathode follower is an impedance-matching device with a very high input impedance and a very low output impedance. Although the voltage gain is less than unity, the power gain may be appreciable. This is so because the signal voltage is the same in both the high-impedance input circuit and the low-impedance output circuit. Since power is proportional to V^2/R, the power amplification is large. In addition, the circuit performance is stable and relatively independent of changes in component values. According to Eq. (5-32), the gain depends only on the amplification factor, which is the most stable of the small signal parameters.

5-11 Difference amplifier

The circuit diagramed in Fig. 5-24 is often used as the input stage of oscilloscope amplifiers and other laboratory instruments,

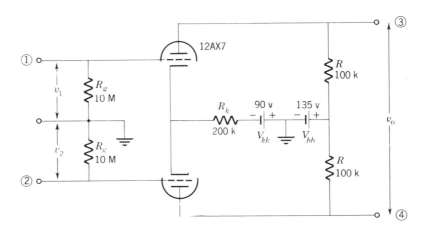

FIGURE 5-24 *Difference amplifier. Half-open tube symbol signifies a dual triode.*

because it yields a signal proportional to the difference between two input voltages. This useful property may be illustrated by analyz-

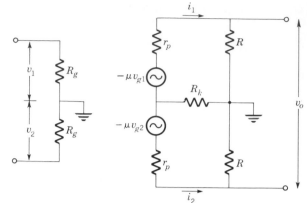

FIGURE 5-25 *Equivalent circuit of difference amplifier.*

ing the equivalent circuit, Fig. 5-25. Kirchhoff's voltage rule applied to both loops results in

$$-\mu v_{g_1} = r_p i_1 + R i_1 + R_k (i_1 + i_2)$$

$$-\mu v_{g_2} = r_p i_2 + R i_2 + R_k (i_1 + i_2)$$ (5-41)

Similarly, the grid-cathode voltages are

$$v_{g_1} = v_1 + R_k (i_1 + i_2)$$

$$v_{g_2} = v_2 + R_k (i_1 + i_2)$$ (5-42)

Equations (5-42) are substituted into (5-41) and the result solved for the two currents. The expression for the current in the upper loop is

$$i_1 = \mu \frac{v_2 - [1 + (r_p + R)/(1 + \mu)R_k]v_1}{\{[1 + (r_p + R)/(1 + \mu)R_k]^2 - 1\}(1 + \mu)R_k}$$ (5-43)

Because of the circuit symmetry, the result for i_2 has the same form with subscripts 1 and 2 interchanged. The plate-to-plate output voltage is

$$v_o = R i_1 - R i_2 = R(i_1 - i_2)$$ (5-44)

Substituting for i_1 and i_2 and simplifying,

$$v_o = \mu(v_2 - v_1) \frac{2 + (r_p + R)/(1 + \mu)R_k}{(1 + r_p/R)[2 + (r_p + R)/(1 + \mu)R_k]}$$ (5-45)

$$v_o = \frac{\mu}{1 + r_p/R} (v_2 - v_1)$$ (5-46)

which is similar to Eq. (5-17) for the amplification of a single triode. According to Eq. (5-46), the output voltage is a constant times the difference between the input signals. This result applies only if the two halves of the circuit are strictly identical. In practical circuits $(1 + \mu)R_k \gg r_p$, and this reduces the effects of any asymmetry.

The *difference amplifier* rejects any voltage signals that are common to both terminals, such that $v_1 = v_2$. At the same time, signals applied from terminal 1 to terminal 2 are amplified normally, since in this case

$$v_1 = \frac{v_i}{2} \quad \text{and} \quad v_2 = -\frac{v_i}{2} \tag{5-47}$$

The output voltage is

$$v_o = \frac{-\mu}{1 + r_p/R} \left(\frac{v_i}{2} + \frac{v_i}{2}\right) = \frac{-\mu}{(1 + r_p/R)} v_i \tag{5-48}$$

which means the circuit simply amplifies the input signal. The same result holds if the input signal is connected between ground and either grid, so that, for example, $v_1 = v_i$ and $v_2 = 0$. Since the circuit rejects *common-mode* signals, resulting from, say, stray electrical fields caused by the 60-cps power mains, it is useful as the input stage of a sensitive amplifier. In addition, the input may be connected to voltage sources that have neither terminal grounded, which is often very convenient.

The output of a difference amplifier is balanced with respect to ground. A single-ended output (one terminal grounded) is obtained by making one of the plate load resistors equal to zero, Fig. 5-26. The circuit has been drawn in this fashion to show that tube

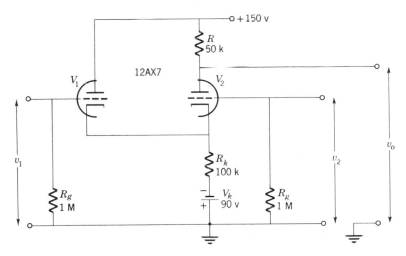

FIGURE 5-26 *Difference amplifier with single-ended output.*

V_1 may be considered as a cathode follower feeding the cathode of tube V_2. The output of V_2 is proportional to its cathode-to-grid voltage and hence approximately proportional to $v_2 - v_1$. The circuit can therefore be analyzed in terms of a simple amplifier preceded by a cathode follower. (See Exercise 5-18.)

Alternatively, the equivalent circuit of Fig. 5-25 can be used with the upper-plate load resistor shorted out. The output signal is

$$v_o = Ri_2 =$$

$$\mu \frac{v_1 - [1 + r_p/(1+\mu)R_k]v_2}{\{[1 + r_p/(1+\mu)R_k][1 + (r_p + R)/(1+\mu)R_k] - 1\}(1+\mu)R_k/R}$$

$$(5\text{-}49)$$

which may be simplified to

$$v_o = \mu \frac{v_2 - v_1 - v_2 r_p/(1+\mu)R_k}{1 + r_p/R[2 + (r_p + R)/(1+\mu)R_k]} \qquad (5\text{-}50)$$

Introducing the approximation $(1+\mu)R_k \gg r_p + R$, this expression reduces to

$$v_o = \frac{\mu}{1 + 2r_p/R}(v_2 - v_1) \qquad (5\text{-}51)$$

Comparing Eq. (5-51) with Eq. (5-46) shows that the single-ended difference amplifier is almost identical with the balanced-output circuit. Actually the approximations introduced in leading to Eqs. (5-46) and (5-51) are slightly more accurate in the case of the balanced circuit. Therefore, the balanced amplifier's ability to reject common-mode signals is superior.

5-12 VTVM

The voltage and power amplification of a vacuum triode results in a sensitive dc *vacuum-tube voltmeter* (*VTVM*) when used in conjunction with a standard d'Arsonval milliammeter. This is possible because of the very great input impedance of vacuum tubes. A common VTVM circuit, Fig. 5-27, is a cathode-follower difference

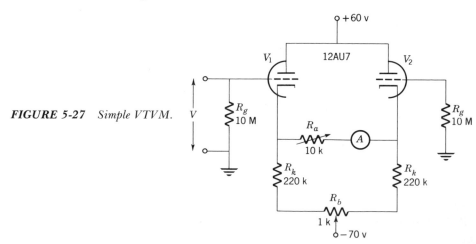

FIGURE 5-27   *Simple VTVM.*

amplifier with the meter connected between the cathodes. The unknown voltage is applied to the grid of one of the triodes. The grid of the other triode is unused and is returned to ground through a grid resistor. Since a cathode follower presents a high input impedance and a low output impedance, this circuit is particularly useful in the VTVM application.

The balanced circuit provides a convenient connection for the d'Arsonval meter which results in zero deflection with zero input signal, even though the quiescent current in each tube is nonzero. Furthermore, the symmetry of the circuit maintains performance stability against component changes caused by aging. Actually the circuit may be looked upon as a bridge comprising a triode in each of two arms together with the cathode resistors in the other two arms. A dc voltage applied to the grid of V_1 changes the tube's resistance and unbalances the bridge. The circuit may be analyzed using vacuum-tube equivalent circuits in the usual fashion (Exercise 5-20).

The adjustable resistor R_a in series with the meter is a calibration resistor in the diagram of Fig. 5-27. The potentiometer R_b is a balance adjustment which corrects for minor asymmetries in the triodes or other components. The circuit is balanced for zero current in the meter by adjusting R_b with zero voltage applied to the grid. It is necessary to readjust the balance control periodically as the tube warms up or as circuit components age.

The grid of V_1 is connected to multiplier resistors in commercial VTVM instruments to achieve multiple-range performance, much as in the case of the VOM circuit. The resistor values are greater in the vacuum-tube instrument, however, because of the much greater sensitivity. An additional feature of interest is that the VTVM may be designed so the maximum meter current, which occurs when one of the tubes is completely cut off, does not damage the meter. Therefore, the meter movement is unharmed, even if the VTVM is inadvertently connected to a voltage source much larger than the full scale value.

Standard VTVM instruments provide for ac measurements by using a diode rectifier circuit, as discussed in the previous chapter. The high input impedance of the cathode-follower difference amplifier is ideally suited to measure the output of the rectifier circuit. In addition to ac and dc voltages, most VTVM instruments also measure resistance with an ohmmeter circuit similar to those discussed in Chap. 1. Again, the difference amplifier is used as the indicator. This permits a very wide range of operation. For example, quite inexpensive instruments are capable of measuring unknown resistances from 1 Ω to 100 MΩ.

5-13 Class A, B, and C amplifiers

The grid signal never exceeds the cutoff voltage, and never becomes positive in all of the circuits examined thus far. Under such conditions, plate current exists at every instant of the input cycle. This is known as *class-A* operation and is the situation in most vacuum-tube applications. The transfer characteristics corresponding to this case, Fig. 5-28a, show that the output waveform is very similar to the input waveform. Some distortion may be introduced by curvature of the tube characteristics, however.

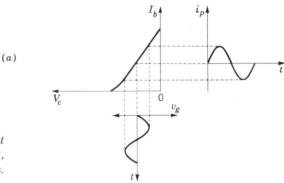

(a)

FIGURE 5-28 *Output current waveforms for (a) class-A, (b) class-B, and (c) class-C operation of amplifiers.*

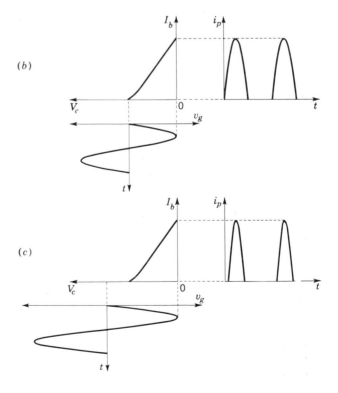

(b)

(c)

If the dc bias equals the cutoff bias of the tube, plate current exists for only one-half of the input cycle, Fig. 5-28*b*. The input signal may be increased considerably without driving the grid positive, and this results in a greater power output. The increased power output of such *class-B* operation is achieved at the expense of the output waveform, for the plate current is a series of near-half-sine waves.

Clearly, class-B operation introduces very large distortions, since the output waveform is no longer a replica of the input signal. By connecting two tubes in a fashion somewhat analogous to the full-wave rectification circuit, it can be arranged that each tube supplies current on alternate half-cycles. Thus the output signal is restored to a replica of the input waveform and the magnitude of the amplified signal is much greater than is possible in class-A operation. This circuit is considered further in Chap. 7. An additional advantage of class-B amplifiers is that the quiescent current is zero, since the dc grid bias is at cutoff. This means that the quiescent power is zero. For this reason, as well as the large plate-current excursions, class-B circuits are very efficient power amplifiers.

Increasing the dc bias beyond cutoff is called *class-C* operation, Fig. 5-28*c*. In this case plate current exists for less than one-half of the input cycle and the input waveform cannot be recovered even with a two-tube circuit. Class-C amplifiers are used exclusively in connection with resonant circuits, where it is necessary to amplify only a single frequency. If the plate load of a class-C amplifier is a parallel resonant circuit having reasonable Q, it is only necessary to excite the resonant circuit once each cycle. The resonant circuit rings and supplies the remainder of the sine-wave signal in the output circuit. The current pulses of the class-C amplifier recur at the resonant frequency and keep the resonant circuit ringing. Because plate current exists for only a portion of the cycle, class-C amplifiers are even more efficient than the class-B circuits.

SUGGESTIONS FOR FURTHER READING

E. J. Angelo, Jr.: "Electronic Circuits," McGraw-Hill Book Company, New York, 1958.

"RCA Receiving Tube Manual," latest edition, Radio Corporation of America, Harrison, N.J.

S. Seely: "Electron Tube Circuits," 2d ed., McGraw-Hill Book Company, New York, 1958.

K. R. Spangenberg: "Vacuum Tubes," McGraw-Hill Book Company, New York, 1948.

EXERCISES

5-1 Plot Child's law, Eq. (5-1), for a type 12AU7 triode and compare with experimental plate characteristics in Appendix 3. Do this by evaluating the constant A using the experimental curve for $V_c = 0$ and evaluating μ for the $V_c = -10$-volt curve.

Ans.: 1.1×10^{-5}; 17.2

5-2 Determine the dynamic transfer characteristic of the type 6SN7 triode amplifier of Fig. 5-4. Compare with the static transfer characteristics of Fig. 5-6.

5-3 Using the results of Exercise 5-2, plot the output-current waveform corresponding to a sinusoidal input signal of 2 volts. Repeat for a 6-volt signal, and note which output signal has greater distortion. Repeat for sawtooth input waveforms having the same peak-to-peak amplitude as the sinusoidal voltages.

5-4 Calculate the small signal parameters corresponding to Exercise 5-2 from the tube's characteristic curves at the operating point. Determine the variation in plate current using Eq. (5-7) for sinusoidal input signals of 2 and 6 volts. Compare with the graphical results obtained in Exercise 5-3.

Ans.: 1560 μmhos, 12.5 kΩ, 19.5; 7.6 ma, 25 ma

5-5 Using the triode equivalent circuit corresponding to Fig. 5-4 and the small signal parameters of Exercise 5-4, calculate the gain of the amplifier. Compare the output signal for 2 volts input with the results of Exercise 5-3. *Ans.*: 13.8; 27.6 volts

5-6 Plot the static transfer characteristics for a type 6AU6 pentode at plate voltages of 100, 200, and 300 volts. Do this with the aid of the plate characteristics given in Fig. 5-11.

5-7 Find the operating point of a type 12AX7 triode amplifier in the circuit of Fig. 5-15 if $R_L = 12,000 \ \Omega$ and $R_k = 2000 \ \Omega$. Use plate characteristics given in Appendix 3. *Ans.*: −3.1 volts, 1.6 ma

5-8 With the aid of Eq. (5-26) plot the gain of the type 6C4 triode amplifier, Fig. 5-15, as a function of frequency. Use a logarithmic frequency scale to cover the interval from 1 to 1000 cps. Assume $\mu = 10$ and $r_p = 6,000 \ \Omega$.

5-9 Determine the operating point of a type 6SF7 pentode amplifier in the circuit of Fig. 5-18. Use the plate characteristics given in Appendix 3. *Ans.*: −6 volts, 1.8 ma

5-10 Determine the operating point of a type 12AU7 triode cathode-follower amplifier, Fig. 5-23. Calculate the input impedance, output impedance, and power gain using values of the small signal parameters determined from the plate characteristics.

Ans.: −3 volts, 3 ma; $2.3 \times 10^7 \ \Omega$, 480 Ω, 4.8×10^4

5-11 Suppose a type 12AX7 triode is inserted into the circuit of Fig. 5-23 with no other changes. Repeat Exercise 5-10 and note that only minor changes result.

Ans.: −1.5 volts, 1.5 ma; 1650 μmhos, 55 kΩ, 96; $9.7 \times 10^7 \ \Omega$, 566 Ω, 1.7×10^5

5-12 Explain why the gain of a difference amplifier, Fig. 5-24, is the same as that of a single triode, even though the cathode resistor is not bypassed. Do this by calculating the ac signal across R_k resulting from a sinusoidal input voltage applied to terminals 1 and 2. Repeat for a signal applied between terminal 1 and ground.

5-13 Analyze the circuit of Fig. 5-24 including a cathode bypass capacitor connected in parallel with R_k. Assume the impedance of the parallel combination is zero at the frequencies of interest. Compare the operation of this circuit with that of a difference amplifier.

5-14 Draw the ac equivalent circuit of the *summing* amplifier in Fig. 5-29. Show that the output voltage is the sum of the input signals.

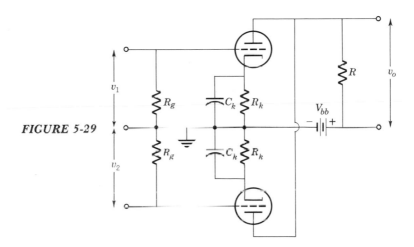

FIGURE 5-29

5-15 Sketch the output waveforms between terminal 3 and ground and also between terminal 4 and ground of the difference amplifier, Fig. 5-24, resulting from a sinusoidal input signal applied between terminal 1 and ground. Pay particular attention to the phase of the output signals. In this application the circuit is called a *phase inverter*.

5-16 Determine the operating point of the type 12AX7 dual-triode difference amplifier, Fig. 5-24. Use plate characteristic curves given in Appendix 3.   *Ans.:* −1.5 volts, 0.22 ma

5-17 Repeat Exercise 5-16 for the single-ended difference amplifier, Fig. 5-26.   *Ans.:* −1.5 volts, 0.5 ma, 0.4 ma

5-18 Analyze the single-ended difference amplifier, Fig. 5-26, by considering the circuit to be a cathode-follower amplifier feeding a triode amplifier with an unbypassed cathode resistor. Do this by using the expressions for each stage found in the text. Compare the result with Eq. (5-51) when the same approximations are introduced.

5-19 With the aid of Eq. (5-46) calculate the output signal of the difference amplifier studied in Exercise 5-16. Use values of small signal parameters given in Table 5-1. Repeat for the single-ended difference amplifier, Fig. 5-26, and compare Eq. (5-50) with Eq. (5-51).

Ans.: 61.7; $28.5(v_2 - v_1) - 1.77 \times 10^{-3}v_2$; $29.7(v_2 - v_1)$

5-20 Analyze the VTVM circuit, Fig. 5-27, by deriving an expression for the meter current I as a function of the dc input voltage V. Insert numerical values given on the circuit diagram, assuming the meter resistance is negligible and the small signal parameters of the tube given in Table 5-1. What is the ohms/volt rating of this meter on the 1-volt scale? Compare with the sensitivity of a VOM using the same 100-μa d'Arsonval meter.

Ans.: $9.2 \times 10^{-5}v$; $10^4 \ \Omega$/volt; $10^7 \ \Omega$/volt

6

TRANSISTORS

The possibilities inherent in electronic circuits were greatly expanded by the invention of the transistor in 1948. Since then the commercial importance of the transistor has spawned a variety of other semiconductor electronic devices. These devices, most notably the transistor, have to a large extent supplanted vacuum tubes in many electronic circuits.

The electronic functions of transistors take place within a solid body. They are small, since they need no complicated mechanical structures or large vacuum enclosures. Their operating life is essentially infinite, because the active element, electrons, cannot wear out. In addition, semiconductor devices require very little power for proper operation and are very efficient circuit elements.

The major disadvantage of semiconductor devices is their poor high-temperature performance, which limits the operating temperature of most devices to a few hundred degrees centigrade. Semiconductors are also sensitive to chemical contamination, so transistors must be carefully protected from the atmosphere. The characteristics of semiconductor devices stem directly from the properties of semiconductor materials. In fact, the great variety of devices that have been developed since the transistor are possible only because of the versatility of semiconductor materials.

SEMICONDUCTORS

6-1 Energy bands

The properties of any solid material, including semiconductors, depend upon the nature of the constituent atoms and upon the way in which the atoms are grouped together. That is, the properties are a function of both the atomic structure of the atoms and the crystal structure of the solid. Experiments have shown that an atom consists of a positively charged nucleus surrounded by electrons located in discrete orbits. Actually electrons can exist in stable orbits near the nucleus only for certain discrete values of energy called *energy levels* of the atom.

The allowed energies of electrons in an atom are illustrated by horizontal lines on an *energy-level diagram,* Fig. 6-1. The curved

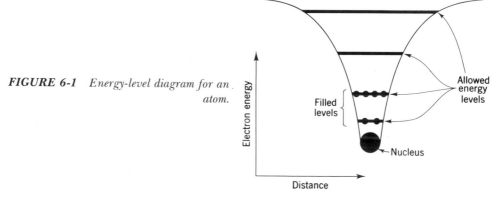

FIGURE 6-1   *Energy-level diagram for an atom.*

lines in the diagram represent the potential energy of an electron near the nucleus, as given by Coulomb's law. As a consequence of the *Pauli exclusion principle*, only a certain maximum number of electrons can occupy a given energy level. The result is that in any atom, electrons fill up the lowest possible levels first. Electrons in occupied levels are indicated by a solid dot in the energy-level diagram.

When atoms come close together to form a solid crystal, electrons in the upper levels of adjacent atoms interact to bind the atoms together. Because of the strong interaction between these outer, or *valence*, electrons, the upper energy levels are drastically altered. This can be illustrated by an energy-level diagram for the entire crystal. Consider first two isolated atoms, each with an energy-level diagram pertaining to the outer electrons as in Fig. 6-2*a*. When these are brought close together, Fig. 6-2*b*, the valence electrons in both atoms are attracted by both nuclei. The result is that the energy required to remove an electron from one nucleus and place it on the other is reduced. This means that an outer electron is equally likely to be located near either nucleus. The appropriate energy-level diagram for the combination of two atoms has two energy levels near each atom core. The higher, un-

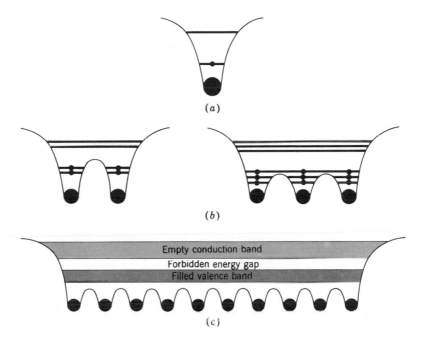

(a)

(b)

(c)

FIGURE 6-2 *Energy-level diagram for (a) isolated atom, (b) two and three atoms close together, and (c) solid crystal. In the crystal, energy levels are broadened into bands.*

occupied, levels are similarly split, indicating that these levels, too, can each contain two electrons. When three atoms are brought together, Fig. 6-2b, the outer electrons of all three atoms can be associated with any of the three nuclei. Consequently, three energy levels are available.

Even the tiniest crystal contains many hundreds of millions of atoms, so that very many energy levels are associated with each nucleus. Since it is impossible to show each of the many millions of levels separately, the energy-level diagram appropriate for the entire crystal has a band of levels. The lowest energy band, called the *valence band* (Fig. 6-2c), is completely filled with electrons for there is one electron for each of the available energy levels. Conversely, the upper energy band is empty of electrons because it corresponds to the unoccupied higher levels in the isolated atom. It is called the *conduction band*, for reasons explained below. The energy region between the valence band and the conduction band is called the *forbidden energy gap* since no electrons with such energies exist in the crystal. The forbidden energy gap corresponds to the energy region between energy levels in the isolated atom, as can be seen by comparing the energy-level diagrams in Fig. 6-2.

This picture of the electronic energy levels in a crystal is known as the *energy-band model* of a crystal. It is very useful in determining the electrical properties of any solid, since it shows how electrons can move in the crystal. While the general features of the band model for any solid are as described, many important details depend upon the specific atomic and crystal structure. In particular, the differences between metals, semiconductors, and insulators are reflected in their energy-band models.

The atomic and crystal structures of metals are such that the valence and conduction bands overlap, as indicated in the conventional energy-band model for a metal, Fig. 6-3a. Since there is no

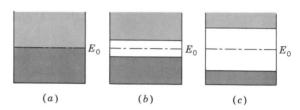

FIGURE 6-3 *Energy-band models for (a) metal, (b) semiconductor, and (c) insulator. Fermi energy level is indicated by E_0.*

(a) (b) (c)

forbidden energy gap in a metal crystal, any of the many valence electrons are free to roam throughout the solid and to move in response to an electric field. Therefore, metals are excellent electric conductors. Electrons in the bands are distributed in accordance with the Pauli exclusion principle. At absolute zero all electrons fill up the lowest levels, and the highest filled level is called the *Fermi level.* At normal temperatures some electrons at the highest energies are excited to levels slightly above the Fermi level by virtue of the heat energy in the crystal. Consequently, a few energy levels below the Fermi level are empty and a few energy levels above the Fermi level are filled. In this situation the Fermi level represents the energy at which the levels are half-filled and half-empty. The position of the Fermi level is indicated on the energy-level diagram of Fig. 6-3a by E_0.

An insulating crystal has a wide forbidden energy gap, Fig. 6-3c. The valence band is completely filled with electrons and the conduction band is completely empty. Obviously the upper band cannot contribute to electric conductivity since no electrons are present to act as carriers. It may seem paradoxical at first, but electrons in the completely filled valence band also cannot conduct electricity. When an electron moves in response to an electric field, it must move slightly faster than before. Consequently, it has greater energy and must find an empty level at a slightly higher energy. Every nearby level is filled, however, so that it is impossible for any electron in the filled valence band to be accelerated by the electric field. The crystal is therefore an insulator.

The energy-band model of a semiconductor, Fig. 6-3b, is similar to that of an insulator except that the forbidden energy gap is comparatively narrow. A few electrons can be promoted from the valence band to the conduction band across the forbidden energy gap by virtue of the thermal energy of the crystal at room temperature. Electrons promoted to the conduction band can conduct electricity. The corresponding electron vacancies in the valence band make it possible for electrons in this band to contribute to conductivity as well. Since the number of carriers is much fewer than in the case of a metal, semiconductors are poorer conductors than metals but better than insulators. A little thought shows that at very low temperatures a semiconductor becomes an insulator. Thermal energies at very low temperatures are insufficient to excite electrons across the forbidden energy gap. Conversely, at sufficiently high temperatures, even insulators conduct electricity because some electrons can be promoted from the valence band to the conduction band.

The width of the forbidden energy gap of semiconductors is of the order of 1 electron volt, as shown in Table 6-1 for several

TABLE 6-1

FORBIDDEN ENERGY GAPS OF TYPICAL SEMICONDUCTORS

Name	*Chemical symbol*	*Forbidden energy gap, ev*
Silicon	Si	1.1
Germanium	Ge	0.72
Gallium arsenide	GaAs	1.34
Indium antimonide	InSb	0.18
Cadmium sulfide	CdS	2.45
Zinc oxide	ZnO	3.3

typical semiconductor crystals. The electron volt, abbreviated *ev*, is equal to the kinetic energy gained by an electron in traversing a potential difference of one volt. It is a convenient energy unit in semiconductor studies. In general, materials with a wide forbidden energy gap are desirable for semiconductor devices. The number of electrons promoted to the conduction band at high temperatures is small and the change in device characteristics with temperature is less severe when the forbidden energy gap is wide. For this reason, silicon crystals are more widely used than germanium crystals even though the latter are easier to prepare and less expensive.

6-2 Electrons and holes

According to the preceding discussion, the net current resulting from electrons in a filled valence band is zero. Formally, this may be written in terms of the current density using Eq. (1-13)

$$J = nev = 0 \tag{6-1}$$

where n is the density of electrons, e is the electronic charge, and v is the average velocity of the electrons in the band. Writing the average velocity explicitly as the average of the velocities of individual electrons,

$$J = ne \frac{1}{n} \sum_{i=1}^{n} v_i = e \sum_{i=1}^{n} v_i = 0 \tag{6-2}$$

Electrons in the valence band of a semiconductor at room temperature can conduct current because of the few vacant levels left behind by electrons excited to the conduction band. To show how this comes about, focus attention upon the jth electron in Eq. (6-2),

$$J = e \sum_{i=1}^{n} v_i = e \sum_{\substack{i=1 \\ i \neq j}}^{n} v_i + ev_j = 0 \tag{6-3}$$

Rearranging,

$$e \sum_{\substack{i=1 \\ i \neq j}}^{n} v_i = -ev_j \tag{6-4}$$

The left side of Eq. (6-4) is the current resulting from all the electrons in the valence band except for the jth one. The right side represents the current density due to one electron but of opposite electric charge. This vacant level in the valence band is called a *hole*. According to Eq. (6-4), holes in the valence band can be treated as positively charged carriers fully analogous to the negatively charged electrons in the conduction band.

The use of holes to represent the behavior of electrons in a nearly filled valence band introduces a considerable conceptual simplification. For example, the conductivity of a semiconductor crystal containing both electrons in the conduction band and holes in the valence band is, by analogy with Eq. (1-16),

$$\sigma = ne\mu_e + pe\mu_h \tag{6-5}$$

where n is the density of conduction-band electrons, p is the density of valence-band holes, and μ_e and μ_h are the respective carrier mobilities.

The energy-band model, Fig. 6-3b, refers to a perfect crystal structure which contains no chemical impurities and in which no atoms are displaced from their proper sites. The properties of the solid are therefore characteristic of an ideal structure, and the crystal is called an *intrinsic semiconductor*. Although it is not possible to achieve perfect structures in real crystals, this ideal may be approached and intrinsic behavior observed experimentally. The number of electrons in the conduction band of an intrinsic semiconductor is equal to the number of holes in the valence band, since both are the result of electron transitions across the forbidden energy gap. This means that the Fermi level is located in the center of the forbidden energy gap, as already indicated on the energy-band diagram. Note that the number of electrons and holes increases at high temperatures, and, according to Eq. (6-5), the conductivity also increases. This is characteristic of semiconductors.

6-3 Extrinsic semiconductors

The electrical properties of a semiconductor are drastically altered when foreign, or *impurity*, atoms are incorporated into the crystal. Since the properties now depend strongly upon the impurity content, the solid is called an *extrinsic* semiconductor. Consider, for example, a single crystal of the important semiconductor material silicon. Each silicon atom has four valence electrons which are part of the filled valence band of a silicon crystal. Suppose now a pentavalent atom, such as phosphorus, arsenic, or antimony, substitutes for a silicon atom in the crystal. Four of the impurity atom's electrons play the same role as the four valence electrons of the replaced silicon atom and become part of the valence band. The fifth valence electron is easily detached by thermal energy and moves freely in the conduction band.

Phosphorus, arsenic, or antimony impurity atoms in silicon donate electrons to the conduction band and are called *donor* impurities. The normal energy level for the extra electron is located at the impurity atom and slightly below the conduction band, Fig. 6-4. One electron is present in the conduction band for each

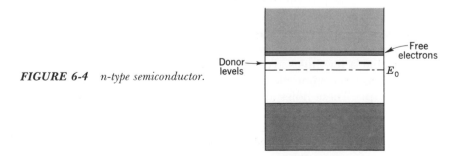

FIGURE 6-4 *n-type semiconductor.*

Donor→ levels

Free electrons

E_0

donor atom in the crystal. Note that there is not an equivalent number of holes in the valence band. The crystal therefore conducts electricity mainly by virtue of electrons in the conduction band. Such a crystal is called an *n-type* semiconductor because of the negative charge on the current carriers. The increased density of electrons in the conduction band means that the Fermi level is located near the donor levels, as indicated in Fig. 6-4.

By comparison, a trivalent atom like boron, aluminum, gallium, or indium substituted for a silicon atom produces a hole in the valence band. Since only three electrons are available, an electron from an adjacent silicon atom transfers to the impurity atom. The foreign atom is said to have accepted a valence electron, and such impurities are termed *acceptors.* Acceptors in a crystal create holes in the valence band and produce a *p-type* semiconductor because of the effective positive charge on each hole. Acceptor energy levels are located just above the valence band, Fig. 6-5. The Fermi level

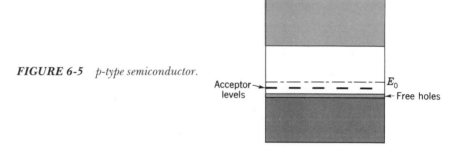

FIGURE 6-5   *p-type semiconductor.*

Acceptor levels

E_0

Free holes

is located nearby since the number of holes in the valence band is greater than the number of electrons in the conduction band.

A crystal containing both donor and acceptor impurities is either *n*-type or *p*-type, depending upon which impurity concentration is greater, because electrons from donor atoms fill up all available acceptor levels. Intrinsic crystals can be produced by including equal concentrations of donor and acceptor impurities, and such crystals are said to be *compensated.* Intrinsic characteristics can also be observed by heating an extrinsic crystal to a high temperature. A great many electrons are excited across the forbidden energy gap from the valence band to the conduction band so there are a great many holes and electrons. Furthermore, the numbers of holes and electrons are nearly equal and the crystal properties become essentially intrinsic.

Note that a few holes are present in the valence band of an *n*-type crystal since some electrons are excited across the forbidden energy gap. These holes are called *minority* carriers and the electrons are called *majority* carriers because of their relative concentration. Conversely, holes are majority carriers in a *p*-type semiconductor, while electrons in the conduction band are minority carriers. Intentionally introducing impurity atoms in semiconductors to obtain a desired concentration of majority carriers is called *doping.*

*PN-*JUNCTION DEVICES

6-4   Energy-band diagram

The junction between a *p*-type region and an *n*-type region in the same semiconductor single crystal, a basic structure in many devices, is called a *pn junction*. Several different techniques for producing *pn* junctions are described in a later section. All result in a transition from acceptor impurities to donor impurities at a given place in the crystal. Electrons in the *n* region tend to diffuse into the *p* region at the junction. At equilibrium, this is compensated by an equal flow of electrons in the reverse direction. The concentration of electrons is much larger in the *n* material, however, and the electron current from the *n* region would be greater except for a potential rise at the junction. This potential difference reduces the electron current from the *n* side. An identical argument applies to the hole currents diffusing across the junction. The magnitude and polarity of the internal potential rise at the junction make the two currents equal. The built-in potential rise leads to excellent rectification in the *pn* junction, as already discussed in Chap. 4.

The Fermi level is continuous throughout the crystal in equilibrium, as shown in the energy-band model for a *pn* junction, Fig. 6-6. Notice that the polarity of the potential rise tends to keep

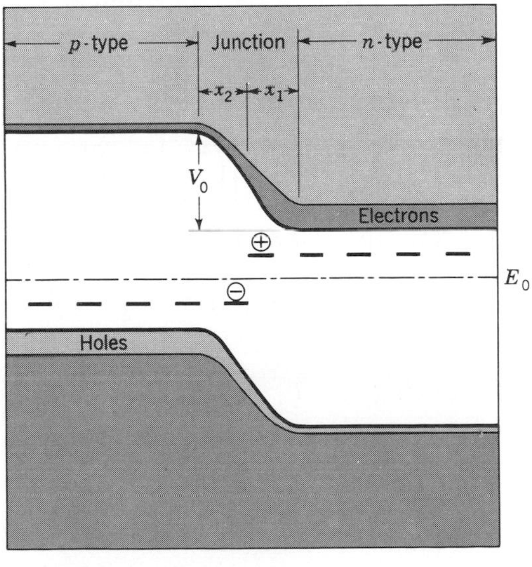

FIGURE 6-6   *Energy-band model of pn junction.*

electrons in the *n* region and holes in the *p* region, as discussed above. The magnitude of the potential step is equal to the difference between the Fermi-level locations on the two sides of the junction. Therefore, the built-in potential of a *pn* junction depends upon the forbidden energy gap, the impurity concentration, and the temperature. In particular, at high temperatures, where the semiconductor becomes intrinsic and the Fermi level is at the center of the forbidden energy gap, the potential rise disappears. Proper device operation is impossible under these conditions.

The potential rise V_0 results from donor electrons at the junction that transfer into nearby acceptor levels. In the case of an *abrupt* junction, one in which the transition from p- to n-type occurs very suddenly in the crystal, the equality of charge transferred from donors to acceptors means that

$$N_d x_1 = N_a x_2 \tag{6-6}$$

where x_1 is the width of the junction in the n region, x_2 is the extent of the junction in the p region, N_d is the donor concentration, and N_a is the acceptor concentration. The magnitude of the potential rise in the n region V_1 is determined by Poisson's equation

$$\frac{d^2 V_1}{dx^2} = \frac{e N_d}{\epsilon_0 \kappa_e} \tag{6-7}$$

where κ_e is the dielectric constant of the semiconductor. The solution is

$$V_1 = \frac{e N_d}{2 \epsilon_0 \kappa_e} x_1^2 \tag{6-8}$$

A similar expression

$$V_2 = \frac{e N_a}{2 \epsilon_0 \kappa_e} x_2^2 \tag{6-9}$$

applies to the p region. The total width of the pn junction is then

$$d = x_1 + x_2 = \left(\frac{2\epsilon_0 \kappa_e}{e}\right)^{1/2} \left[\left(\frac{V_1}{N_d}\right)^{1/2} + \left(\frac{V_2}{N_a}\right)^{1/2}\right] \tag{6-10}$$

Using Eqs. (6-6) to (6-8),

$$\frac{V_1}{V_2} = \left(\frac{x_1}{x_2}\right)^2 \frac{N_d}{N_a} = \frac{N_a}{N_d} \tag{6-11}$$

Introducing $V_0 = V_1 + V_2$ and Eq. (6-11) into Eq. (6-10),

$$d = \left[\frac{2\epsilon_0 \kappa_e V_0}{e(N_a + N_d)}\right]^{1/2} \left[\left(\frac{N_a}{N_d}\right)^{1/2} + \left(\frac{N_d}{N_a}\right)^{1/2}\right] \tag{6-12}$$

If the donor concentration on the n side is much greater than the acceptor concentration on the p side, $N_d \gg N_a$, Eq. (6-12) reduces to

$$d = \left(\frac{2\epsilon_0 \kappa_e V_0}{e N_a}\right)^{1/2} \tag{6-13}$$

Furthermore, the potential rise is almost entirely confined to the p region, as can be seen from Eq. (6-11).

According to Eq. (6-13), the junction is narrow for high impurity concentrations. This principle is used to set the breakdown voltage of Zener diodes at the desired potential. The avalanche breakdown process discussed in Chap. 4 depends upon the electric field in the junction. Therefore, the voltage at which breakdown occurs is small in narrow junctions and large in wide junctions.

6-5 Parametric diodes

A pn junction is a double layer of opposite charges separated by a small distance and so has the properties of a capacitance. Furthermore, the capacitance can be varied by applying a reverse-bias voltage. This is so because reverse bias increases the magnitude of the potential rise at the junction, and the width of the junction increases, according to Eq. (6-13). The junction capacitance is calculated from the expression for a parallel-plate capacitor, Eq. (2-28),

$$C = \frac{\epsilon_0 \kappa_e A}{d} \tag{6-14}$$

Substituting for d from Eq. (6-13),

$$C = A \left(\frac{\epsilon_0 \kappa_e e N_a / 2}{V_0 + V} \right)^{1/2} \tag{6-15}$$

where the reverse-bias potential V is explicitly indicated. According to Eq. (6-15) the junction capacitance decreases as the reverse-bias potential is increased.

The variation of capacitance with reverse bias for a typical *parametric diode*, Fig. 6-7, is in good agreement with Eq. (6-15). The name of this useful semiconductor device describes the ability of the pn junction to adjust one of its electrical parameters, capaci-

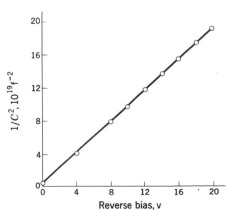

FIGURE 6-7 *Variation of capacitance of parametric diode with reverse-bias potential. Linear trend is in agreement with Eq. (6-15).*

tance, in response to an applied voltage. Correspondingly, the particular circuit developed to take advantage of this property is termed a parametric amplifier, which is a very sensitive microwave amplifier. Parametric diodes are also used as electrically controlled tuning capacitors in radio receivers to replace conventional variable capacitors, particularly in automatically or remotely tuned receivers.

6-6 Minority-carrier injection

The internal potential barrier is reduced when a *pn* junction is biased in the forward direction. The forward current results from holes diffusing across the junction from the *p*-type side and electrons diffusing across from the *n*-type side. The result is that holes are injected into the *n* region and electrons are injected into the *p* region, where in each case they are minority carriers. This *minority-carrier injection* at a *pn* junction is the basis for transistor action in semiconductors, as described in the next section. It is usually desirable that the forward current be carried predominantly by either holes or electrons in order to enhance the injection effect. The way this is accomplished can be seen from the rectifier equation, Eq. (4-13),

$$I = (C_1 n_p + C_2 p_n)(e^{eV/kT} - 1) \tag{6-16}$$

where, it is recalled, n_p is the equilibrium concentration of electrons in the *p* region and p_n is the equilibrium concentration of holes in the *n* region. If the *n* region is lightly doped and the *p* region is heavily doped, $n_p \ll p_n$, Eq. (6-16) reduces to

$$I = C_2 p_n (e^{eV/kT} - 1) \tag{6-17}$$

This means that the forward current is carried by holes and, consequently, a large excess hole concentration is injected into the *n* region. If the doping ratio is interchanged, the reverse situation is true and electrons are injected into the *p* region.

The concentration of holes injected into the *n* region, $p(0)$, is simply the number in the *p* region with sufficient energy to surmount the reduced barrier. This is, from the relation corresponding to Eq. (4-8),

$$p(0) + p_n = \frac{I_2}{C_2} = p_0 e^{-e(V_0 - V)/kT} \tag{6-18}$$

where p_0 is the concentration of holes in the *p* region. The injected holes diffuse away from the junction because of their concentration gradient. As they diffuse, they combine with the majority carriers, electrons, so that far from the junction the hole concentration is characteristic of the *n*-type semiconductor. The excess hole concentration $p(x)$ decreases in moving away from the junction according to

$$p(x) = p(0)e^{-x/L_p} \qquad (6\text{-}19)$$

where the constant L_p is called the *diffusion length*. The concentration of holes in the various regions is indicated schematically in Fig. 6-8.

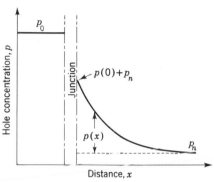

FIGURE 6-8   *Hole concentration near pn junction under forward bias.*

The current carried across the junction by the diffusing holes is simply

$$I_p = -AD_p e \left(\frac{dp}{dx}\right)_{x=0} \qquad (6\text{-}20)$$

where A is the junction area and D_p is called the *diffusion constant*. The current may be calculated by inserting Eq. (6-19) into Eq. (6-20). Comparing the result with Eq. (6-17) permits the constant C_2 to be evaluated,

$$C_2 = eA\frac{D_p}{L_p} \qquad (6\text{-}21)$$

A similar expression may be developed for the constant C_1. In this way the dependence of the reverse saturation current upon material parameters is determined.

JUNCTION TRANSISTORS

6-7   Theory of junction transistors

A junction transistor consists of two parallel *pn* junctions juxtaposed in the same single crystal and separated by less than a minority-carrier diffusion length. Two distinct types are possible, the *pnp* transistor and the *npn* transistor, depending upon the conductivity type of the common region. The operation of the two is conceptually identical except for the interchange of minority and majority carrier types (and the polarity of the bias potentials), so that it suffices to discuss the *pnp* transistor. Examples of structures having this dual junction arrangement are described in a following section.

The operation of a junction transistor can be derived from the properties of *pn* junctions. The energy-band model for a *pnp* structure in the absence of applied bias voltages, Fig. 6-9*a*, is

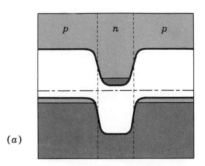

(*a*)

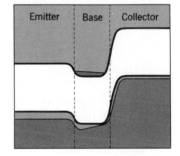

(*b*)

FIGURE 6-9 (*a*) *Energy-band diagram of pnp transistor in equilibrium, and* (*b*) *under operating bias;* (*c*) *hole concentration for case* (*b*).

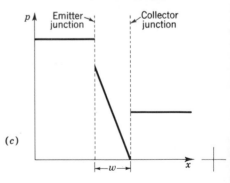

(*c*)

simply that of two *pn* junctions placed back to back. In operation, one junction, called the *emitter*, is biased in the forward direction and the other, the *collector*, is biased in the reverse direction, as in Fig. 6-9*b*. Holes injected into the *n*-type *base* region at the emitter junction diffuse across to the collector junction where they are collected by the electric field at the junction. The hole concentration in the various regions is sketched in Fig. 6-9*c*.

Variations in the emitter-base bias voltage change the injected current correspondingly, and this signal is observed at the collector junction. The forward-biased emitter represents a small resistance and the reverse-biased collector a large resistance. Since nearly the same current is in both, a large power gain results. Thus the transistor is basically a power amplifier. For maximum amplification, it is desirable that the collector current be as large a fraction of the emitter current as possible. The current through the emitter junction should be carried primarily by holes, since electrons injected from the base to the emitter cannot influence the collector current. According to Eq. (6-16), this can be accomplished if the p-type emitter region is heavily doped while the n-type base region is lightly doped. Secondly, the base region must be thin compared with a minority-carrier diffusion length so that few holes are lost before reaching the collector junction. It is convenient to dope the collector region lightly in order to increase the junction width. This reduces the capacitance of the collector junction and also increases the reverse breakdown voltage.

A useful figure of merit for a transistor is the *current-gain factor* α, which is the ratio of the change in collector current to the change in emitter current for constant collector voltage. Alpha is the product of two terms, the emitter efficiency γ and the base transport efficiency ϵ, so that

$$\alpha = \epsilon\gamma \qquad\qquad (6\text{-}22)$$

The emitter efficiency is defined as the fraction of the emitter-junction current carried by holes (for a *pnp* transistor), while ϵ is the ratio of the collector current to the hole current injected into the base at the emitter. In terms of these definitions, the carrier currents in the various regions of a transistor are given in Fig. 6-10, using the emitter current I_e as a starting point. The current I_e in the emitter junction results in a hole current γI_e injected into the

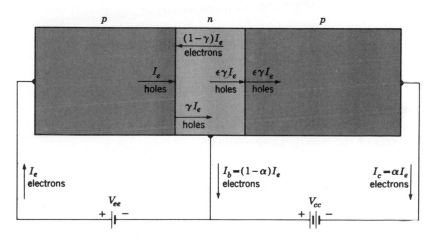

FIGURE 6-10   *Currents in pnp transistor expressed in terms of emitter current, emitter efficiency, and current gain.*

base, and a collector current $\epsilon \gamma I_e$. The difference between the emitter and collector currents $(1 - \alpha)I_e$ appears at the external connection to the base. Obviously, when the current gain is unity, all the emitter current appears in the collector circuit and the base current is zero.

The emitter efficiency in a transistor structure is larger than that for an isolated *pn* junction because the collector acts as a sink for holes in the base. The hole concentration in the base falls more rapidly with distance, Fig. 6-9c, compared with the exponential decrease near an isolated junction, Fig. 6-8. Therefore, the concentration gradient of holes at the base side of the emitter junction is greater because of the presence of the collector. According to Eq. (6-20), the forward hole current is increased correspondingly. Using Eqs. (6-19) and (6-20), the hole gradient for an isolated junction is $-p(0)/L_p$. Since the hole concentration in the base region of a transistor is nearly linear (for a thin-base region), the gradient in this case is $-p(0)/W$, where W is the width of the base. Thus the forward hole current in the emitter is increased by the factor L_p/W and the emitter efficiency is similarly larger. The emitter efficiency can easily be made to exceed 0.995 when the doping ratio between the emitter and base is large and when $W \ll L_p$.

With a thin-base region the base transport efficiency can be 0.999, so that the current gain α is typically of the order of 0.995 $\times$ 0.999 = 0.994. Actually, since α is very nearly unity for most devices the base-collector current gain β is a more sensitive measure of transistor quality. The relation between the base-collector current gain and α is, from Fig. 6-10,

$$\beta = \frac{I_c}{I_b} = \frac{\alpha}{1 - \alpha} \tag{6-23}$$

The base-collector current gain is large when α approaches unity. Typical values of β range from 20 to 10^3 in practical transistors.

Minority carriers injected into the base move to the collector by diffusion, and the finite time taken by the carriers to cross the base limits the high-frequency usefulness of transistors. By ingenious fabrication techniques it is possible to achieve very narrow base widths ($\sim 5 \times 10^{-7}$ m) and obtain useful amplification at frequencies of 10^3 Mc. It is also necessary to reduce the area of the junctions in high-frequency transistors in order to minimize adverse effects of the junction capacitances.

6-8 The T-equivalent circuit

A convenient way to represent the current-voltage characteristics of a transistor is the collector characteristics, Fig. 6-11, for different values of emitter current. When $I_e = 0$ the characteristic is simply the reverse saturation curve of the collector junction.

Emitter current translates the curve along the current axis.   Note that the curves are very flat, straight, and uniformly spaced.   This indicates that the transistor is a very useful amplifier and that

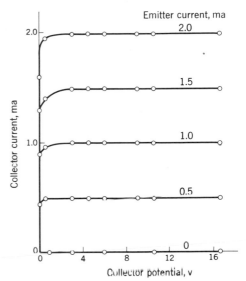

FIGURE 6-11   *Experimental collector characteristics of pnp transistor.*

successful operation is possible even for applied potentials of less than 1 volt.

The electrical characteristics of a junction transistor can be represented by a *T-equivalent circuit*, Fig. 6-12, which corresponds to

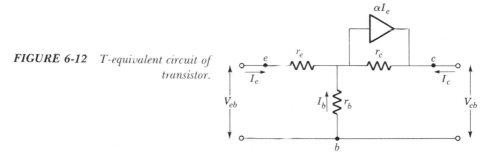

FIGURE 6-12   *T-equivalent circuit of transistor.*

the diagram of Fig. 6-10.   This configuration is called the *grounded-base* circuit because the base terminal is common to both input and output.   In the T-equivalent circuit the constant-current generator αI_e is in parallel with the collector-junction resistance r_c.   The collector resistance is the reciprocal of the slope of the collector characteristic curves.   An analytical expression for the collector-junction resistance can be developed by differentiating the rectifier equation, Eq. (4-13), with respect to current,

$$\frac{dI}{dI} = 1 = \frac{I_0 e}{kT} e^{eV/kT} \frac{dV}{dI} \tag{6-24}$$

$$r = \frac{kT}{eI_0} e^{-eV/kT} \tag{6-25}$$

According to Eq. (6-25) the collector reverse resistance is very large for negative collector potentials. Secondary effects such as leakage currents across the junction at the transistor surface reduce the resistance below that corresponding to an ideal *pn* junction. Therefore values of r_c must be determined experimentally and in practice are of the order of 1 to 10 MΩ.

The emitter resistance r_e is the forward resistance of the emitter junction. This is given by Eq. (6-25) with $I_0 \exp (eV/kT)$ replaced by the forward emitter current I_e. This substitution is possible because commonly used values of positive forward-bias potentials make the exponential term much larger than unity in the rectifier equation. Therefore the emitter resistance is

$$r_e = \frac{kT/e}{I_e} = \frac{26}{I_e} \quad \Omega \tag{6-26}$$

The numerical value in Eq. (6-26) is appropriate for room temperature and for the emitter current expressed in milliamperes. Accordingly, the emitter resistance of a transistor is 26 Ω at a quiescent bias current of 1 ma.

The base resistance in the T-equivalent circuit arises from two sources; the ohmic resistance of the base region (which may be appreciable since the base is so thin) and a feedback effect between the collector and the base. The origin of this effect is the decrease in base width as the collector junction widens with collector voltage. The narrower base width increases the base transport efficiency and also tends to increase the emitter efficiency. Therefore a smaller emitter-base voltage is required to maintain a constant collector current. This is exactly the effect a series resistance r_b has in the T-equivalent circuit since it reduces the influence of the input voltage. A typical value for the base resistance arising from these combined effects is 500 Ω.

The T-equivalent circuit for transistors is used in circuit analysis analogously to the vacuum-tube equivalent circuit. The T equivalent is particularly appropriate because its parameters are directly related to the basic physical structure of the transistor. Note that the T-equivalent circuit involves a direct connection between the input and output terminals, which differs from the vacuum-tube case. This may be illustrated explicitly by solving the T-equivalent circuit, Fig. 6-12, for the various currents and voltages. Using Kirchhoff's rules,

$$I_e + I_b + I_c = 0$$

$$V_{eb} = I_e r_e - I_b r_b \tag{6-27}$$

$$V_{cb} = (\alpha I_e + I_c) r_c - I_b r_b$$

Solving for I_c and V_{eb},

$$V_{eb} = [r_e + (1 - \alpha) r_b] I_e + \frac{r_b}{r_c} V_{cb} \tag{6-28}$$

$$I_c = -\alpha I_e + \frac{1}{r_c} V_{cb} \qquad (6\text{-}29)$$

where the approximation $r_c \gg r_b$ has been introduced. Thus, two equations are necessary to describe the operation of a transistor, whereas a single expression is sufficient in the case of a vacuum triode. Actually, Eq. (6-29) is quite analogous to the corresponding expression for a triode and should be compared with Eq. (5-7). The other relation, Eq. (6-28), indicates that the input voltage depends upon the output voltage V_{cb} as well as upon the input current I_e. No such expression is necessary in the case of a triode since the grid is not electrically connected to the plate or cathode.

6-9 Fabrication of transistors

Of the several ways to produce a semiconductor single crystal containing two *pn* junctions, four types are most popular: the grown-junction, alloy-junction, diffused-mesa, and planar transistors, Fig. 6-13. Many modifications of these four types have been devised, but they differ only in minor details from the ones shown. The grown-junction transistor was the first junction type to be fabricated and has now been largely supplanted by the other three. It is prepared during crystal growth from the melt by altering the impurity content of the melt as the solidified crystal is slowly withdrawn. To obtain a *pnp* transistor, for example, the process is started with a *p*-type melt. After crystal growth has proceeded sufficiently to form a collector region of the desired length, enough *n*-type impurities are added to overcome the original *p*-type concentration. When the *n*-type base region has grown as wide as desired, the melt is made *p*-type again by further addition of *p*-type impurities and the emitter region is grown. The resultant single crystal has a thin planar *n* region perpendicular to the direction of growth together with a strongly *p*-type emitter region and a lightly *p*-type collector region. Since a typical crystal may be 1 to 2 cm in diameter, while a single transistor is only about 1 mm square, many transistors can be obtained by cutting up the original crystal. Connections are soldered to the emitter, base, and collector regions. Solder containing a small amount of impurity corresponding to the conductivity type being soldered is used in order to provide good electric contacts. Thus, indium is introduced into the solder for the contacts attached to the *p* regions and antimony is added to the solder for the base. This is particularly important in making the connection to the very narrow base region because the *n*-type impurity produces a good electric connection to the *n*-type base and at the same time forms a *pn* junction with the *p* regions. This means that the soldered base contact is effectively electrically isolated from the emitter and collector regions, even though it may physically extend beyond the thin base region.

The *pnp* alloy-junction transistor is produced from a thin wafer of *n*-type single-crystal material by placing indium pellets on opposite surfaces and heating. As the indium melts it dissolves

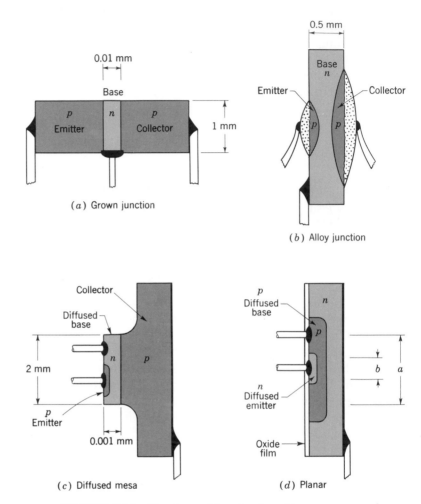

(a) Grown junction

(b) Alloy junction

(c) Diffused mesa

(d) Planar

FIGURE 6-13 *Structures of junction transistors.*

some of the germanium beneath it. During subsequent cooling the dissolved germanium recrystallizes upon the base crystal and incorporates many indium atoms into its structure. The recrystallized material is therefore *p*-type, and a transistor structure results. It is convenient to make the collector pellet larger than the emitter pellet, Fig. 6-13*b*, for in this way carriers injected at the emitter junction are collected more efficiently. Thus, the alloy junction is inherently a more satisfactory transistor geometry than the simple grown-junction shape. A micrograph of the cross section of an actual alloy-junction transistor is shown in Fig. 6-14.

The emitter and collector junctions are made visible by chemical etching and the recrystallized regions and indium pellets are clearly apparent.

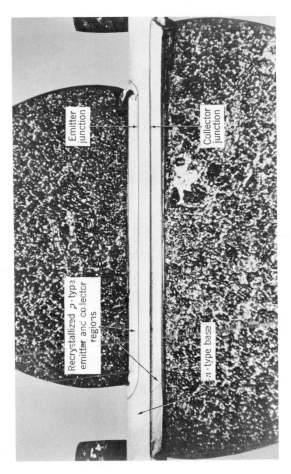

FIGURE 6-14 Micrograph of cross section of alloy-junction transistor. Emitter and collector junctions, revealed by chemical etching, are clearly visible. (Courtesy Amperex Electronic Corporation.)

As discussed earlier, it is necessary to make the dimensions of the transistor region as small as possible in order to achieve satisfactory high-frequency performance. This is difficult in the case of the alloy-junction transistor, although many ingenious variations of the above process have been developed to accomplish this goal. The diffused-mesa transistor, Fig. 6-13c, however, is much more adaptable to high-frequency transistors because the junction fabrication process can be precisely controlled. The collector junction is formed by placing a p-type single-crystal wafer in a hot gas of, say, antimony atoms. As the wafer is heated, antimony atoms diffuse into the crystal to a depth of approximately 10^{-3} mm. The crystal is subsequently masked and chemically etched to produce a small elevated region, or mesa, about 2 mm in diameter. The mesa top is then suitably masked so that two regions 0.3 mm in diameter are exposed and appropriate metals are deposited by evaporation in high vacuum. Next, the slab is maintained at an elevated temperature while the two metal deposits diffuse into the *n* region. This results in the formation of a *p*-type emitter region by one of the metal deposits while the other one forms a contact to the base region.

The area of the collector junction is defined exactly by the size of the mesa while the emitter junction is set by the area of the vapor-deposited metal. Both processes can be precisely controlled and result in an extremely tiny active volume. The width of the base region is determined by the gaseous diffusion process and subsequent diffusion of the deposited metal. Both processes can be adjusted easily by the temperature of the wafer to yield a very thin, yet accurately defined, base region. Therefore, the entire fabrication technique lends itself to precise control of transistor geometry. Very tiny active regions are produced on a wafer which is large enough to handle conveniently.

The mesa transistor, like the grown-junction and alloy-junction transistors, is so constructed that the emitter and collector junctions are exposed at the surface of the semiconductor. The electrical properties of the junction are extremely sensitive to chemical impurities from the surrounding atmosphere because of the high electric fields at the junction. Minute traces of foreign atoms on the surface in the junction region greatly degrade the performance of actual transistors compared with theoretical expectations. For this reason, transistors are hermetically sealed in carefully cleansed metal enclosures after fabrication.

A more satisfactory solution to the surface-contamination problem is to grow a thin oxide film on the surface of the semiconductor by heating in an oxidizing atmosphere. This technique, applicable primarily to silicon because of the favorable properties of silicon oxide, results in a semiconductor device completely protected from atmospheric contamination. In addition, the oxide film is a barrier to gaseous diffusion of impurities so the film itself acts as a mask during fabrication. This technique makes possible the planar transistor, Fig. 6-13*d*, so called because the entire transistor appears to be a simple plane wafer of silicon.

Construction of a planar *npn* transistor begins with a single-crystal wafer of *n*-type silicon. A thin oxide layer is grown on the top surface by heating in an oxygen atmosphere. The oxide is chemically etched away in a circular region of diameter *a*. The wafer is then exposed to a hot boron gas atmosphere. Boron atoms diffuse into the exposed silicon, forming a *p*-type base region and the collector junction. Boron atoms also diffuse laterally under the oxide film so that the base region is somewhat larger than the diameter *a* and the collector junction is protected at the surface by the oxide layer. Next, the wafer is reoxidized to produce a film covering the entire area once again. After the oxide is etched away in an area of diameter *b*, the wafer is again exposed to a hot impurity gas, this time phosphorus. These *n*-type impurity atoms diffuse into the silicon, forming the emitter region and the emitter junction. Lateral diffusion of phosphorus atoms under the oxide film again ensures that the emitter junction is protected by the oxide layer.

Finally, electric contacts are provided by vapor deposition and alloying as in the case of the mesa transistor. The result is an *npn* transistor entirely contained in one plane wafer and completely encased in an impervious oxide film. Geometric definition of the junction positions and the base width is extremely accurate because of the easily controlled gaseous diffusion doping technique. Several hundred transistors can be fabricated simultaneously from one silicon wafer a centimeter or so in diameter. These are subsequently cut into individual units by sawing up the wafer. The planar transistor design is also suitable for high-power transistors because good-quality large-area junctions are easily produced by the gaseous diffusion process.

6-10 Hybrid parameters

Although the T-equivalent circuit is a satisfactory representation of transistor operation, it is fairly difficult to determine the various resistance parameters of the circuit by direct measurements on actual transistors. For this reason an equivalent circuit which involves so-called *hybrid parameters* is more commonly employed in circuit analysis. This representation may be illustrated by writing Eqs. (6-28) and (6-29) as

$$v_{cb} = h_{ib}i_e + h_{rb}v_{cb} \tag{6-30}$$

$$i_c = h_{fb}i_e + h_{ob}v_{cb} \tag{6-31}$$

where the *h*'s are the hybrid parameters and lowercase symbols are used to represent ac values of the currents and voltages in conformity with vacuum-tube terminology. The significance of the *h*-parameter subscripts is as follows: the subscripts *i*, *r*, *f*, and *o* refer to input, reverse, forward, and output, respectively, which may be understood by examining the meaning of each coefficient in Eqs. (6-30) and (6-31). The subscript *b* signifies the common-base configuration for which these equations have been developed. This designation distinguishes these parameters from those appropriate for the common-emitter and common-collector connections discussed below. A summary of the subscript notations is presented in Table 6-2.

According to Eq. (6-30) it is possible to determine h_{ib} from the ratio of the emitter-base voltage to the emitter current v_{eb}/i_e with the collector shorted to ground so that $v_{cb} = 0$. Similarly, the ratio of collector current to emitter current i_c/i_e with the collector shorted yields h_{fb}, using Eq. (6-31). When the emitter is open-circuited, $i_e = 0$, so that $h_{rb} = v_{eb}/v_{cb}$ and $h_{ob} = i_c/v_{cb}$. Note that the conditions $v_{cb} = 0$ and $i_e = 0$ refer to ac signals; the dc potentials

TABLE 6-2

SUBSCRIPT NOTATION FOR h PARAMETERS

Subscript	Meaning
i	Input parameter
r	Reverse parameter
f	Forward parameter
o	Output parameter
e	Common emitter
b	Common base
c	Common collector

are maintained at the proper operating point for the transistor. Because of the small emitter resistance and large collector resistance of a transistor it is particularly easy to achieve an open-circuited emitter or a short-circuited collector for ac signals while maintaining the desired dc potentials. In this way the small signal h parameters can be measured using ac bridge techniques. The great virtue of the hybrid parameters is the fact that they can be measured directly with relative ease.

The circuit of a grounded-base amplifier corresponding to Fig. 6-10, but ignoring bias voltages for the moment, is illustrated in Fig. 6-15a. This diagram uses the conventional circuit symbol for

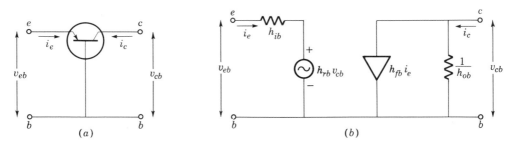

FIGURE 6-15   (a) *Grounded-base transistor amplifier (bias voltages not shown) and* (b) *its hybrid equivalent circuit.*

a *pnp* transistor. The symbol for an *npn* transistor is similar except that the direction of the arrow on the emitter points away from the base. This suggests that the current through the device is in the opposite direction. The *hybrid equivalent circuit* representing the transistor in this configuration is given in Fig. 6-15b, as can be determined by inspecting Eqs. (6-30) and (6-31). Kirchhoff's rule applied to the input loop yields Eq. (6-30) directly. The voltage equation around the output loop gives

$$v_{cb} = \frac{1}{h_{ob}} (i_c - h_{fb}i_e) \tag{6-32}$$

Solving for i_c yields Eq. (6-31). Therefore this hybrid equivalent circuit represents the operation of the transistor as given by Eqs. (6-30) and (6-31). These equations, in turn, are based on the fundamental processes associated with pn junctions in the transistor structure.

The direct connection between input and output is not so immediately apparent in the hybrid equivalent circuit as compared with the T-equivalent. Note, however, that the voltage generator in the input circuit $h_{rb}v_{cb}$ involves the collector-base voltage and that the current generator in the output circuit $h_{fb}i_e$ includes the emitter current. Thus, the input and output circuits are indeed coupled. According to Fig. 6-15b, h_{ib} represents a resistance, h_{ob} is a conductance, while h_{rb} and h_{fb} are simple numerics. These quantities represent different physical entities and are therefore termed hybrid parameters. The relation between hybrid parameters and T-equivalent parameters may be determined directly by comparing Eq. (6-30) with (6-28) and Eq. (6-31) with (6-29). These relations are summarized in Table 6-3.

The common-emitter configuration, Fig. 6-16a, is more widely used than the common-base circuit. While it is possible to re-

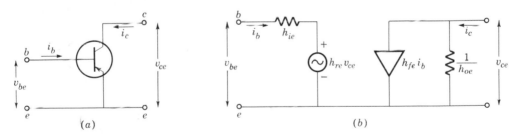

FIGURE 6-16   (a) Grounded-emitter transistor amplifier (bias voltages not shown) and (b) its hybrid equivalent circuit.

arrange the equivalent circuit appropriate for the common-base configuration to apply to the common-emitter case, it is much more convenient to employ the same form of equivalent circuit. The parameters of the circuit are suitably adjusted for the common emitter. Accordingly, the hybrid-parameter equivalent circuit appropriate for the grounded-emitter amplifier is as shown in Fig. 6-16b. The corresponding circuit equations are

$$v_{be} = h_{ie}i_b + h_{re}v_{ce} \tag{6-33}$$

$$i_c = h_{fe}i_b + h_{oe}v_{ce} \tag{6-34}$$

where the h-parameter subscripts are taken from Table 6-2.

TABLE 6-3

TRANSISTOR PARAMETER RELATIONS

Common-base parameters	Common emitter	Common collector	T-equivalent
$h_{ib} =$	$h_{ie}/(1 + h_{fe})$	$-h_{ic}/h_{fc}$	$r_e + (1 - \alpha)r_b$
$h_{rb} =$	$h_{ie}h_{oe}/(1 + h_{fe}) - h_{re}$	$h_{re} - 1 - h_{ic}h_{oc}/h_{fc}$	r_b/r_c
$h_{fb} =$	$-h_{fe}/(1 + h_{fe})$	$-(1 + h_{fc})/h_{fc}$	$-\alpha$
$h_{ob} =$	$h_{oe}/(1 + h_{fe})$	$-h_{oc}/h_{fc}$	$1/r_c$

Common-collector parameters	Common emitter	Common base	T-equivalent
$h_{ic} =$	h_{ie}	$h_{ib}/(1 + h_{fb})$	$r_b + r_e/(1 - \alpha)$
$h_{rc} =$	$1 - h_{re}$	1	$1 - r_e/(1 - \alpha)r_c$
$h_{fc} =$	$-(1 + h_{fe})$	$-1/(1 + h_{fb})$	$-1/(1 - \alpha)$
$h_{oc} =$	h_{oe}	$h_{ob}/(1 + h_{fb})$	$1/(1 - \alpha)r_c$

Common-emitter parameters	Common base	Common collector	T-equivalent
$h_{ie} =$	$h_{ib}/(1 + h_{fb})$	h_{ic}	$r_b + r_e/(1 - \alpha)$
$h_{re} =$	$h_{ib}h_{ob}/(1 + h_{fb}) - h_{rb}$	$1 - h_{rc}$	$r_e/(1 - \alpha)r_c$
$h_{fe} =$	$-h_{fb}/(1 + h_{fb})$	$-(1 + h_{fc})$	$\alpha/(1 - \alpha)$
$h_{oe} =$	$h_{ob}/(1 + h_{fb})$	h_{oc}	$1/(1 - \alpha)r_c$

T-equivalent parameters	Common emitter	Common base	Common collector
α	$h_{fe}/(1 + h_{fe})$	$-h_{fb}$	$(1 + h_{fc})/h_{fc}$
r_c	$(h_{fe} + 1)/h_{oe}$	$(1 - h_{rb})/h_{ob}$	$-h_{fc}/h_{oc}$
r_e	h_{re}/h_{oe}	$h_{ib} - (1 + h_{fb})h_{rb}/h_{ob}$	$(1 - h_{rc})/h_{oc}$
r_b	$h_{ie} - h_{re}(1 + h_{fe})/h_{oe}$	h_{rb}/h_{ob}	$h_{ic} + h_{fc}(1 - h_{rc})/h_{oc}$

To show that the equivalent circuit in Fig. 6-16b does in fact represent the common-emitter amplifier, begin with the already established equations (6-30) and (6-31). Using the two additional equations

$$v_{be} + v_{cb} + v_{ec} = 0 \qquad (6\text{-}35)$$

$$i_b + i_e + i_c = 0 \qquad (6\text{-}36)$$

(which apply to any circuit configuration) to eliminate i_e and v_{cb}, Eqs. (6-30) and (6-31) may be put in the form

$$v_{be} = \left(\frac{h_{ib}}{1 + h_{fb}}\right) i_b + \left(\frac{h_{ib}h_{ob}}{1 + h_{fb}} - h_{rb}\right) v_{ce} \qquad (6\text{-}37)$$

$$i_c = \left(\frac{-h_{fb}}{1 + h_{fb}}\right) i_b + \left(\frac{h_{ob}}{1 + h_{fb}}\right) v_{ce} \qquad (6\text{-}38)$$

The approximation that h_{rb} and h_{ob} are very small has been introduced in arriving at Eqs. (6-37) and (6-38). This is permissible
since they are both essentially equal to the reciprocal of the
collector resistance, according to Table 6-3. Comparing these
equations with Eqs. (6-33) and (6-34) establishes the validity of the
proposed equivalent circuit. Furthermore, the common-emitter h
parameters are related to the common-base h parameters by these
equations. The relationships are summarized in Table 6-3.

The third possible transistor amplifier configuration is the
common-collector circuit, Fig. 6-17a, which is also termed an

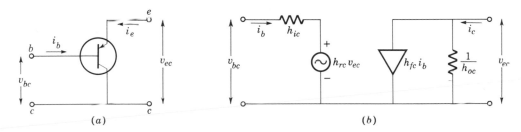

FIGURE 6-17 (*a*) *Grounded-collector transistor amplifier (bias voltages not
shown) and (b) its hybrid equivalent circuit.*

emitter follower by analogy with the vacuum-tube cathode follower. Here again, the convenient equivalent circuit takes the
same form, Fig. 6-17b, and the circuit equations are

$$v_{bc} = h_{ic}i_b + h_{rc}v_{ec}$$
$$i_e = h_{fc}i_b + h_{oc}v_{ec} \qquad (6\text{-}39)$$

The relation between the grounded-collector h parameters and
those corresponding to the other equivalent circuits can be developed by network analysis identical to that carried out above.
Again, the results are summarized in Table 6-3. The h parameters
appropriate for any of the three circuit configurations depend
upon the dc operating point of the transistor as well as upon the
particular transistor type. It is common practice for transistor data
sheets to specify the h parameters for the grounded-emitter or
grounded-base configurations. The relations in Table 6-3 can be
used to determine other parameters as needed. In addition, the
variation of the parameters with operating point is usually specified so that appropriate corrections can be applied to the given
values.

Illustrative values of the common-emitter h parameters and their
variation with emitter current are given in Fig. 6-18. Note that the
forward current gain h_{fe} and the reverse voltage amplification
factor h_{re} are sensibly constant, while both the input resistance h_{ie}

and output conductance h_{oe} vary considerably. The change in h_{ie} results mainly from the decrease of emitter-junction resistance with current. This may be noted from the relationship in Table 6-3 and Eq. (6-26). (See Exercise 6-4.)

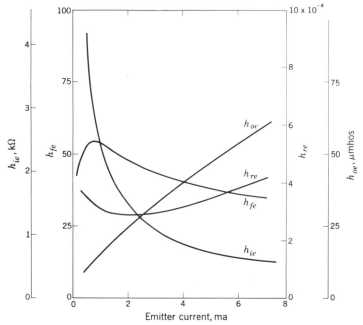

FIGURE 6-18   *Variation of hybrid parameters with emitter current.*

The two most sensitive measures of transistor quality are the emitter-collector current gain h_{fe} and the grounded-base output conductance h_{ob}. Large values of current gain are desirable to achieve maximum amplification, as explained in connection with Eq. (6-23). Note that h_{fe} and β as previously defined are two commonly used symbols for the same quantity. Similarly, small values of h_{ob} are desirable since then the output resistance is large and the feedback effect small. A small h_{ob} implies a large value of collector resistance (compare Table 6-3). Thus the two major parameters h_{fe} and h_{ob} reveal the quality of the emitter junction, base region, and collector junction.

TRANSISTOR CIRCUITS

6-11   Biasing

Since the emitter junction requires forward bias and the collector junction reverse bias, it is quite straightforward to supply the proper biases from a single battery. Consider, for example, the

simple grounded-emitter amplifier, Fig. 6-19, in which the base
bias current is supplied by the resistor R_B. Because the forward

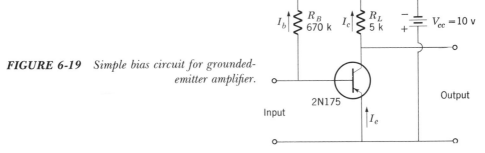

FIGURE 6-19   *Simple bias circuit for grounded-*
emitter amplifier.

resistance of the emitter junction is very small, the base current is
given by

$$I_b = \frac{V_{cc}}{R_B} \qquad\qquad (6\text{-}40)$$

An approximate value of the collector current is then $h_{fe}I_b$, and the
operating point is completely determined.

The forward current gain h_{fe} is itself a function of current, however, so that graphical methods are generally used to determine the
operating point. The load line is plotted on the common emitter
characteristic curves, Fig. 6-20, in the usual fashion. The inter-

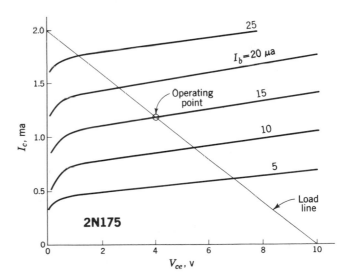

FIGURE 6-20   *Determination of operating*
point of amplifier in Fig. 6-19 using
grounded-emitter collector characteristics.

section of the load line with the curve for the base current given by
Eq. (6-40) represents the operating point. Note that the common-
emitter characteristic curves make it possible to determine an

approximate value of h_{fe} by directly comparing I_c from the curve for a given I_b. Similarly, the output conductance h_{oe} is determined from the slope of the curves. Since these parameters are most important in describing a transistor, the common-emitter characteristics are most often provided by transistor manufacturers.

The simple bias circuit, Fig. 6-19, is not generally satisfactory because it is possible for the operating point to shift drastically with temperature. The reverse saturation current of the collector junction increases exponentially with temperature, according to Eq. (4-15). Therefore, the common-emitter characteristics, Fig. 6-20, shift to larger currents as the temperature increases. Since the base bias current is fixed by the circuit, it is possible for the operating point to move into an unusable portion of the transistor characteristics.

An even more drastic effect, called *thermal runaway*, may also occur. Collector current heats the collector junction because of I^2R losses in the transistor. The corresponding increase in junction temperature, in turn, causes the collector current to increase further. This succession of events may become cumulative and the ratings of the transistor exceeded. Even if the current is limited by the circuit so that the transistor is not destroyed, the operating point is shifted enough to make the circuit inoperative.

Some improvement in operating-point stability is obtained by deriving base bias from the collector circuit, Fig. 6-21. Thus, if the

FIGURE 6-21   *Improved bias circuit for transistor amplifier.*

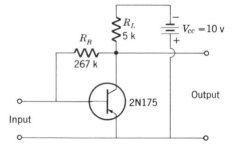

collector current increases because of a temperature rise, the drop across R_L increases and the base current is reduced. This means that the net change in operating point is smaller. A disadvantage of this circuit is that the overall amplification is reduced because the collector signal is also fed back to the base terminal. This reduces the net input signal (see Exercise 6-6). The procedure for determining the operating point is to plot the load line and then calculate the collector current from

$$I_c = \frac{V_{cc} - I_b R_B}{R_L} \tag{6-41}$$

for several assumed values of I_b. These points are plotted on the transistor characteristics and connected by a line; the intersection with the load line is the operating point.

The most satisfactory transistor bias circuit is obtained by including a resistor in the emitter circuit, Fig. 6-22. The voltage

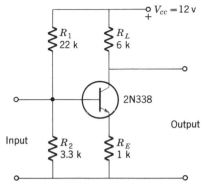

FIGURE 6-22   *Practical transistor bias circuit. Note
type 2N338 npn transistor is used. Circuit applies
equally to pnp type if polarity of V_{cc} is reversed.*

drop across R_E tends to bias the emitter junction in the reverse
direction and the voltage divider comprising R_1 and R_2 sets the
base voltage so that the base-emitter potential is in the forward
direction.   This circuit has the advantage that an increase in transistor current changes the voltage drop across R_E such that the base
bias current is reduced, much as in the case of cathode bias of a
vacuum tube.
   The bias circuit of Fig. 6-22 is best analyzed by converting the R_1
and R_2 voltage divider to its Thévenin equivalent circuit.   Using
Eqs. (1-76) and (1-77), the equivalent battery and series resistance
are

$$V_{eq} = \frac{R_2}{R_1 + R_2} V_{cc}$$

and

$$R_{eq} = \frac{R_1 R_2}{R_1 + R_2} \qquad\qquad (6\text{-}42)$$

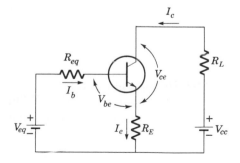

FIGURE 6-23   *The dc equivalent circuit of Fig.
6-22 is used to determine operating point.*

as shown in Fig. 6-23.   With this dc equivalent circuit the quiescent
operating point is found as follows.   First, the appropriate load
line, which includes both R_L and R_E, is plotted on the transistor
characteristics, Fig. 6-24.   Next, writing Kirchhoff's voltage equation around the base circuit,

$$V_{eq} = I_c R_e + I_b R_{eq} + V_{be} \tag{6-43}$$

and around the collector loop,

$$V_{cc} = I_c(R_e + R_L) + V_{ce} \tag{6-44}$$

In Eqs. (6-43) and (6-44) the approximation $I_e = I_c$ has been made. These equations are solved for V_{ce} in terms of I_b. The result is

$$V_{ce} = V_{cc} - (V_{eq} - V_{be}) \left(1 + \frac{R_L}{R_E}\right) + R_{eq} \left(1 + \frac{R_L}{R_E}\right) I_b \tag{6-45}$$

In most circuits V_{be} may be considered to be a constant equal to 0.2 volt for germanium transistors and 0.6 volt for silicon units. The reason for this difference is that a larger forward bias is necessary

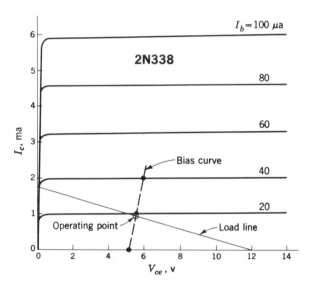

FIGURE 6-24 *Determining operating point for circuit of Fig. 6-22 using common-emitter collector characteristics.*

when the forbidden energy gap is larger, in conformity with Eq. (6-16). The fact that V_{be} is essentially a constant is a result of the steepness of the forward characteristic of a *pn* junction (refer to Fig. 4-9).

Choosing values of I_b, the collector current is calculated from Eq. (6-45) and corresponding points plotted on the transistor characteristics. The intersection of this bias curve with the load line gives the operating point, as illustrated in Fig. 6-24.

Actually, transistor collector characteristics are so linear and evenly spaced (compare Fig. 6-24) that it is often possible to determine the operating point analytically, rather than graphically. The manufacturer usually specifies a dc current gain h_{FE}, which is the ratio of the dc collector current to the dc base current. Thus, $h_{FE}I_b$ is substituted for I_c in Eq. (6-43) and the equation immediately solved for I_b. This determines the operating point since then I_c is also known.

The bias circuit of Fig. 6-22 is the most popular for the grounded-emitter configuration because of its superior stability characteristics. It is used in the common-collector and common-emitter amplifier circuits as well. In the grounded-emitter case, the emitter bias resistor R_E is bypassed with a low-reactance capacitor. This eliminates the ac signal across R_E from the input circuit.

To design a transistor amplifier circuit such as in Fig. 6-22, it is first necessary to choose the operating point corresponding to desired values of the h parameters. This is best done after consulting the transistor manufacturer's data sheets for a given transistor type. Next, a value for R_L is selected to suit gain requirements (see discussion in the next section) and output impedance considerations. In order that the potential divider made up of R_1 and R_2 may not seriously impair the amplification, R_{eq} should be larger than h_{ie} by a factor of 5 or 10. The emitter resistor should be chosen so that $R_E \approx R_{eq}/5$ to ensure satisfactory stability of the operating point. Then, the required dc supply voltage V_{cc} is $I_c(R_L + R_E) + V_{ce}$. The value of R_{eq} selected above, together with Eq. (6-45), yields simultaneous equations for R_1 and R_2, which completes the design. It is apparent from this brief description that the design of a transistor circuit is not completely determined by the usual requirements specified in advance. For this reason many different circuits have been developed. Each of these optimizes some particular feature of interest such as gain, minimum current requirement, or stability of operating point.

6-12 Common-emitter amplifier

The complete circuit of a practical common-emitter amplifier using an *npn* transistor is shown in Fig. 6-25. The input and out-

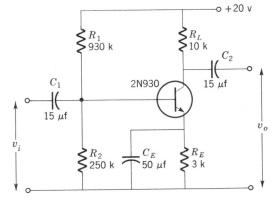

FIGURE 6-25 *Practical common-emitter amplifier using npn type 2N930 transistor.*

put coupling capacitors C_1 and C_2 pass ac signal voltages and assure that the dc operating point of the transistor is independent of the source and load conditions. The reactance of the emitter bypass capacitor C_E is made approximately one-fifth of the emitter bias resistor at the lowest frequency of interest.

Assuming that the reactance of all three capacitors is small, the hybrid equivalent circuit of Fig. 6-25 is shown in Fig. 6-26. The

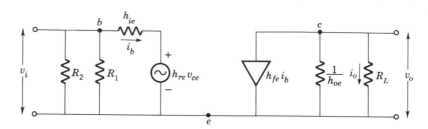

FIGURE 6-26 *Hybrid equivalent circuit of amplifier in Fig. 6-25.*

output voltage can be written directly as the current through the parallel combination of $1/h_{oe}$ and R_L

$$v_o = -h_{fe}i_b \frac{R_L}{1 + h_{oe}R_L} \tag{6-46}$$

Kirchhoff's rule applied to the input circuit yields

$$v_i = h_{ie}i_b + h_{re}v_o \tag{6-47}$$

Equation (6-47) is solved for i_b and this is substituted into Eq. (6-46). The result is arranged to give the voltage gain

$$a = \frac{v_o}{v_i} = -\frac{1}{h_{ie}(1 + h_{oe}R_L)/R_L h_{fe} - h_{re}} \tag{6-48}$$

By referring to Table 6-3 to compare the h parameters with the T-equivalent parameters, it may be seen that h_{re} is small and that $h_{oe}R_L$ may be neglected with respect to unity. Therefore Eq. (6-48) has the approximate form

$$a = -h_{fe} \frac{R_L}{h_{ie}} \tag{6-49}$$

According to Eq. (6-49), the voltage gain is approximately equal to the forward current gain of the transistor times the ratio of the load resistance to the input resistance. The voltage gain of the common-emitter amplifier is appreciable since both factors are large. The minus sign signifies that the input and output signals are 180° out of phase.

The transistor is basically a current-controlled device, and the current gain, which is the ratio of the output current to the input current, is also important. The output current is determined from Eq. (6-46)

$$i_o = \frac{v_o}{R_L} = -\frac{h_{fe}i_b}{1 + h_{oe}R_L} \tag{6-50}$$

For simplicity, the effect of R_{eq} in the bias network is assumed negligible, so the current gain is

$$g = \frac{i_o}{i_b} = -\frac{h_{fe}}{1 + h_{oe}R_L} \tag{6-51}$$

Here again, $h_{oe}R_L \ll 1$, so the approximate current gain is just h_{fe}.

The input resistance of the common-emitter amplifier is the ratio of the input voltage to the input current, or

$$R_i = \frac{v_i}{i_b} = \frac{h_{ie}i_b + h_{re}v_o}{i_b}$$

$$= h_{ie} - h_{re}h_{fe}R_L \tag{6-52}$$

In arriving at Eq. (6-52), Eqs. (6-47) and (6-46) have been used and the effect of R_{eq} has again been neglected. If necessary, R_{eq} may be included by calculating the parallel combination of R_{eq} and R_i. In Eq. (6-52), the second term is often negligible, so the input resistance is approximately h_{ie}. Note, however, that the exact input resistance depends upon the value of the load resistance R_l. This illustrates the coupling between input and output terminals inherent in transistors.

The output resistance of the amplifier is slightly more complicated to determine. First of all, the internal resistance of the input signal source must be included because of the coupling between input and output terminals. Accordingly, the appropriate equivalent circuit is shown in Fig. 6-27. The effective internal

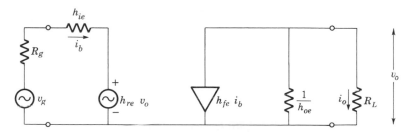

FIGURE 6-27   *Equivalent circuit used to calculate output impedance of transistor amplifier.*

resistance of the amplifier as viewed from the output terminals is determined using the Thévenin equivalent circuit. As discussed in Chap. 1, the equivalent internal resistance in the Thévenin circuit is the ratio of the open-circuit ($R_L = \infty$) voltage to the short-circuit ($R_L = 0$) current. Thus

$$R_o = \frac{(v_o)_{oc}}{(i_o)_{sc}} = -\frac{(h_{fe}/h_{oe})(i_b)_{oc}}{-h_{fe}(i_b)_{sc}} \tag{6-53}$$

The numerator uses Eq. (6-46) with $R_L = \infty$, and the denominator comes from the output loop of Fig. 6-27. Kirchhoff's rule applied to the input loop yields

$$v_g + i_b(R_g + h_{ie}) + h_{re}v_o = 0 \tag{6-54}$$

where v_g and R_g are the voltage and internal resistance of the signal source, respectively. Equation (6-54) may be solved for i_b and used to evaluate $(i_b)_{oc}$ by introducing v_o from Eq. (6-46). Similarly, $(i_b)_{sc}$ results from setting $v_o = 0$ in Eq. (6-54). Substituting these values into Eq. (6-53) gives the following expression for the output resistance of the amplifier,

$$R_o = \frac{1}{h_{oe} - h_{re}h_{fe}/(h_{ie} + R_g)} \tag{6-55}$$

The output impedance depends upon the source impedance, again indicative of the input-output coupling in a transistor. To the same degree of approximation introduced previously, the output resistance is just $1/h_{oe}$, which is a fairly high value.

In summary, the common-emitter transistor amplifier yields both voltage and current gain. It has a modestly high input resistance and large output resistance. Because of the favorable values of these four quantities, it is the most commonly used transistor amplifier circuit. Table 6-4 illustrates the magnitude of these important parameters, calculated from the h parameters of Fig. 6-18 at an emitter current of 2 ma. The various approximations introduced above have been used in preparing this table.

TABLE 6-4

APPROXIMATE PARAMETERS OF TRANSISTOR AMPLIFIERS *

Circuit configuration	Voltage gain	Current gain	Input resistance, Ω	Output resistance, Ω
Common emitter	280	47	1700	4×10^4
Common base	280	0.98	35	1.9×10^6
Common collector	1	48	5×10^5	22

* Using Fig. 6-18 for $I_E = 2$ ma; $R_L = 10^4\ \Omega$.

6-13 Grounded-base amplifier

A typical common-base amplifier circuit using an *npn* transistor is shown in Fig. 6-28. Careful comparison of this circuit with the common-emitter configuration, Fig. 6-25, reveals that the bias arrangements are identical. Therefore, bias considerations and the techniques for determining the operating point previously described for the common-emitter amplifier apply to the grounded-base circuit as well.

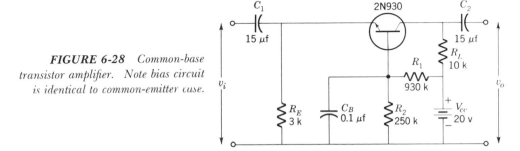

FIGURE 6-28 *Common-base transistor amplifier. Note bias circuit is identical to common-emitter case.*

Capacitor C_B bypasses the base resistor R_2, and R_1 is shorted out for ac signals by the low impedance of the battery. Consequently, in the appropriate hybrid equivalent circuit, Fig. 6-29, these resistors are absent. The properties of this circuit can be found directly by comparing Fig. 6-29 with the hybrid equivalent of the

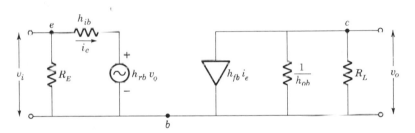

FIGURE 6-29 *Equivalent circuit of common-base amplifier in Fig. 6-28.*

common-emitter case, Fig. 6-26. The two are identical in form so that the previous results for the voltage and current gain, Eqs. (6-48) and (6-51), and for the input and output resistance, Eqs. (6-52) and (6-55), apply directly upon substituting the applicable h parameters. Note also that R_E replaces R_{eq} and i_e replaces i_b in converting the equations to the common-base configuration.

The approximate voltage gain in this case is $-h_{fb}R_L/h_{ib}$, which can be made large, but only if R_L is very great. This is so because the current gain is only $-h_{fb}$, which is approximately equal to unity. Note that h_{fb} is inherently a negative quantity (Table 6-3), so that the input and output voltage signals are in phase. The approximate input resistance h_{ib} is very low because it is essentially the resistance of the forward-biased emitter junction. Conversely, the output resistance $1/h_{ob}$ is the resistance of the reverse-biased collector junction and is therefore very large. This wide disparity between input and output resistance makes the grounded-base circuit less popular than the common-emitter amplifier, except for special applications. A summary of typical common-base circuit properties is presented in Table 6-4.

6-14 The emitter follower

The common-collector amplifier, Fig. 6-30, is more often termed the emitter follower because of its similarity to the cathode-follower

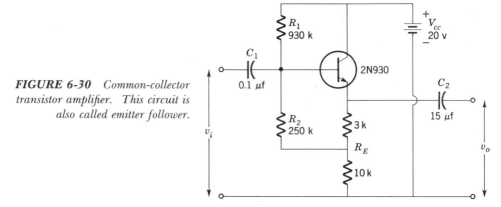

FIGURE 6-30 *Common-collector transistor amplifier. This circuit is also called emitter follower.*

circuit. Here again, bias considerations are identical with those previously discussed. The hybrid equivalent circuit, Fig. 6-31,

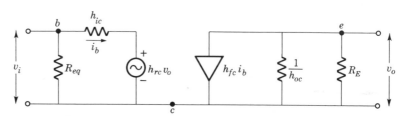

FIGURE 6-31 *Equivalent circuit of emitter-follower amplifier.*

neglects the reactance of the input and output capacitors, as usual. Since this equivalent circuit also has the same form as Fig. 6-26, the circuit properties are obtained directly from the previous equations upon making the appropriate substitutions.

Values of the common-collector h parameters (Table 6-3) are such that the voltage gain $1/h_{rc}$ is approximately unity. Furthermore, the output signal is in phase with the input. The approximate current gain $-h_{fc}$ is equal to $1/(1 - \alpha)$ and is large. If the effect of R_{eq} can be neglected, the input resistance is simply $-h_{rc}h_{fc}r_e$, which is equal to $r_e/(1 - \alpha)$ in terms of transistor parameters. Thus, the input impedance is the emitter resistance divided by a small factor and is appreciable. The approximate output impedance reduces to $(1 - \alpha)(r_b + R_g)$. Therefore, the output impedance of the amplifier itself is very small since the internal resistance R_g is associated with the signal source.

All these properties, summarized in Table 6-4 for the common-collector transistor amplifier, are similar to the cathode-follower vacuum-triode circuit. Therefore it is not surprising that the two circuits find similar applications. In particular, transistor differential amplifiers similar to the triode circuits discussed in Chap. 5 are often used. (See Exercise 6-14.)

6-15 Complementary symmetry

One of the more intriguing circuit applications of transistors is based on the combination of *npn* and *pnp* transistors, with their symmetrically inverted bias and signal voltage polarities. Consider, for example, the *complementary-symmetry* circuit, Fig. 6-32, em-

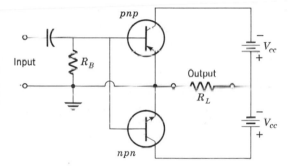

FIGURE 6-32 *Complementary-symmetry amplifier employing pnp and npn transistors.*

ploying *npn* and *pnp* grounded-emitter amplifiers having common input and output connections. The base bias on both transistors is zero so in the absence of signal the transistors are cut off and each unit operates as a class-B amplifier. Therefore, current is present in each transistor only when the input signal voltage biases its emitter junction in the forward direction. This happens on alternate half-cycles of the input voltage waveform because of the opposite polarities of the two transistors. Thus, the *npn* transistor delivers current to the load resistor when the *pnp* unit is cut off, and vice versa. The output signal is a replica of the input waveform, even though each transistor operates only half the time (see Exercise 6-15).

This particularly simple circuit is an efficient power amplifier since the quiescent current is zero and each transistor operates over the entire range of its characteristics. Furthermore, I^2R losses are small because the dc current in the load resistor is zero at all times. Unfortunately, it is not easy to fabricate *npn* and *pnp* transistors with identical characteristics. Also, the center-tapped collector supply voltage having neither terminal at ground is an awkward complication. For these reasons, the advantages of complementary symmetry are not widely used, although Fig. 6-32 does demonstrate the potential benefits that can be achieved in suitable circuits.

OTHER SEMICONDUCTOR DEVICES

Although the junction transistor undoubtedly is the most important semiconductor device, a number of others have been developed which in the aggregate are of equal significance. The junction rectifier, Zener diode, and parametric diode are typical examples of the versatility inherent in semiconductors and semiconductor devices. Several additional devices are briefly described in this section.

6-16 Field-effect transistors

The input impedance of conventional transistor amplifiers is characteristically small because of the low resistance of the forward-biased emitter junction. Although this is of little consequence in most circuit applications, it is often convenient, particularly in the input stage of an amplifier, to have a high input impedance in order to minimize loading of the signal source. Conventional transistors are also limited in high-frequency performance by the

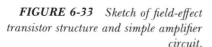

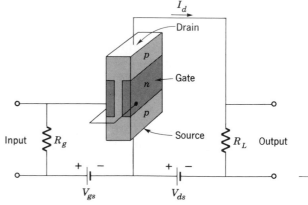

FIGURE 6-33   Sketch of field-effect transistor structure and simple amplifier circuit.

time minority carriers take to diffuse across the base region. This time is reduced if the base is very thin, but this limits the maximum permissible collector potential. The collector voltage cannot exceed the value which makes the collector junction penetrate completely through the base region. Both of these unfavorable characteristics are absent in the *field-effect transistor* (FET), in which the flow of majority carriers is controlled by a signal voltage applied to a reverse-biased *pn* junction. The reverse-biased junction results in a high input impedance, and the acceleration of majority carriers in response to the applied electric field reduces the carrier transit time from input to output. This improves high-frequency performance.

A typical FET, indicated schematically in Fig. 6-33, involves a simple *p*-type semiconductor crystal with an ohmic contact called the *source* at one end and a similar contact, the *drain,* at the other. Carriers traveling from the source to the drain in response to the voltage V_{ds} pass through a channel between two *n* regions. This *pn* junction is called the *gate* because the width of the reverse-biased gate junction determines the width of the channel and controls the current between the source and drain. Variations in the gate voltage cause corresponding variations in the channel width, which means that the resistance of the semiconductor between source and drain changes in response to the applied signal.

The current-voltage characteristics of a typical FET, Fig. 6-34, are quite reminiscent of the plate characteristics of a vacuum pentode, except that the maximum source-drain voltage is limited

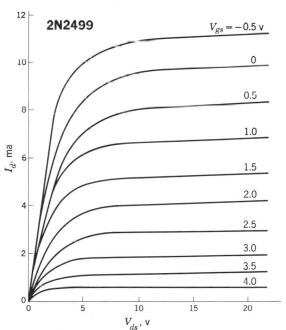

FIGURE 6-34   Current-voltage characteristic of type 2N2499 field-effect transistor.

by reverse breakdown of the gate junction. The gate potential is analogous to the pentode's grid voltage. The high reverse resistance of the gate junction leads to a large input resistance. This means that the ac equivalent circuit appropriate for the FET is similar to the Norton equivalent used for the pentode in Chap. 5. Generally it is necessary to include the capacitance of the gate junction in the equivalent circuit for high-frequency considerations.

An elementary FET voltage-amplifier circuit, Fig. 6-35, uses a source bias resistor to develop the necessary gate voltage. It is often useful to add a resistor from the gate to V_{dd} in order to

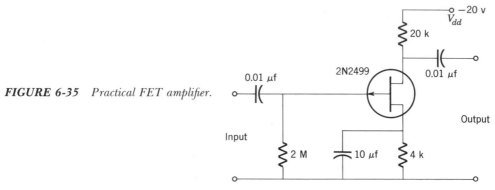

FIGURE 6-35   *Practical FET amplifier.*

stabilize the operating point, particularly against temperature changes. The operating point and circuit performance are determined much as in the case of the vacuum pentode (see Exercise 6-17). In addition to the simple common-source amplifier circuit of Fig. 6-35, a number of other FET circuit configurations have been developed to take advantage of the high input impedance of this semiconductor device.

6-17   Silicon controlled rectifiers

It is now possible to describe in greater detail the *silicon controlled rectifier* (SCR) originally discussed in Chap. 4. The useful performance of this device is obtained by adding a third *pn* junction to the junction transistor structure. The resulting *pnpn* four-layer device, Fig. 6-36a, is also called a *four-layer diode* when connections are made only to the two outer layers. A positive

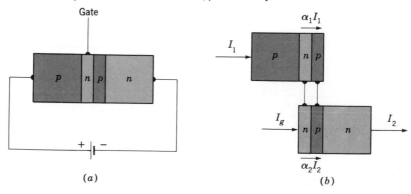

FIGURE 6-36   *(a) Sketch of SCR and (b) its interpretation in terms of pnp transistor coupled to npn transistor.*

potential applied to the p-type terminal puts the center pn junction under reverse bias while the two outer junctions are forward-biased. The device may be looked upon as the back-to-back combination of a pnp transistor together with an npn transistor, Fig. 6-36b, the two transistors having a common collector junction.

Note that I_1 is the emitter current in the pnp transistor and that $\alpha_1 I_1$ is the collector current. Similarly, I_2 is the emitter current of the npn unit and $\alpha_2 I_2$ is the collector current. Using Kirchhoff's current rule at the collector junction,

$$I_2 = \alpha_1 I_1 + \alpha_2 I_2 \tag{6-56}$$

Considering the overall current input to the device

$$I_2 = I_g + I_1 \tag{6-57}$$

where I_g is the current into the gate terminal. Substituting for I_1 in Eq. (6-56) and solving the result for I_2 yields

$$I_2 = \frac{-\alpha_1}{1 - (\alpha_1 + \alpha_2)} I_g \tag{6-58}$$

According to Eq. (6-58), if the sum of the current gains $\alpha_1 + \alpha_2$ is near unity, the current I_2 can be very large even though the gate current is small. In fact, if $\alpha_1 + \alpha_2 = 1$, the current is large and limited only by the ohmic resistance of the semiconductor, even if there is no gate current.

The current-voltage characteristics of a four-layer diode, Fig. 4-29, are interpreted in terms of Eq. (6-58) as follows. For low terminal voltages the current corresponds to the minuscule reverse current of the collector junction and the current gain factors are small. At a critical applied voltage, avalanche breakdown at the collector junction increases the current through the device and the α's increase (compare Fig. 6-18). When $\alpha_1 + \alpha_2$ equals unity, the device switches to the high-conductance state. According to Eq. (6-58) the current can also be increased by introducing a current into the gate terminal. Thus the transition can be made to occur at a lower terminal voltage than that corresponding to current avalanche at the collector junction. Once triggered into the conducting state by gate current, the gate current may be reduced to zero since the device current itself maintains $\alpha_1 + \alpha_2$ equal to unity.

The great utility of the SCR in control circuitry has already been explored in Chap. 4. Devices covering a broad range of power-handling ability are readily available. The four-layer diode is useful as a voltage-operated switch, particularly in pulse circuits (Chap. 10) and relaxation oscillators (Chap. 9). In another four-layer device the switching current is supplied by the photocurrent generated when light energy falls on the collector junction. Such a *light-activated switch* can control considerable amounts of electrical power directly from a light beam.

6-18 Tunnel diodes

A very useful effect occurs in *pn* junctions in which the impurity concentrations on both the *n* and *p* sides are very great. The carrier concentrations are large and the Fermi level lies in the valence and conduction bands on the two sides of the junction. The energy-band model of the junction is shown in Fig. 6-37*a* for the case of zero applied voltage.

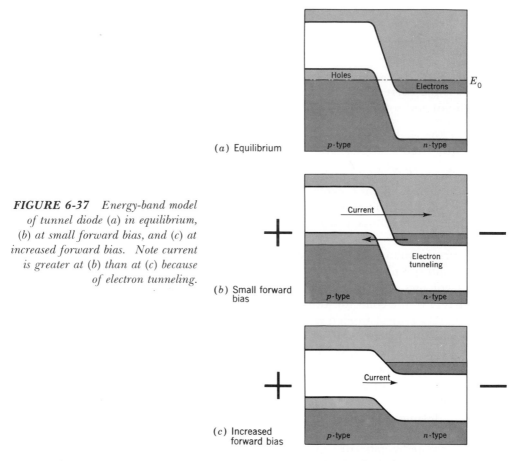

(*a*) Equilibrium

FIGURE 6-37 *Energy-band model of tunnel diode (a) in equilibrium, (b) at small forward bias, and (c) at increased forward bias. Note current is greater at (b) than at (c) because of electron tunneling.*

(*b*) Small forward bias

(*c*) Increased forward bias

Very large impurity concentrations also mean that the junction is very narrow, according to Eq. (6-12). Widths of the order of 10 to 100 atomic diameters are easily achieved in germanium diodes and similar devices. In this situation it is possible for an electron in the conduction band on the *n* side to jump to the valence band on the *p* side by a process called electron tunneling. The tunneling transition takes place with no change in the energy of the electron. The ability of an electron to tunnel through the potential barrier of the junction is a result of the wavelike nature of the electron. The probability that an electron will penetrate a potential barrier can be calculated from the principles of quantum mechanics. The tunneling current depends upon the junction width, upon the number of electrons capable of tunneling, and upon the number of empty energy levels into which they can transfer. In equilibrium, Fig. 6-37a, the tunneling currents across the junction in the two directions are equal and the net current is zero.

At a small forward-bias potential, electrons tunnel from the conduction band on the n side to empty levels in the valence band on the p side and a forward current results. The current increases with voltage until the electrons on the n side are in line with the holes on the p side, Fig. 6-37b. As the bias is increased beyond this point, electrons in the conduction band are raised above the valence-band states and the tunnel current is reduced. In this range of forward bias each increment in voltage causes a decrease in current. Finally, Fig. 6-37c, the electrons and holes are completely out of line and the junction current corresponds to the normal forward pn-junction current.

The current-voltage characteristic of a *tunnel diode* (also referred to as an *Esaki diode* after its discoverer), Fig. 6-38, shows how the

FIGURE 6-38 *Experimental current-voltage characteristic of tunnel diode. Negative resistance region exists between peak and valley currents.*

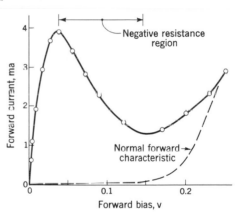

current rises to a maximum, corresponding to the condition of Fig. 6-37b, and then decreases as the forward bias is increased. The interval between the peak and valley of the characteristic curve exhibits a negative resistance effect since each voltage increase reduces the current. The usefulness of this effect stems from the fact that all conventional electronic circuit components have positive resistance and therefore dissipate power. If a tunnel diode is placed in a resonant circuit, Fig. 6-39, so the net resistance vanishes, no power loss results. The circuit therefore oscillates at its

FIGURE 6-39 *Tunnel-diode oscillator.*

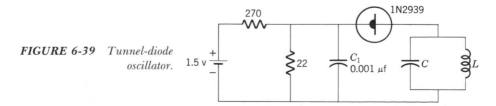

resonant frequency. (See Exercise 6-18.) The purpose of the battery and resistors in Fig. 6-39 is to bias the diode to the negative resistance point.

The tunnel diode makes possible very simple ac generator circuits which are particularly useful at extremely high frequencies. Tunneling takes place essentially instantaneously so that excellent high-frequency performance is achieved. Circuits that oscillate at frequencies as high as 10^{11} cps have been designed. Furthermore, the input power requirements are extremely small, as can be seen from Fig. 6-38.

6-19 Heterojunctions

A single crystal having two different semiconductor materials directly attached to each other can be produced by a process called *epitaxial growth*. Consider, for example, a single crystal of gallium arsenide (GaAs) placed in a hot gas of germanium. As Ge atoms deposit on the face of the GaAs crystal, they line up with the gallium and arsenic atoms so that the regularity of the single crystal is preserved. The result is a single crystal in which the semiconductor switches from GaAs to Ge at a certain place. The forbidden energy gaps of the two semiconductors are different, so that such a *heterojunction* has a potential difference across it much as does a *pn* junction.

The energy-band model of an *n*-type heterojunction is sketched in Fig. 6-40*a*. Both the narrow forbidden energy gap material on one side of the junction and the wide forbidden energy gap semiconductor on the other side are *n*-type crystals. Just as in the *pn* junction, electrons diffuse across the boundary until the two sides are in equilibrium and the Fermi levels line up. The result is a potential rise containing a sharp spike as shown. Note that the potential difference is present even though the semiconductor is *n*-type on both sides of the junction. This comes about because of the difference in forbidden energy gaps of the two semiconductors. An exactly analogous situation occurs in the case of a *p*-type heterojunction.

Heterojunctions have rectification properties since under reverse bias, Fig. 6-40*b*, only a few electrons have sufficient energy to surmount the energy spike and move from the wide-gap material to the narrow-gap side. Conversely, under forward bias, Fig. 6-40*c*, many electrons can move across the lowered potential barrier from the narrow-gap side to the wide-gap material. The rectification properties of an *n*-type (or *p*-type) heterojunction are not as favorable as for a *pn* junction, however, since the ratio of forward current to reverse current depends on the size of the potential spike. The spike is inherently smaller than the potential rise at a *pn* junction. Notice, though, that current is carried across an *n*-

type heterojunction exclusively by electrons, contrary to carrier injection at a *pn* junction. This means that the injected majority carriers do not recombine with their opposite carrier type after

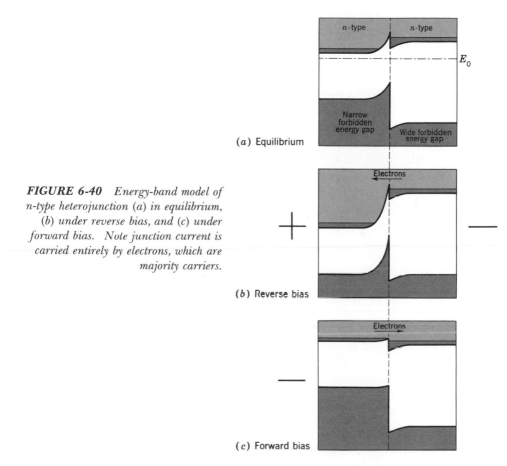

(*a*) Equilibrium

FIGURE 6-40   Energy-band model of n-type heterojunction (a) in equilibrium, (b) under reverse bias, and (c) under forward bias. Note junction current is carried entirely by electrons, which are majority carriers.

(*b*) Reverse bias

(*c*) Forward bias

crossing the junction. The performance of ordinary *pn* junctions is degraded at high frequencies where the recombination time is appreciable with respect to the period of the signal. Heterojunctions, on the other hand, do not have this limitation. Accordingly, they are useful in very-high-speed applications such as digital computers.

6-20 Injection lasers

Electrons injected into the *p* region of a forward-biased *pn* junction recombine with holes in a time which depends upon the type of recombination transition. In certain semiconductors, most notably GaAs, recombination takes place very rapidly by means of transitions from the conduction band to the valence band. Each such transition is accompanied by the emission of a light photon.

The photon wavelength corresponds to the energy of the forbidden energy gap since the electron must lose this amount of
energy in making the transition. The width of the forbidden
energy gap in GaAs is such that the emitted light is in the near-
infrared region. Such junctions are efficient light sources and the
light intensity is easily modulated by altering the strength of the
forward current.

Since each electronic transition is independent of all the others,
the photons are emitted randomly in all directions. The light output is similar to that from conventional light sources such as
fluorescent lamps. It is possible, however, to influence the recombination transitions by shining light of the same wavelength on the
junction. This additional light stimulates the recombinations, and
the emitted light energy simply adds to the incident light, thereby
making it more intense. The stimulation of recombination transitions can be indicated on an energy-band model of a forward-
biased *pn* junction, as in Fig. 6-41. The *pn* junction, therefore, acts

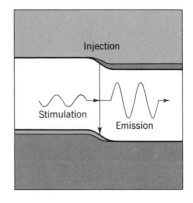

FIGURE 6-41 *Energy-band model of injection laser.
Recombination of electrons and holes injected by forward
bias is stimulated by incident radiation. Emitted photons are
amplification of incident radiation.*

as a light amplifier. The phenomenon is termed light amplification by stimulated emission of radiation, commonly shortened to
laser.

It is not actually necessary to shine light on the junction in order
for laser action to occur since emission from one transition is sufficient to stimulate other recombinations. Consider, for example, a
pn junction with optically polished and parallel sides perpendicular
to the plane of the junction. Photons traveling parallel to the junction are reflected back and forth between the polished sides and
thereby repeatedly traverse the junction region. Light emitted in
this direction from a single transition stimulates other transitions so
that additional light is emitted in this direction. This continues
until all of the emitted photons are in the same direction. Any
photons that may be emitted at an angle to the plane of the junction are not amplified efficiently because they are not reflected back
and forth in the same region. One of the sides is purposely made
to be an imperfect reflector so that a portion of the light energy is
transmitted as an emerging beam.

The characteristics of the light emission from an *injection laser* are much different from those from conventional light sources since the emitted light from a stimulated transition is simply an amplification of the incident light. This means all the light is emitted at the same wavelength, rather than spread over a range of wavelengths. A familiar acoustic analogy to this optical phenomenon is the difference between a pure flute tone and the noise of a cymbal clash. Furthermore, the light beam from an injection laser is strictly parallel since only light energy moving parallel to the plane of the junction is amplified.

The injection laser is a newly developed device and its full potential is yet to be realized. It seems certain that the extreme spectral purity and parallelism of the emitted radiation can be used, for example, in communications systems. If the junction current is varied in accordance with a signal, the emitted beam is correspondingly modulated. The signal is recovered at the receiving station by directing the laser light onto a photocell. The advantages of this system result from the characteristics of the laser beam which permit an extremely large amount of information to be transmitted. In another potential application, lasers are used in very-high-speed electronic computers. Signals are transported at the speed of light from one part of the computer to another.

6-21   Integrated circuits

The properties of semiconductors make it possible to produce an entire electronic circuit within one single crystal. Such an *integrated circuit* miniaturizes electronic networks and also reduces the number of individual components in complex electronic circuits. This is so because an entire integrated circuit represents, in effect, only one component.

The integrated-circuit idea can be illustrated most easily by considering a rudimentary transistor amplifier circuit, Fig. 6-42*a*. The six individual components of this circuit are usually fastened to a common support and connected by metal wires. Since the resistance of a simple piece of semiconductor can be adjusted by controlling the impurity content, the resistors in the circuit can be made of the same substance as the transistor, namely, silicon. Similarly, the capacitance of a *pn* junction can be used for the input and output capacitors. Thus, the circuit can be assembled entirely from pieces of silicon connected by wires, Fig. 6-42*b*. It is not really necessary to connect semiconductor pieces of the same conductivity type with wires, however, so the circuit can be reduced to only three components, Fig. 6-42*c*. Through judicious geometric arrangement these can all be combined into one single-crystal semiconductor slab, as in Fig. 6-42*d*. The single slab contains the proper structure of *n*-type, *p*-type, and insulating intrinsic regions.

Forgetting for the moment that Fig. 6-42*d* was developed by start-ing with a conventional circuit, the final result looks like a single semiconductor device. Yet this one component performs the func-tion of an entire amplifier.

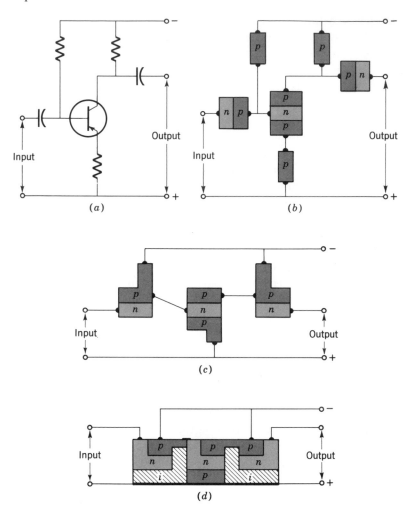

FIGURE 6-42 *Development of integrated-circuit amplifier from conventional transistor circuit.*

This elementary example presents only the rudiments of the integrated-circuit approach. Actually entire amplifiers, radio re-ceivers, and computer subassemblies have been fabricated. In all these circuits careful attention must be given to unwanted stray capacitances and leakage resistances present between different regions of the crystal. These arise because all circuit components are contained within one semiconductor crystal. Another problem is the difficulty of producing inductances by integrated-circuit techniques. To circumvent this difficulty, *RC* networks with res-onancelike effects, such as the Wien bridge or the twin-T network discussed in Chap. 3, are often used. It seems clear that as circuit engineers gain experience in the design of integrated circuits their applications are destined to become widespread.

SUGGESTIONS FOR FURTHER READING

Leonid V. Azároff and James J. Brophy: "Electronic Processes in Materials," McGraw-Hill Book Company, New York, 1963.

James J. Brophy: "Semiconductor Devices," McGraw-Hill Book Company, New York, 1964.

"General Electric Transistor Manual," latest edition, General Electric Company, Semiconductor Products Department, Syracuse, N.Y.

R. F. Shea: "Transistor Applications," John Wiley & Sons, Inc., New York, 1964.

Joseph A. Walston and John R. Miller (eds.): "Transistor Circuit Design," McGraw-Hill Book Company, New York, 1963.

EXERCISES

6-1 Determine the impurity concentration and internal potential rise of the parametric-diode pn junction corresponding to Fig. 6 7 from the slope and intercept of the line and with the aid of Eq. (6-15). The area of the junction is 4.5×10^{-7} m² and the dielectric constant of silicon is 11. Also calculate the width of the junction and the electric field in the junction at a reverse potential of 10 volts.

   Ans.: 7.1×10^{16} cm⁻³; 0.36 volt; 2.98×10^{-7} m; 3.5×10^7 volts/m

6-2 Sketch the energy-band model for an npn transistor in equilibrium and biased for transistor operation.

6-3 Calculate an approximate value of r_b for a transistor 1 mm × 1 mm in cross section assuming that the base resistance is entirely a result of the ohmic base region. The resistivity of the base region is 10^{-2} Ω-m; the base width is 10^{-3} cm and the base contact covers one edge of the base region. *Ans.:* 500 Ω

6-4 Derive a set of idealized common-emitter h parameters and their variation with emitter current corresponding to Fig. 6-18. Use Eqs. (6-25) and (6-26); assume α is a constant equal to 0.99, $I_o = 10 \times 10^{-6}$ amp, and r_b is as calculated in Exercise 6-3.

   Ans.: 1 ma, 1 volt; 3100 Ω, 3.1×10^{-16}, 99, 1.2×10^{-18} mho

6-5 Calculate an approximate value of h_{fe} for the type 2N175 transistor from the characteristic curves in Appendix 3. Repeat for h_{oe}.

   Ans.: 83, 5×10^{-5} mho

6-6 Determine the operating point of a type 2N175 transistor in the grounded-emitter circuit, Fig. 6-21. Draw the ac equivalent circuit of the amplifier and calculate the gain assuming $h_{ie} = 1000$ Ω, $h_{re} = 3 \times 10^{-4}$, and the other parameters are as in Exercise 6-5. Repeat for the circuit of Fig. 6-19 and compare the gain of the two amplifiers. *Ans.:* 10 μa, 1 ma; 262, 415

6-7 Determine the operating point of the *npn* grounded-emitter amplifier, Fig. 6-22, using a 2N338 transistor, if $R_E = 470\ \Omega$, $R_1 = 16,000\ \Omega$, $R_2 = 6200\ \Omega$, $R_L = 700\ \Omega$, and $V_{cc} = 12$ volts. Use the characteristic curves in Appendix 3. *Ans.:* 75 μa, 4 ma

6-8 Design a common-emitter amplifier corresponding to Fig. 6-22 for the type 2N35 transistor. The operating point is $V_{ce} = 6$ volts, $I_c = 1$ ma, and $I_b = 20 \times 10^{-6}$ amp. Assume $R_L = 10,000\ \Omega$ and $h_{ie} = 2000\ \Omega$. Characteristic curves of the 2N35 are in Appendix 3.

6-9 Determine the operating point of the 2N930 common-emitter amplifier, Fig. 6-25. Characteristic curves of the 2N930 are in Appendix 3. *Ans.:* 4 μa, 1 ma

6-10 Calculate the voltage and current gain and the input and output impedance of the amplifier of Exercise 6-9. The h parameters are $h_{ie} = 3600\ \Omega$, $h_{re} = 3 \times 10^{-3}$, $h_{fe} = 150$, $h_{oe} = 1.4 \times 10^{-4}$ mho. Assume the reactances of all capacitors in the circuit are negligible and that the source resistance is 1000 Ω. Compare the calculated values with approximations introduced in the text.
Ans.: 362, 416; 62.4, 150; 8100 Ω, 3600 Ω; $4.2 \times 10^3\ \Omega$, $7.1 \times 10^3\ \Omega$

6-11 Determine the operating point of the 2N930 grounded-base amplifier, Fig. 6-28. Assuming the hybrid parameters given in Exercise 6-10, calculate the voltage and current gain and the input impedance for this circuit. Compare these with the approximations discussed in the text. Take $R_g = 100\ \Omega$.
Ans.: 200, 413; 0.99, 0.994; 27.5 Ω, 24 Ω

6-12 Determine the operating point of the type 2N930 emitter-follower amplifier, Fig. 6-30. Given the h parameters of Exercise 6-10, calculate the voltage and current gain and the input and output impedance for this circuit. Compare these results with the approximations introduced in the text. The source resistance is 10,000 Ω.
Ans.: 2.5 μa, 0.75 ma; 1, 1; 63, 151; $1.5 \times 10^6\ \Omega$, $1.5 \times 10^6\ \Omega$; 90 Ω

6-13 Connect the input of the emitter-follower amplifier of Exercise 6-12 to the output of the common-base amplifier of Exercise 6-11 and calculate the overall voltage and current gain using the h parameters listed in Exercise 6-10. Note that part of the load of the common-base amplifier is the input impedance of the common-emitter amplifier. *Ans.:* 413, 62.6

6-14 Draw the hybrid equivalent circuit of the transistor differential amplifier in Fig. 6-43. Plot the output signal as a function of the input signal. The appropriate h parameters are $h_{ie} = 1260\ \Omega$, $h_{re} = 1.5 \times 10^{-3}$, $h_{fe} = 44$, and $h_{oe} = 2.7 \times 10^{-5}$ mho.

6-15 Consider the complementary-symmetry amplifier, Fig. 6-32. Assuming that both transistors have characteristics similar to the type 2N35 in Appendix 3 (except for the reversed current and voltage polarities of the *pnp* unit) plot the dynamic transfer characteristic of the circuit. This is a plot of the output current as a function of the input current. Do this by considering each half of the circuit separately and then combining the individual characteristics according to the polarities of the currents of the two transistors. Assuming that the input signal is sinusoidal, sketch the current waveform in each transistor and the current waveform in the load resistance.

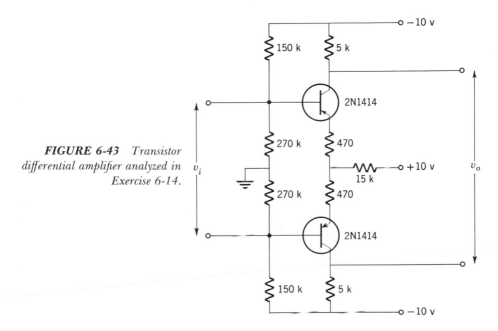

FIGURE 6-43   *Transistor differential amplifier analyzed in Exercise 6-14.*

6-16 Suggest a reason why it is not desirable to use a very large value of load resistance in order to make the voltage gain of the grounded-base stage very large. *Hint:* Consider the collector supply potential needed and the base-collector voltage if the input signal drives the transistor into cutoff.

6-17 Determine the operating point of the 2N2499 FET amplifier, Fig. 6-35, using the characteristic curves given in Appendix 3. Calculate the approximate voltage gain of the amplifier.

$$\text{Ans.: } -3.5 \text{ volts, } 0.9 \text{ ma; } 24$$

6-18 Draw an approximate equivalent circuit for the tunnel-diode oscillator, Fig. 6-39. Assume all circuit losses can be represented by a resistance in series with the diode. Calculate the current in the inductance resulting from an assumed series voltage generator and derive the condition for sustained oscillation, i.e., current even without the generator. Note that this result suggests that the current becomes infinite. In a practical circuit, what limits the current? *Hint:* Consider the extent of the negative-resistance region in the current-voltage curve of the tunnel diode, Fig. 6-38.

6-19 Sketch the energy-band diagram of a *p*-type heterojunction.

6-20 Sketch the energy-band diagram of a *pn* heterojunction if the forbidden energy gap of the *p*-type side is larger than the forbidden energy gap of the *n*-type side. Repeat for the reverse situation.

7
AMPLIFIERS

The principal applications of transistors and vacuum tubes are based on their ability to amplify electric signals. Some circuits amplify minute voltage signals by factors of many million, while others increase the electric power of a signal in order to operate a mechanical device such as an electric motor. Still other circuits amplify currents. In each of these applications the frequency range of the input signal is important. Different circuits have been developed for dc amplification and for use at high radio frequencies.

Most often, the signal level is increased in several successive amplifier stages to attain the desired output signal magnitude. In this case, the interaction of amplifier stages must be considered and fairly complicated networks are involved. Fortunately, the techniques of circuit analysis developed in previous chapters, in particular the ac equivalent circuits for tubes and transistors, are sufficient for a satisfactory understanding of complete amplifier circuits.

VOLTAGE AMPLIFIERS

7-1   Cascading

The transistor and vacuum-tube circuits discussed in previous chapters are ideally suited to amplify voltage signals with minimum waveform distortion.   Gain factors greater than those possible with a single-stage amplifier are obtained by *cascading* several amplifier stages.   The output of one amplifier stage is amplified by another stage or stages until the desired signal voltage level is achieved.

Consider, for example, the two-stage cascaded triode amplifier, Fig. 7-1.   Two individual circuits similar to those discussed in

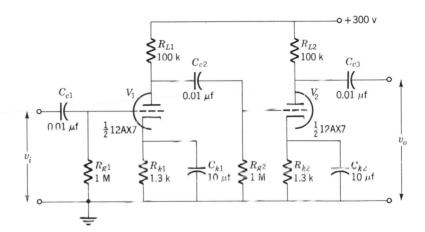

FIGURE 7-1   *Two-stage amplifier using triodes connected in cascade.*

Chap. 5 are connected with the coupling capacitor C_{c2}.   This capacitor passes the amplified ac signal from V_1 to the grid of V_2. At the same time it blocks the positive plate voltage of V_1 from the grid of the second triode.   Similarly, capacitors C_{c1} and C_{c3} isolate the input and output circuits insofar as dc potentials are concerned.

The entire ac equivalent circuit of this amplifier may be drawn using the principles discussed in Chap. 5.   The performance of the system is determined from a complete ac-circuit analysis.   Actually, this procedure is unwieldy because of the number of loops in the network and is rarely attempted.   Rather, the circuit is analyzed in several separate steps, each of which has a minimum of mathematical complexity.   This has the further advantage that the important effects can be isolated and more clearly examined.

For example, the reactances of both cathode bypass capacitors are assumed small enough to be negligible.   Accordingly, these components are absent in the ac equivalent circuit of the amplifier, Fig. 7-2.   The reactances of the coupling capacitors are also ignored, even though they are included in the equivalent circuit for clarity. With these simplifications, the output voltage may be immediately written as

$$v_o = v_{g2} \frac{-\mu_2}{1 + r_{p2}/R_{L2}} = v_{g1} \frac{-\mu_1}{1 + r_{p1}/R'_{L1}} \times \frac{-\mu_2}{1 + r_{p2}/R_{L2}} \qquad (7\text{-}1)$$

where the load resistance of the first stage R'_{L1} is the parallel combination of the plate resistor R_{L1} and the second-stage grid resistor R_{g2}.

According to (7-1), the overall gain of this two-stage amplifier is simply

$$a = a_1 a_2 \qquad (7\text{-}2)$$

where a_1 and a_2 are the gains of each stage. The expression for the gain of the first stage a_1 includes the input impedance of V_2 as

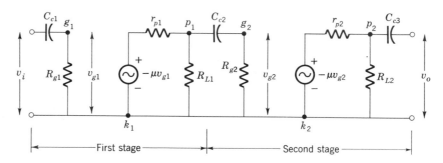

FIGURE 7-2 *Equivalent circuit of the two-stage cascaded amplifier of Fig. 7-1.*

part of the load resistance. Usually, $R_{g2} \gg R_{L1}$, however, so a_1 is essentially the gain of the isolated V_1 stage. Equations (7-1) and (7-2) give the *midband gain* of the amplifier since the reactances of the coupling capacitors and the cathode bypass capacitors are assumed negligible. This approximation applies to signal frequencies which are neither so low that the reactances cannot be ignored nor so high that other effects reduce the gain. These other frequency regions are discussed in the following section.

Cascaded transistor voltage amplifiers most often employ the grounded-emitter configuration because of the combined voltage and current gain of this circuit. Neither the common-base nor the emitter-follower configuration achieves as great overall voltage amplification when cascaded. This is a result of the great impedance mismatch between the output impedance of one stage and the input impedance of the succeeding stage. A typical transistor voltage amplifier, Fig. 7-3, uses interstage coupling capacitors as in the vacuum-tube case to isolate the dc bias voltages of the two stages. Note that the bias resistors of the second stage are different from those of the first stage, even though both transistors are identical. The operating points are set at different places in order to obtain most favorable values of the h parameters in each stage.

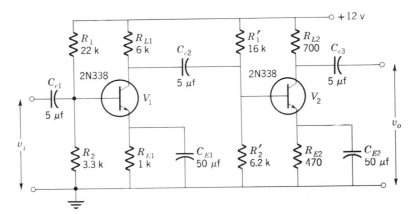

FIGURE 7-3   *Two-stage cascaded transistor amplifier.*

In the appropriate equivalent circuit of the amplifier, Fig. 7-4, the base bias resistors are replaced by their parallel combination, as explained in the previous chapter. Here again, the overall gain

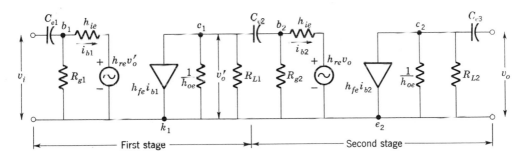

FIGURE 7-4   *Equivalent circuit of the two-stage transistor amplifier of Fig. 7-3.*

is the product of the individual gain of each stage, Eq. (7-2). The loading effect of the second stage upon the output of the first stage cannot be ignored in calculating the gain because of the inherently low input impedance of transistors. In fact, it is necessary to work backward through the circuit starting at the output terminals because the input impedance of a transistor amplifier depends upon the output load impedance. With the output load specified, the gain and input impedance of the second stage are calculated using the results developed in the previous chapter. This input impedance is part of the load for the preceding stage and its gain and input impedance are calculated accordingly. Thus, detailed analysis of transistor circuits is somewhat more complicated than is the case for vacuum-tube amplifiers, basically because of the input-output coupling in a transistor. Nevertheless, transistor circuits are treated quite satisfactorily by straightforward ac-circuit analysis of the equivalent circuit.

7-2 Low-frequency gain

At sufficiently low frequencies the capacitive reactances may no longer be neglected. The effect of the coupling capacitors is usually of greater significance than that of the cathode bypass capacitors, although both tend to reduce the gain at low frequencies. It is not practical to make the coupling capacitors large. Large values of capacitance imply increased leakage current, which upsets grid bias of vacuum tubes. This situation is aggravated by the fact that the coupling capacitor is connected between the large positive plate potential and the low grid voltage and by the large value of grid resistance. Consequently, practical coupling capacitors are limited to values below about 0.5 μf.

No such restrictions are placed on cathode bypass capacitors since they are connected in low-impedance, low-voltage circuits where leakage currents are insignificant. Electrolytic capacitors are common in this position and values ranging up to 100 μf are used. Special low-voltage electrolytics are used in transistor amplifiers as both coupling capacitors and bypass capacitors since the impedance levels are low in both places. Nevertheless, leakage currents must be minimized into the base terminal so a limit to the capacitance exists in this case as well. The low-frequency gain of cascaded transistor amplifiers is also determined primarily by the reactance of the interstage coupling capacitors.

Because the overall gain of cascaded stages is the product of individual stage gains, it is only necessary to examine the effect of the coupling capacitor reactance for an isolated amplifier stage. According to the ac equivalent circuits of both vacuum-tube and transistor amplifiers, Figs. 7-2 and 7-4, this effect can be treated by considering the simple RC circuit comprising the coupling capacitor and the input impedance of the amplifier.

This part of both equivalent circuits is shown separately in Fig. 7-5 for clarity. The input impedance R_i is simply the grid resistor

FIGURE 7-5

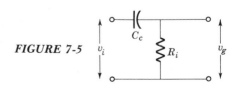

in the case of the tube amplifier, but in the transistor amplifier it includes the input impedance of the transistor itself. In either case, the output voltage of the stage is

$$v_o = av_g = a \frac{v_i}{R_i + 1/j\omega C_c} R_i$$

$$= \frac{av_i}{1 - j/\omega R_i C_c} \tag{7-3}$$

As discussed in Chap. 2, it is appropriate to define the characteristic frequency

$$2\pi f_0 = \omega_0 = \frac{1}{R_i C_c} \tag{7-4}$$

Substituting Eq. (7-4) into Eq. (7-3), the gain v_o/v_i is

$$a(f) = \frac{a}{1 - jf_0/f} \tag{7-5}$$

where a is the midband gain. Note that the gain is reduced when the signal frequency is smaller than the characteristic frequency. At the same time a phase shift is introduced between the input and the output signals. Both effects are important in determining the waveform distortion of the amplifier. Recall that in the Fourier analysis of a complex signal waveform, both the amplitudes and relative phases of all frequency components must be preserved if the output wave is to be an amplified replica of the input signal.

It is convenient to rationalize Eq. (7-5),

$$a(f) = -\frac{a}{\sqrt{1 + (f_0/f)^2}} \tag{7-6}$$

so that the gain at any frequency can be immediately calculated. Note that Eq. (7-6) shows that the gain is $a/\sqrt{2}$, or about 70 percent of the midband gain, when $f = f_0$. It is important to recognize that Eq. (7-6) applies to an individual stage. The low-frequency response of the entire amplifier is always poorer than that of any individual stage because the gain of cascaded stages is the product of individual stage gains.

7-3 High-frequency gain

The high-frequency gain of any amplifier is reduced by stray capacitive effects that are not purposely made part of the circuit. Referring to a simple triode amplifier, Fig. 7-6, these are the grid-cathode capacitance C_1, the grid-plate capacitance C_2, and the plate-cathode capacitance C_3 of the tube itself. Also included in C_1 and C_3 are stray capacitances between the wires and components attached to the grid and plate terminals. All three of these capacitors shunt the signal to ground at frequencies high enough that the capacitive reactances are significant.

The effect of the grid-plate capacitance is particularly important. Consider the pertinent equivalent circuit, Fig. 7-7, in which C_2 is

connected between the grid and plate terminals. For the moment
the effect of the other capacitors is ignored. The input impedance

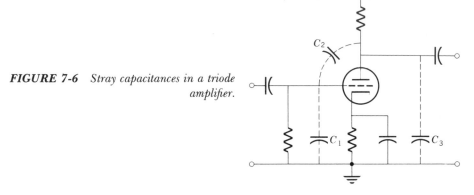

FIGURE 7-6   *Stray capacitances in a triode
amplifier.*

of the amplifier is calculated by assuming that the reactance of C_2
is the controlling factor,

$$Z_i = \frac{v_i}{i_i} \cong \frac{v_i}{(v_i + \mu v_i)/(1/j\omega C_2)} \qquad (7\text{-}7)$$

$$Z_i = \frac{1}{j\omega(1+\mu)C_2} \qquad (7\text{-}8)$$

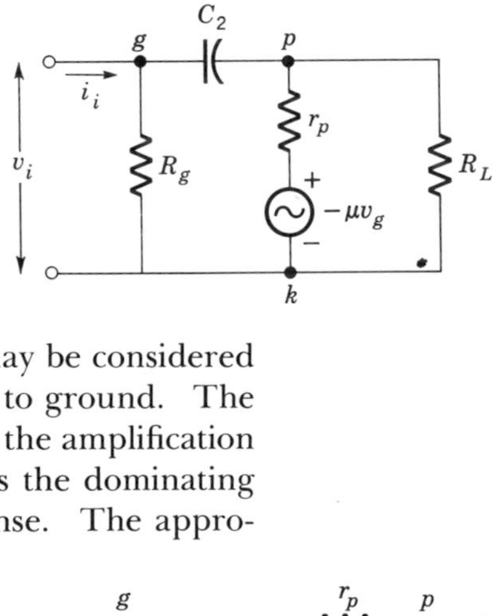

FIGURE 7-7

This result indicates that the input impedance may be considered
to be a capacitor $(1 + \mu)C_2$ connected from grid to ground. The
increase in effective shunt capacitance caused by the amplification
factor of the tube is called the *Miller effect* and is the dominating
effect in determining the high-frequency response. The appro-

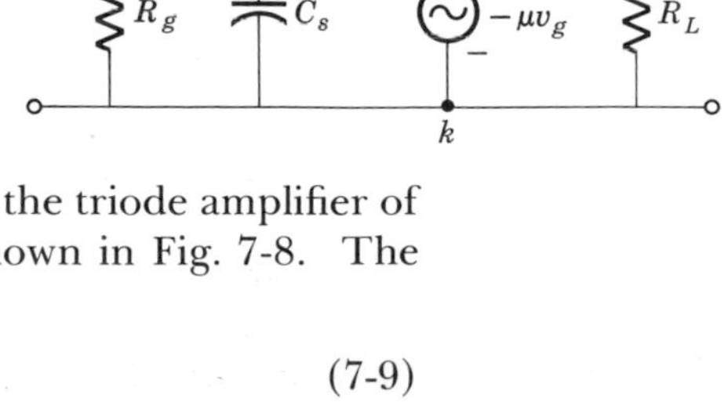

FIGURE 7-8   *High-frequency equivalent circuit
of triode amplifier includes shunt capacitance C_s.*

priate high-frequency equivalent circuit for the triode amplifier of
Fig. 7-6 includes a shunt capacitance, as shown in Fig. 7-8. The
magnitude of this capacitance,

$$C_s = C_1 + C_3 + (1+\mu)C_2 \qquad (7\text{-}9)$$

includes the plate-cathode capacitance of the previous stage C_3 in the total shunt capacitance, as indicated by Eq. (7-9).

Shunt capacitance is less important in a transistor amplifier, Fig. 7-9, because of the small input impedance of the transistor com-

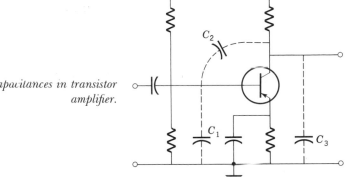

FIGURE 7-9 *Stray capacitances in transistor amplifier.*

pared with the vacuum tube. Nevertheless, the collector-junction capacitance C_2 and the emitter-junction capacitance C_1 must be accounted for in assessing the high-frequency response. As in the case of the triode amplifier, capacitances C_1 and C_3 also include the effect of stray wiring capacitances.

The effect of the collector-junction capacitance is enhanced by the Miller effect of the transistor. The magnitude is found by a procedure identical to that used for the triode amplifier and results in a total shunt capacitance given by

$$C_s = C_1 + C_3 + (1 - h_{fe})C_2 \qquad (7\text{-}10)$$

Because h_{fe} is inherently negative, the third term in Eq. (7-10) is most important. The corresponding high-frequency equivalent circuit of the transistor amplifier is illustrated in Fig. 7-10.

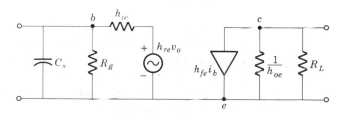

FIGURE 7-10 *High-frequency equivalent circuit of a transistor amplifier includes shunt capacitance C_s.*

According to Figs. 7-8 and 7-10, the high-frequency gain of both triode and transistor amplifiers is accounted for by the input shunt capacitor C_s. This is evaluated using the simple circuit, Fig. 7-11, which also includes the effect of the source resistance R_s. The input resistance R_i is essentially the grid resistance R_g in the case of the vacuum tube but includes the total input impedance in the case of the transistor amplifier.   The

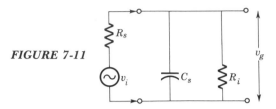

output voltage of either amplifier is found by analyzing the circuit of Fig. 7-11,

$$v_o = a'v_g = a' \frac{v_i}{R_s + Z} Z$$

where

$$\frac{1}{Z} = \frac{1}{R_i} + j\omega C_s$$

and a' is the midband gain of the stage with no load.   Substituting for Z and simplifying,

$$v_o = \frac{a'v_i}{(1 + R_s/R_i) + j\omega R_s C_s} \qquad (7\text{-}11)$$

The characteristic frequency of this circuit is defined as

$$2\pi f_0 = \omega_0 = \frac{1}{C_s}\left(\frac{1}{R_s} + \frac{1}{R_i}\right) \qquad (7\text{-}12)$$

Introducing Eq. (7-12) into Eq. (7-11) and solving for the gain v_o/v_i gives

$$a(f) = \frac{a'}{1 + R_s/R_i} \frac{1}{1 + jf/f_0} \qquad (7\text{-}13)$$

The denominator of the first term in Eq. (7-13) accounts for the loading of the amplifier input upon the previous stage.   As previously discussed, this effect is usually included in the determination of the true midband gain of the entire amplifier. Accordingly, the variation of the gain at high frequencies is conveniently written, after rationalization, as

$$a(f) = \frac{a}{\sqrt{1 + (f/f_0)^2}} \qquad (7\text{-}14)$$

where a is the true midband gain.

This result shows that the gain is reduced at high frequencies. Note also, Eq. (7-13), that phase shift is introduced between input and output signals, and this is equally significant in preserving the signal waveform.   In the case of the vacuum-tube amplifier, the input resistance is essentially equal to the grid

resistor R_g.   Since $R_g \gg R_s$, the high-frequency performance
is controlled by the output impedance of the preceding stage,
according to Eq. (7-12).   Conversely, $R_i < R_s$ in the case of the
transistor amplifier, so the transistor input impedance is the
dominating factor.   As in the low-frequency case, the overall
high-frequency response of the complete amplifier is poorer
than that of any individual stage.

Actually, the high-frequency amplification of many transistors
is limited by the transit time of carriers diffusing across the base
region.   This effect results in a high-frequency gain given by an
expression identical to Eq. (7-14) except that f_0 is determined by
physical constants of the transistor, such as the width of the base.
This characteristic frequency is usually specified by the transistor
manufacturer.   In specially designed high-frequency transistors
the *alpha falloff frequency* is high enough that the gain is limited by
circuit parameters, as discussed above.

Using Eqs. (7-6) and (7-14), the *frequency response* of any voltage
amplifier is similar to that illustrated in Fig. 7-12a.   The *low-fre-*

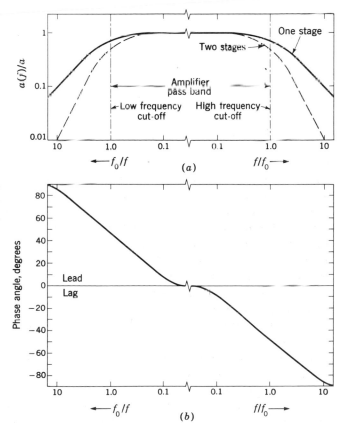

FIGURE 7-12   (a) Frequency-
response characteristic of single
amplifier stage.   Characteristic
of two-stage amplifier is shown
dashed.   (b) Phase-shift
characteristic of single amplifier
stage.

quency cutoff for each stage is determined from Eq. (7-4) while the
high-frequency cutoff for each stage is found using Eq. (7-12).   The
bandpass of the complete amplifier is the frequency interval be-

tween the high- and low-frequency points where the gain falls to $1/\sqrt{2}$ of the midband gain. Since the power output is reduced to $\frac{1}{2}$ of the midband value at these frequencies, they are generally referred to as the half-power points (see Chap. 2). It is conventional to employ logarithmic scales on both axes of bandpass characteristics such as Fig. 7-12a because the range of gains and frequencies is so great. The vertical scale is often put in terms of a unit called the *decibel,* abbreviated *db,* defined as

$$db = 20 \log \frac{a(f)}{a} \qquad (7\text{-}15)$$

Correspondingly, the midband gain is often quoted in terms of decibels using the definition

$$db = 20 \log \frac{v_o}{v_i} \qquad (7\text{-}16)$$

The advantage of this unit is that the total gain in db of several amplifier stages is simply the sum of the individual gains in terms of decibels. Note that, according to Eq. (7-15), the amplifier gain is down 3 db at the upper and lower half-power points.

The phase-shift characteristics of a single-stage amplifier are illustrated in Fig. 7-12b. The output signal leads the input at frequencies below the low-frequency cutoff and lags at frequencies above the high-frequency cutoff. The phase-shift characteristics of an entire amplifier are determined by adding the contributions from each stage.

Often an amplifier must have a wide bandpass in order to minimize waveform distortion. A number of minor circuit alterations have been developed to accomplish this end. For example, the cathode or emitter bypass capacitors may purposely be made small so that the capacitive reactance is appreciable except at frequencies near the high-frequency cutoff. This reduces the midband gain, according to Eq. (5-26), but increases the gain at high frequencies where the capacitive reactance becomes small. The net result is an extended high-frequency response, although at the expense of smaller overall amplification (see Exercise 7-3). If necessary, the loss in gain can be made up by adding another stage.

A second useful way of extending the high-frequency response is to include a small inductance as part of the plate load, Fig. 7-13. The load impedance increases at high frequencies and the gain of the amplifier is larger (see Exercise 7-4). This technique is called *peaking* since the resulting frequency-response characteristic tends to be peaked at the high-frequency end. The high-frequency response of this amplifier is further improved by the use of a pentode because of the much smaller grid-plate capacitance.

Improved low-frequency response can be achieved by adding a series resistor-capacitor combination R_3 and C_3 to the output

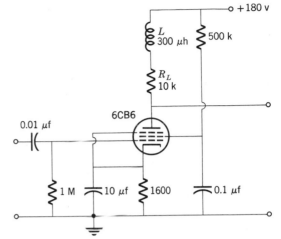

FIGURE 7-13   Small inductance in load
impedance improves high-frequency response
because gain is increased by higher load
impedance.

circuit, Fig. 7-14.   The gain at frequencies where the reactance of C_3 is small includes the effect of R_3 in the ac load resistance.

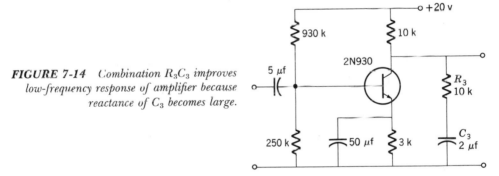

FIGURE 7-14   Combination R_3C_3 improves
low-frequency response of amplifier because
reactance of C_3 becomes large.

At low frequencies the gain increases as the reactance of the capacitor increases and removes R_3 as part of the output load. The result is an extended low-frequency response at the expense of midband gain (see Exercise 7-5).

7-4   Decoupling

When three or more stages of amplification are cascaded it is usually necessary to *decouple* the power supply of the input stage from the remainder of the amplifier.   The reason for this is that the supply voltage changes with current because of the effective internal impedance of the power supply.   Any small change in the power-supply voltage alters the bias on the first stage, and this change is amplified in the same fashion as an input signal. If the change in bias increases the current in the first stage, current in the second stage is reduced because of the 180° phase shift in the input amplifier. The current in the third stage is increased, however, because of the second 180° phase shift in the second stage. The change in the third stage is much larger than the original disturbance because of the gain of the amplifier. The additional load causes a decrease in the power-supply voltage. This, in turn, further alters the bias on the first stage and the process is cumulative. The changes continue until one tube or transistor is driven to cutoff or into saturation, which reduces the overall gain to zero. The power-supply voltage then returns to normal and the process repeats itself. The result of this *feedback* from output to input is that the amplifier rapidly oscillates from cutoff to saturation at a rate which is a function of the circuit components.

A low-pass *RC* filter inserted in the power-supply lead to the first stage, Fig. 7-15, circumvents this difficulty. The time con-

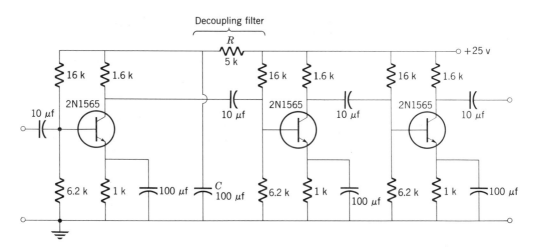

FIGURE 7-15 *Simple RC decoupling filter eliminates instability in multistage amplifier by reducing feedback effects resulting from common power supply.*

stant of this decoupling filter is selected so that power-supply variations are sufficiently attenuated and feedback is eliminated. Actually, the characteristic filter frequency is put below the low-frequency cutoff of the amplifier where the gain is insufficient to support feedback oscillations.

POWER AMPLIFIERS

7-5 Transformer coupling

When transistor or vacuum-tube amplifiers deliver appreciable amounts of power, it is no longer feasible to use resistors in the collector or plate circuit. The I^2R losses become significant at the high currents associated with large powers. Instead, a transformer couples the circuit to the load, Fig. 7-16. The dc collector current

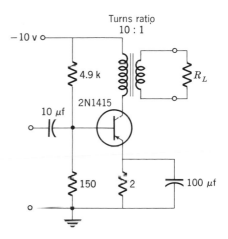

FIGURE 7-16 *Power amplifiers use transformer to couple transistor to load to reduce dc power lost in load resistance.*

in the winding resistance introduces only a small power loss, yet the reflected resistance of R_L into the primary circuit provides the proper ac load impedance for the amplifier. Furthermore, the output impedance of the amplifier is matched to the load by the transformer and the actual load resistance can be any convenient value.

The dc load line is essentially vertical on the collector characteristic curves, Fig. 7-17, because of the small winding resistance of the transformer primary. The quiescent operating point is determined exactly as outlined in Chap. 6. The ac load line corresponding to the reflected load resistance R_L' as seen from the primary side of the output transformer passes through the operating point. The slope of the ac load line is $-1/R_L'$, as shown in Fig. 7-17.

The operating point of a power amplifier is chosen to maximize the efficiency of the amplifier and to minimize the possibility of thermal runaway. Power dissipation in the transistor due to collector current is limited by the allowable temperature rise of the collector junction. If the maximum permissible temperature of the collector junction is T_M, the power dissipation must not exceed

$$P_M = KT_M \tag{7-17}$$

where K is a constant involving the thermal conductance and other

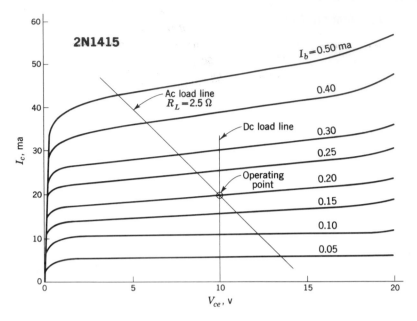

FIGURE 7-17   *Location of operating point and dc and ac load lines for power amplifier in Fig. 7-16.*

geometrical factors. Writing the power dissipation in the transistor as $I_c V_c$, the product must never exceed KT_M. The relation

$$I_c V_c = P_M \qquad (7\text{-}18)$$

is a hyperbola on the collector characteristics, as indicated by the dashed line in Fig. 7-18. The permissible operating range of collector current and voltage is to the left of this *maximum-power hyperbola*.

Power transistors firmly mounted on a good heat conductor make K in Eq. (7-17) larger. This moves the maximum-power hyperbola farther away from the origin and extends the permissible operating current and voltage range. In addition, cooling fins are often provided to maximize heat conduction away from the transistor.

The operating point is located so that the largest possible ac signals can be developed in order to maximize the power output without distortion. The maximum instantaneous collector potential is limited by reverse breakdown at the collector junction. Similarly, the maximum instantaneous transistor current corresponds to collector saturation, where the collector current no longer increases with emitter-junction current. The output waveform is badly distorted if either of these limits is exceeded because the peaks of the signal wave are clipped. Therefore, the optimum position for the operating point is in the center of the rectangle bounded by collector breakdown, collector saturation, zero collector current, and zero collector voltage, Fig. 7-18.

Here, the collector current and voltage excursions on either side of the operating point are maximized without distortion.

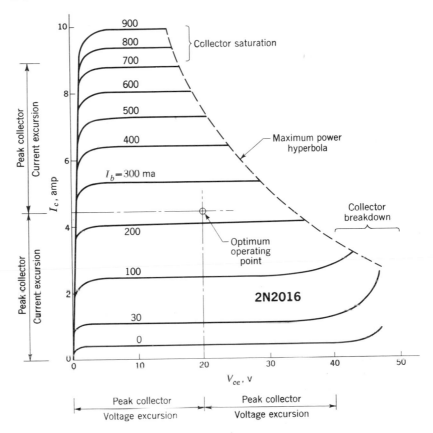

FIGURE 7-18 *Optimum location of operating point for class-A power amplifier is determined by collector saturation and collector breakdown.*

The efficiency of a power amplifier is equal to the ratio of the ac signal power to the dc or average power consumed by the amplifier. The average power is simply the product of the quiescent current times the quiescent collector voltage $I_c V_c$. If the operating point is located at the optimum position, the peak output signal current is equal to I_c and the peak output signal voltage is equal to V_c. Consequently, the efficiency is

$$\eta = \frac{(I_c/\sqrt{2})(V_c/\sqrt{2})}{I_c V_c} = \frac{1}{2} \tag{7-19}$$

Thus, the maximum efficiency of a class-A power amplifier is 50 percent. Practical transistor amplifiers approach this ideal quite closely, even though for minimum distortion the signal excursions must be somewhat smaller than the ideal case considered above. Efficiencies of the order of 48 percent are achieved in practice.

The plate characteristics of vacuum tubes are not nearly so ideal as are transistor collector characteristics. Curvature in the characteristics is considerably greater. Consequently, peak signal voltages and currents are smaller and the efficiency is correspondingly less. Pentodes are much more satisfactory than triodes in this respect, but the efficiency of practical circuits rarely exceeds 30 percent.

An equivalent-circuit representation of power amplifiers is not feasible because of the large signal voltage excursions. Consequently, all analyses are carried out graphically. It is most useful to determine the dynamic transfer characteristic of the amplifier, which is a plot of the collector output current as a function of base input current, Fig. 7-19. The transfer characteristic is determined

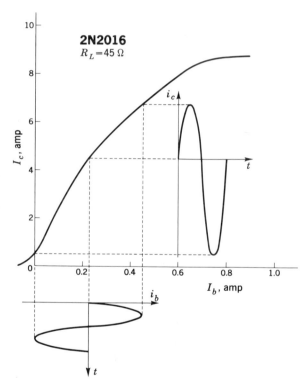

FIGURE 7-19 Dynamic transfer characteristic is used to determine amplified waveform of 2N2016 power amplifier. Note distortion in output current caused by nonlinear transfer characteristic.

from intersections of the collector characteristic curves, Fig. 7-18, with the dynamic load line. For minimum distortion the transfer characteristic should be a straight line since any curvature introduces irregularities into the output waveform.

7-6 Push-pull amplifier

The two-transistor *push-pull* amplifier, Fig. 7-20, has increased power output, efficiency, and less distortion than a single-transistor circuit. The center-tapped input transformer drives each of the transistors with signals 180° out of phase, which accounts for the name of the circuit. The amplified collector currents combine in the center-tapped output transformer to produce a load current

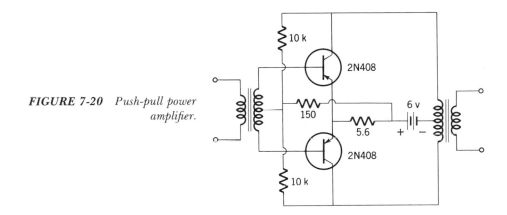

FIGURE 7-20 *Push-pull power amplifier.*

waveform that is a replica of the input signal. The input transformer also matches the driver stage to the input impedance of the amplifier.

Increased efficiency results when the push-pull amplifier is biased for class-B operation. Because each transistor is biased near cutoff, the quiescent current is very small and the signal voltage and current excursions can be equal to the maximum permissible collector voltage and current, Fig. 7-21. Each tube delivers one-half of a sine-wave signal to the output transformer and the output waveform is preserved even though signal currents in each transistor represent only one-half of the input signal. This action has already been noted in the complementary-symmetry amplifier discussed in Chap. 6. In push-pull operation the peak output voltage can equal the maximum collector potential, which is the same as the dc collector supply voltage (see Fig. 7-21). Correspondingly, the peak signal current is equal to the maximum collector current. The average power of the stage is equal to the power of a half-sine wave, since only one tube conducts at a time. Therefore, the efficiency of a class-B push-pull amplifier is

$$\eta = \frac{P_o}{P_{dc}} = \frac{(V_c/\sqrt{2})(I_c\sqrt{2})}{(2/\pi)V_cI_c} = \frac{\pi}{4} \qquad (7\text{-}20)$$

According to Eq. (7-20), the maximum efficiency is 78 percent, a considerable improvement over the single-transistor class-A amplifier.

The required power output P_o of any push-pull amplifier is specified by the particular application. The peak output-signal voltage is limited by the collector reverse breakdown potential V_c, however, which means that the collector-to-collector load resistance must be

$$R_L = \frac{V_c^2}{2P_o} \tag{7-21}$$

It usually turns out that the value of R_L determined by Eq. (7-21) is smaller than the output impedance of the transistors, and maxi-

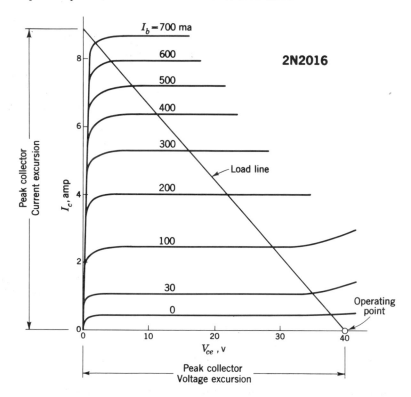

FIGURE 7-21 *Operating point for class-B push-pull operation permits voltage to swing over maximum range of collector characteristics.*

mum power transfer conditions are not possible. Nevertheless, the turns ratio of the output transformer is selected to reflect the proper value of R_L corresponding to the actual load resistance.

A small quiescent base bias current minimizes *crossover* distortion resulting from nonlinearity in the transfer characteristic of each transistor at small currents. This is illustrated in Fig. 7-22, where the transfer characteristics of the two transistors are plotted in opposite quadrants corresponding to their reversed signal polarities. The composite transfer characteristic of the entire amplifier is the average of the individual curves and is much more linear than either one. In particular, the nonlinearities cancel each other near the origin where both transistors are active. The cancellation effect means that the push-pull circuit has much less distortion than a single-ended stage. For this reason class-A push-pull amplifiers are often used, even though the power efficiency is no greater than that of the single-tube circuit.

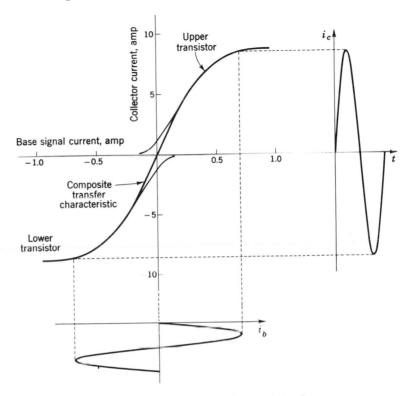

FIGURE 7-22 *Composite transfer characteristic of push-pull power amplifier is more linear than that associated with each transistor. Compare output-signal current amplitude and waveform with single transistor case, Fig. 7-19.*

Transistors are so inherently temperature-sensitive that it is necessary to compensate for temperature changes which tend to alter the bias current. This situation is compounded in class-B power amplifiers where a rather critical value of bias is necessary to maintain class-B conditions. According to Eq. (6-25), the emitter resistance of a transistor decreases significantly with increasing temperature, which means that for a constant base bias the transistor may be near class-C operation at low temperatures and class-A operation at high temperatures. A temperature-sensitive resistor can be included in the bias circuit to counteract this undesirable variation. In the practical circuit of Fig. 7-23, a silicon diode D_1 performs this function. The changes in D_1 with temperature correspond exactly to those of the emitter junction of the transistor. The value of resistor R_1 in the bias network is chosen to keep D_1 biased in the forward direction under all conditions.

Alternatively, temperature compensation can be achieved by making resistor R_1 temperature-sensitive. In this case R_1 has a positive temperature coefficient and base bias is reduced at elevated temperatures.

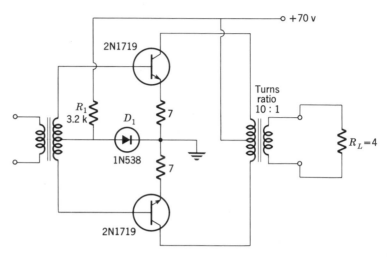

FIGURE 7-23 *A 5-watt power amplifier using diode in bias circuit to compensate for temperature changes.*

Note that the emitter resistors are not bypassed in the circuit of Fig. 7-23. The reason for this is the clamping action at the rectifying emitter junction, which is inherent in class-B operation. The clamp would charge a bypass capacitor to the peak value of the input signal and thereby maintain the transistor at cutoff at all times. The loss in gain resulting from the unbypassed emitter resistors is usually not serious, in view of the considerable improvement in bias stability achieved. Emitter bypass capacitors are permissible in class-A operation since both transistors conduct continuously.

Vacuum-tube circuits equivalent to the transistor versions are equally useful. In particular, consider the push-pull pentode amplifier illustrated in Fig. 7-24. Here the out-of-phase grid signals are provided by a single-tube *phase inverter*, which performs the same function as the difference amplifier discussed in Chap. 5. It is usually not necessary to use an input transformer in vacuum-tube circuits because of the high input impedance. Although pentodes are commonly used as power amplifiers, triodes are also satisfactory because distortions tend to cancel in the push-pull circuit. Nevertheless, the power efficiency of vacuum-tube power amplifiers is not as high as is the case for transistors.

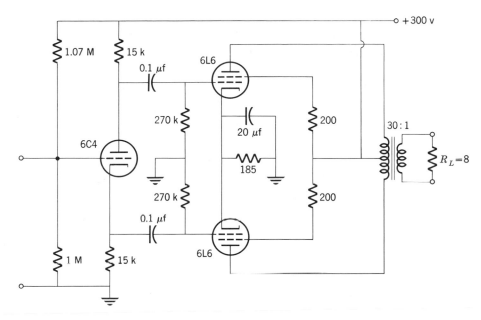

FIGURE 7-24 *Push-pull pentode power amplifier using phase-inverter driving stage.*

TUNED AMPLIFIERS

7-7 Tuned coupling

Resonant circuits couple the output of one stage to the input of the next when it is only necessary to amplify signals of a single frequency or of a narrow band of frequencies. The impedance of parallel resonant circuits is very great at resonance, as discussed in Chap. 3. Therefore, appreciable gain is achieved at the resonant frequency when a *tuned circuit* is the load impedance of a vacuum-tube or transistor amplifier. A tuned amplifier also rejects signals far from the resonant frequency, which is often a considerable advantage. In addition, stray circuit capacitances are incorporated into the resonant circuit and do not shunt the signal at high frequencies.

The elementary two-stage transistor tuned amplifier, Fig. 7-25, uses parallel resonant circuits for the input circuit and output load of each transistor. The coupling capacitor C_c carries the signal from one stage to the next. The operating point for each transistor is determined in the standard fashion. It is common practice to make the tuning capacitors C_1, C_2, C_3, and C_4 adjustable so that each circuit can be brought to the same resonant frequency including the effect of all stray capacitances in each stage. Tuned circuits are resistive at resonance, which means that the amplifier can be analyzed by the methods previously developed. Stray capacities can be neglected, however, and values of the h parameters appropriate at the frequency of interest must be used.

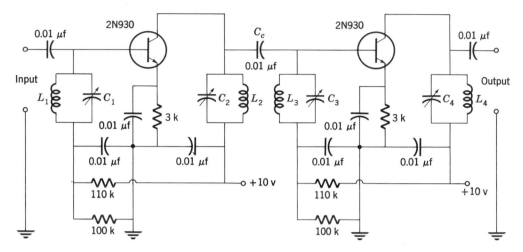

FIGURE 7-25 *Two-stage tuned amplifier.*

Circuit analysis at other than the resonant frequency is rather complicated because of reactance effects, but can be treated straightforwardly using the ac equivalent circuit.

If all four resonant circuits are tuned to the same frequency, the response characteristic is sharply peaked at the resonant frequency, Fig. 7-26 (also see Exercise 7-13). Such a characteristic is useful

FIGURE 7-26 *Response characteristic of sharply tuned amplifier.*

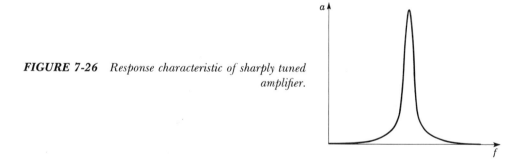

when signals having one specific frequency are amplified. Alternatively, each circuit can be tuned to a slightly different frequency, Fig. 7-27, in which case the response characteristic becomes flat-topped. This permits amplification over a band of frequencies such as for the modulated sine wave discussed in Chap. 4. The midband gain of such a *stagger-tuned* amplifier is less than that of the single-frequency circuit since the maximum amplification of each stage occurs at different frequencies.

If L_2 and L_3 are wound on the same core the response characteristic may be double-peaked, Fig. 7-28, even though both primary and secondary windings are tuned to the center frequency. This is caused by mutual inductance between the windings, which are said to be *overcoupled*. The mutual inductance is altered by chang-

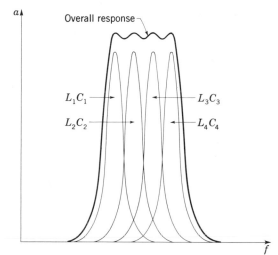

FIGURE 7-27 *Stagger-tuned amplifier has response characteristic with relatively flat top.*

ing the distance between the two coils. In this way the frequency-response curve is either sharply peaked, as in Fig. 7-26, or relatively flat-topped, as in Fig. 7-28. The overcoupled case is

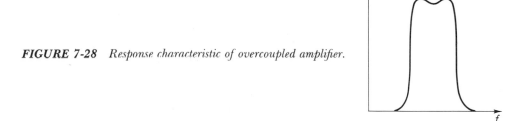

FIGURE 7-28 *Response characteristic of overcoupled amplifier.*

particularly useful because the midband gain is greater than in the stagger-tuned amplifier and the sides of the response curve rise much more steeply. The circuit thus rejects signals at frequencies immediately outside of the passband. Note that the coupling capacitor is no longer necessary since the signal is coupled from one stage to the next by the mutual inductance. In fact, the combination L_2C_2 and L_3C_3 is looked upon as a tuned transformer.

7-8 Neutralization

The collector-junction capacitance in many transistors is large enough to cause an undesirable feedback effect between the collector and base. At high frequencies the capacitive reactance becomes small and the amplifier oscillates because the amplified collector signal is returned to the input where it is reamplified, etc. The circuit is useless as an amplifier when this occurs. The effect of the collector capacitance can be *neutralized* by feeding the base a signal of the same amplitude as that produced by the feedback capacitance but 180° out of phase so that the two feedback signals cancel each other. One technique for accomplishing this is illustrated in Fig. 7-29. Here, a portion of the output signal is fed back

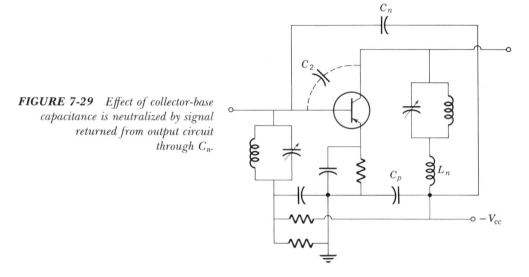

FIGURE 7-29 *Effect of collector-base capacitance is neutralized by signal returned from output circuit through C_n.*

to the input by the neutralizing capacitor C_n. The magnitude of the return signal is determined by the relative values of the small series inductance L_n and the capacitor C_p, as well as the value of C_n. The return signal is 180° out of phase with that due to the collector capacitance because of the inductive phase shift introduced by the series inductance. Other circuit configurations are also used. In transistor design, every effort is made to minimize collector capacitance so that neutralization is unnecessary.

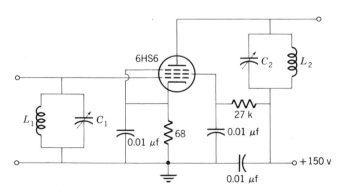

FIGURE 7-30 *Pentode tuned amplifier.*

A similar effect occurs in a triode vacuum tube because of the grid-plate capacitance. For this reason pentodes are almost universally used in preference to triodes as high-frequency amplifiers except for certain very-high-power class-C stages. A typical tuned amplifier stage employing a pentode is illustrated in Fig. 7-30. Analysis of the circuit using the equivalent circuit is quite direct (see Exercise 7-14).

The feedback effect in transistor amplifiers can be circumvented by employing the grounded-base configuration, Fig. 7-31. In this

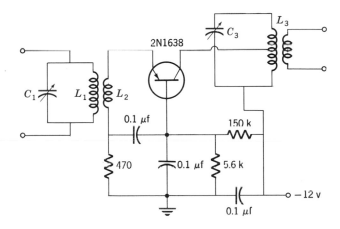

FIGURE 7-31   *Grounded-base tuned amplifier.*

circuit the collector-emitter capacitance is so small that neutralization is unnecessary. Furthermore, the grounded-base h parameters are relatively independent of frequency so that the transistor is a useful amplifier at frequencies very close to the α-cutoff frequency. The low input impedance of the grounded-base stage can be matched using a tuned transformer. The winding L_2 has only a few turns, and it is usually not advantageous to resonate the secondary of the transformer.

In the circuit of Fig. 7-31, the collector is tapped down on the inductance of the resonant circuit L_3C_3. This reduces the loading of the transistor output impedance upon the resonant circuit, thereby increasing the Q and making the resonance curve sharper. Furthermore, the collector capacitance is much less significant in determining the resonant frequency. This is important because of the change in collector capacitance with temperature. If the collector is connected across the entire resonant circuit, the collector capacitance is effectively in parallel with the tuning capacitor C_3 and the resonance frequency varies with temperature.

NOISE

Any spurious currents or voltages extraneous to the signal of interest are termed *noise* since they interfere with the signal. Noise voltages arise in the basic operation of electronic devices or are the result of improper circuit design and use. It is important to minimize noise effects in order to characterize the signals with the greatest possible precision and to permit the weakest signals to be amplified. A convenient measure of the influence of noise on any signal is the *signal-to-noise* ratio, the ratio of the signal power to the noise power at any point in a circuit.

7-9   Nyquist noise

When a number of amplifier stages are cascaded a random noise voltage appears at the output terminals, even in the absence of an input signal. This output voltage is caused by a random voltage generated in the input resistor. The noise voltages that appear across the terminals of any resistor are attributed to the random motion of the free electrons in the material of the resistance. Electrons in a conductor are free to roam about by virtue of their thermal energy and at any given instant more electrons may be directed toward one terminal of the resistor than toward the other. The result is a small potential difference between the terminals. The magnitude of the potential fluctuates rapidly as the number of electrons moving in a given direction changes from instant to instant.

Since the noise voltage across a resistor fluctuates randomly, it has Fourier components covering a wide range of frequencies. It is convenient, therefore, to specify the noise voltage in terms of the mean square noise voltage per unit cycle of bandwidth. For a resistor R this quantity is

$$\langle \Delta v^2 \rangle = 4kTR \tag{7-22}$$

where k is Boltzmann's constant, and T is the absolute temperature. The noise voltage given by Eq. (7-22) is variously called *Nyquist noise*, after the physicist who derived this equation, or *thermal noise*, since its origin is a result of the thermal agitation of free electrons.

The meaning of Eq. (7-22) is as follows. A noise voltage appears between the terminals of any resistance. The magnitude of the noise voltage actually measured with any instrument depends upon the frequency response of the instrument. For example, the rms noise voltage of a 1000-Ω resistor at room temperature as measured by a voltmeter with a bandwidth of 10,000 cps is, using Eq. (7-22),

$$v = (1.65 \times 10^{-20} \times 10^3 \times 10^4)^{1/2} = 4.1 \times 10^{-7} = 0.41 \ \mu v \qquad (7\text{-}23)$$

This rather small voltage is not inconsequential. For example, the output voltage of an amplifier with a 10-kc bandpass and a gain of 10^6 is nearly $\frac{1}{2}$ volt if the input resistor is 1000 Ω. This output voltage is present even when no input signal is applied.

The Nyquist expression for the noise voltage of resistances, Eq. (7-22), may be understood in the following way. Replace the actual resistor by an equivalent circuit, Fig. 7-32, containing a noise volt-

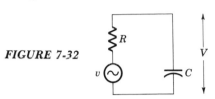

FIGURE 7-32

age generator in series with a noiseless resistor and in parallel with a capacitor representing the inherent stray capacitance of the actual resistor. The square of the voltage across the capacitor is simply

$$V^2 = \frac{v^2}{1 + (\omega RC)^2} \qquad (7\text{-}24)$$

The condition of the circuit is completely determined if the voltage across the capacitor is known; in thermodynamic terms the circuit is a system with 1 degree of freedom. According to the equipartition theorem in thermodynamics, the total energy of the capacitor, therefore, must equal $\frac{1}{2}kT$. Thus, using Eq. (7-24),

$$\tfrac{1}{2}kT = \tfrac{1}{2}CV^2 = \tfrac{1}{2}C \int_0^\infty \frac{v^2 df}{1 + (\omega RC)^2} \qquad (7\text{-}25)$$

where the result of Exercise 2-16 for the energy of a charged capacitor has been employed. The integration extends over all frequencies because of the random nature of the noise voltage.

Equation (7-25) determines the magnitude of the noise voltage v^2. We proceed by assuming that the noise voltage is independent of frequency, so v^2 may be brought out from under the integral sign. Therefore, Eq. (7-25) becomes

$$kT = Cv^2 \int_0^\infty \frac{df}{1 + (\omega RC)^2} = \frac{v^2}{4R} \qquad (7\text{-}26)$$

Solving Eq. (7-26) for v^2 yields the Nyquist expression.

This development indicates that the noise voltage of resistances is independent of frequency. Accordingly, Nyquist noise is called "white" noise by analogy with the uniform spectral distribution of white light energy. As indicated by Fig. 7-32, the presence of Nyquist noise in any circuit is accounted for by including a noise generator given by Eq. (7-22) in series with a noiseless resistor. In practice it is usually necessary to consider the Nyquist noise of only those resistors in the input circuit of an amplifier. The gain of the first stage makes the amplified noise of the input resistor larger than the noise of resistors in succeeding stages.

Nyquist noise is a fundamental and unavoidable property of any resistance. An amplifier should have a bandwidth only as wide as is necessary to adequately amplify all signal components in order to minimize the ever-present Nyquist noise voltages. If it is desired to amplify a single-frequency signal, for example, the frequency response of the amplifier should be sharply peaked at that frequency, as in Fig. 7-26. The total noise voltage at the output is therefore reduced since only noise components having frequencies in the amplifier passband are amplified. The signal-to-noise ratio is enhanced and weak signals can be amplified usefully.

7-10   1/*f* noise

Noise voltages in excess of Nyquist noise are observed experimentally in certain resistances when a direct current is present. Although the physical origins of this additional noise are not clear, many experiments have shown that the noise is largest at low frequencies and that it increases with the square of the current. An empirical expression for this effect is

$$\langle \Delta v^2 \rangle = K \frac{I^2}{f} \qquad\qquad (7\text{-}27)$$

where K is an empirical constant involving the geometry of the resistor, the type of resistance material, and other factors; I is the dc current; and f is the frequency. According to Eq. (7-27) the mean square noise voltage per unit bandwidth decreases inversely with frequency and the phenomenon is therefore called *1/f noise*. Since the noise also depends on I, it is sometimes referred to as *current noise*.

The magnitude of 1/*f* noise varies markedly with the material of the conductor and its physical form. It is absent entirely in metals, so that only Nyquist noise is observed in wire-wound resistors. Composition resistors, on the other hand, generate a large 1/*f* noise level, Fig. 7-33, which is associated with the intergranular contacts in such resistors. Although such contacts are known to be important, 1/*f* noise is also observed in single-crystal semiconductors where contact effects are negligible.

To minimize the low-frequency noise level, resistor types in which the 1/*f* noise is small, such as wire-wound units, are selected. Fortunately, at high frequencies where wire-wound resistors are unsuitable because of their inductance, the 1/*f* noise of composition resistors is usually negligible compared with Nyquist noise. In other situations the direct current in noisy components is minimized to reduce the current noise generated. The total current noise voltage in any given circuit is found by integrating Eq. (7-27) over the frequency response characteristic of the amplifier.

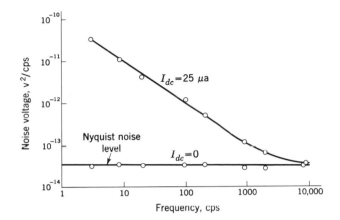

FIGURE 7-33 *Experimental noise voltage of 2.2-MΩ composition resistor. Note spectrum is 1/f noise when dc current is present and white Nyquist noise in absence of current.*

Low-frequency $1/f$ noise is also present in vacuum tubes and transistors. In the former it is often known as *flicker noise* and originates in the semiconducting cathode material, particularly at the emitting surface. The noise in transistors results from semiconductor properties, in which surface conditions are very important. In general, $1/f$ noise is more prevalent in germanium devices than in silicon units.

7-11   Noise in tubes and transistors

Other noise effects are also present in tubes and transistors. *Shot noise* in vacuum tubes is a result of the random emission of electrons from the cathode. Since each electron represents an increment of current, the plate current fluctuates slightly about the dc value. This effect is analogous to the noise of raindrops on a tin roof. That is, the basic reason for shot noise is that the electron is a discrete unit of electrical charge.

An expression for the magnitude of shot noise can be developed as follows. Suppose that n is the average number of electrons emitted from the cathode in a time interval t. The direct current is then, from Eq. (1-10),

$$I = \frac{en}{t} \qquad\qquad (7\text{-}28)$$

According to a general principle of statistical phenomena the variance in n is equal to its average value, so that

$$\langle \Delta n^2 \rangle = n = \frac{It}{e} \qquad (7\text{-}29)$$

Therefore, the current fluctuations in the time interval t are

$$\langle \Delta I^2 \rangle = \left(\frac{e}{t}\right)^2 \langle \Delta n^2 \rangle = \frac{e}{t} I \qquad (7\text{-}30)$$

Finally, it can be shown that the relation between the total fluctuations in a given time interval and the mean square fluctuation per unit bandwidth is given by

$$\langle \Delta i^2 \rangle = 2t \langle \Delta I^2 \rangle \qquad (7\text{-}31)$$

Introducing Eq. (7-30), the current fluctuations are

$$\langle \Delta i^2 \rangle = 2eI \qquad (7\text{-}32)$$

The quantity $\langle \Delta i^2 \rangle$ is analogous to $\langle \Delta v^2 \rangle$ in the Nyquist expression, Eq. (7-22), except that the noise is expressed here in terms of current fluctuations. The mean square noise voltage output of a tube is simply Eq. (7-32) multiplied by the square of the load resistance. Note that shot noise is a white noise since the right side of Eq. (7-32) is independent of frequency.

The basic expression for shot noise, Eq. (7-32), applies to the situation in which each electron emitted from the cathode proceeds to the anode independently of all other electrons. As discussed in Chap. 4 in connection with Child's law, this is not the case in practical vacuum tubes. Each electron is influenced by the presence of all the others. The result of this interaction is to make the electron current more uniform and thereby reduce the magnitude of shot noise. It turns out that the actual value is a function of the operating point. A full analysis of this effect is complicated because it depends upon subtle details of the emission current and electric field.

It is convenient to express the effective shot noise in terms of the Nyquist noise of an equivalent resistor in the grid circuit. The magnitude of the equivalent noise resistor in the case of a triode is given by

$$R_{neq} = \frac{2.5}{g_m} \,\Omega \; (g_m \text{ in micromhos}) \qquad (7\text{-}33)$$

The meaning of R_{neq} is simply that the effective shot noise of the triode can be represented by a noise voltage generator in the grid circuit given by the Nyquist expression, Eq. (7-22), using the resistance value determined from Eq. (7-33). Therefore, the appropriate equivalent circuit, Fig. 7-34, includes two noise generators, one associated with Nyquist noise of the grid resistor and the other associated with the effective shot noise of the tube. According to

Eq. (7-33), the effective shot noise is smallest for tubes having a large mutual transconductance and is of the order of 250 Ω for the lowest-noise triodes listed in Table 5-1. The internal noise

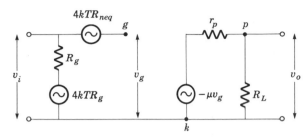

FIGURE 7-34 *Equivalent circuit of triode including noise generators.*

as a function of frequency for typical triodes is illustrated in Fig. 7-35. In these curves the output noise level is referred to a noise voltage generator in the grid circuit. Any contribution due to the

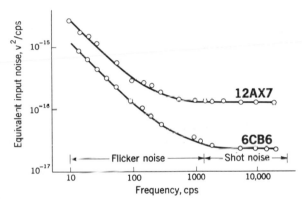

FIGURE 7-35 *Experimental internal noise levels of 12AX7 triode and triode-connected (screen tied to plate) 6CB6. Note flicker noise at low frequencies and white shot noise at high frequencies.*

grid resistor has been eliminated simply by shorting the grid to ground. The flicker-noise and shot-noise regions can be easily discerned.

Noise voltages are treated by including noise voltage generators in the equivalent circuits. The effect of the amplifier passband, which may be determined by stray shunt capacitance or by tuned circuits, is included in assessing the magnitude of the noise voltages. The noise resulting from each generator may be treated separately since random noise voltages are independent. The total output noise voltage is therefore simply the sum of all noise effects. As mentioned previously, it is not necessary to consider the noise of the resistors r_p and R_L in Fig. 7-34 because the amplified noise of the input circuit is much larger than the Nyquist noise of these resistors.

An expression analogous to Eq. (7-32) applies to each electrode in pentode and other multigrid tubes where the appropriate value of current to each electrode is used. The total noise is the sum of the individual electrode noises, suitably modified by the internal conditions. The sum is known as *partition noise* since the total tube current is divided among several electrodes. Pentodes are therefore noisier than triodes and the latter are universally used when it is necessary to obtain the largest possible signal-to-noise ratio. Note that this applies principally to the input stage of an amplifier. The gain of the first stage increases the signal level sufficiently so that noise effects in succeeding stages are negligible. The signal-to-noise ratio of any circuit is determined primarily by conditions in the first amplifier stage.

The input signal to any circuit has associated with it a given signal-to-noise ratio since Nyquist noise corresponding to the source resistance is present, at least. An ideal amplifier amplifies the incoming signal and the incoming noise equally and introduces no additional noise. Therefore, the original signal-to-noise ratio is preserved at the output. Practical amplifiers are not ideal because of Nyquist noise of the input circuit and shot noise of the first stage. A useful figure of merit for any circuit is the *noise figure, NF*, which is defined as the input signal-to-noise ratio divided by the output signal-to-noise ratio. An ideal amplifier has a noise figure of unity and many practical circuits approach this value fairly closely.

The noise of transistors is a result of Nyquist noise of the semiconductor resistance, $1/f$ noise caused by current in the semiconductor crystal, and shot noise of carriers crossing the junctions. In addition, still another noise phenomenon has been observed in semiconductors. Electrons are promoted randomly from the valence band to the conduction band and also return randomly to the valence band, keeping the proper average number of carriers in each band. Random generation and recombination of carriers is caused by thermal energies and produces a conductivity fluctuation of the semiconductor. This generates a noise voltage when a direct current is present; this second type of current noise in semiconductors is termed *generation-recombination*, or *g-r noise*.

Analysis of noise phenomena in transistors is complicated by these many factors and by the inherent input-output coupling. It turns out that at intermediate frequencies the noise figure of a transistor can be expressed as

$$\text{NF} = 1 + \frac{r_b}{R_s} + \frac{r_e}{2R_s} + \frac{(R_s + r_b + r_e)^2}{2h_{fe}r_e R_s} \tag{7-34}$$

where R_s is the source resistance and the other symbols have their usual meaning. According to Eq. (7-34) the noise figure approaches unity if the emitter and base resistances are small with respect to the source resistance and if the forward current gain h_{fe} is large. Note that the internal noise of a transistor depends upon the operating point, much as is the case for a vacuum tube.

Equation (7-34) ignores $1/f$ noise, which increases the noise level at low frequencies, Fig. 7-36. Additionally, an increase in noise at frequencies of the order of the α-cutoff frequency is observed. The latter effect, also apparent in Fig. 7-36, can be quite well explained on the basis of the influence of current gain and the α-cutoff frequency upon g-r noise.

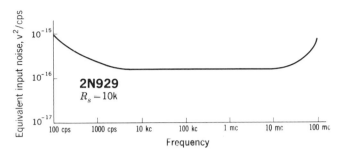

FIGURE 7-36 Experimental internal noise level of a type 2N929 transistor with a source resistance of 10,000 Ω.

7-12 Stray pickup

Noise is often introduced in practical circuits by extraneous voltage signals coupled into the circuit from the surroundings. The most common source of this noise comes from the 60-cps electric and magnetic fields produced by power mains. The 60-cps signal induced by these fields is called *hum* because it is audible as a low-frequency tone in amplifiers connected to a loudspeaker. Other *stray pickup* may result from electric fields generated by nearby electronic equipment, electric motors, lightning discharges, etc.

It is useful to *shield* those portions of a circuit where the signal level is small and, consequently, where noise voltages are most troublesome. Electric fields induce noise voltages capacitively, so it is only necessary to surround the circuit with a grounded conducting shield in order to reduce stray pickup. This is illustrated schematically in Fig. 7-37, where the capacitive coupling to external sources in Fig. 7-37a is interrupted by interposing a grounded conductor, Fig. 7-37b. Such shielding is also effective in reducing so-called *crosstalk* between different stages of the same circuit as, for example, between the input stage and the power output stage of a complete amplifier.

Additionally, it is useful to shield a circuit to minimize induced currents resulting from stray magnetic fields. This is accomplished with high-permeability ferromagnetic enclosures which reduce the intensity of the magnetic field inside. Such shielding is never complete because of the properties of ferromagnetic materials, and it is always advantageous to minimize the area of the circuit by using the shortest possible signal leads. According to

Eq. (2-66) the induced voltage in any circuit resulting from changing magnetic fields decreases if the enclosed area of the circuit is
reduced. Transformers are particularly troublesome with respect

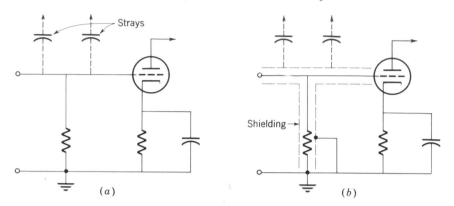

FIGURE 7-37   (a) *Stray capacitive coupling introduces
noise pickup signals into sensitive circuits. (b) Grounded
conductor shields the circuit from surroundings.*

to inductive pickup because of their many turns of wire. They
are kept well removed from all power transformers because of the
strong magnetic fields generated by such units.

In general it is good practice to keep all circuits physically small
in order to minimize stray pickup, crosstalk, and stray capacitance.
All grounded components, such as bypass capacitors, pertaining
to a given stage are returned to a single point. This reduces so-
called *ground loops,* which are current paths through the metal
chassis on which electronic circuits are often mounted. If all components of one stage are not grounded at the same point, the currents may cause undesirable signal coupling between stages.

Vacuum tubes are also *microphonic* in that noise voltages are
generated by movement of the grid wires caused by mechanical
vibration or shock. Transistors are much superior in this respect
because of their simpler mechanical construction. On the other
hand, the lower impedance level in transistor circuits makes them
more susceptible to induced magnetic pickup because the induced
currents are larger. Hum may also result from an inadequate
power-supply filter or the ac heater-current wires. It is common
practice to twist heater-current wires tightly together to reduce the
net magnetic field from the current. In very sensitive circuits hum
pickup from this source is reduced by heating the cathodes of the
input stages with direct current.

When a number of individual electronic units are interconnected, shielded cable is used for all signal leads between units.
The shield is used as the ground lead, as illustrated in Fig. 7-38.
It is important that the entire system be grounded at only one
point, usually the input terminal. If each unit is grounded sepa-

rately, as shown by dashed lines in Fig. 7-38, large 60-cps currents can be induced in the circuit because of the large area encompassed. The current induced in loop A by stray 60-cps magnetic fields introduces a large stray pickup signal into the amplifier.

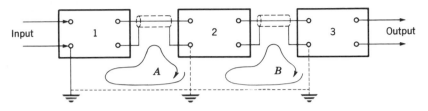

FIGURE 7-38   *When several electronic devices are connected, system must be grounded only at one point, preferably at input. Multiple grounds can lead to large ground-loop currents.*

Note that the capacitance between the central wire and its shield tends to shunt the signal at high frequencies. For this reason such cables are kept as short as possible. The circuit output impedance is also made small since this reduces the effect of shunt capacitance. Therefore, the output stage of many electronic circuits is a cathode or emitter follower.

SPECIAL CIRCUITS

7-13   Cascode amplifier

A unique circuit employing two identical triodes, shown in Fig. 7-39, combines the low-noise features of a triode with the superior high-frequency performance of a pentode. This *cascode amplifier*

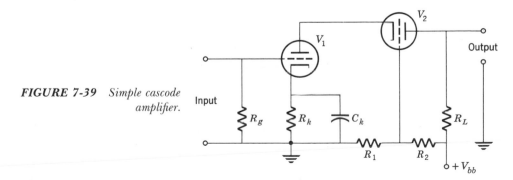

FIGURE 7-39   *Simple cascode amplifier.*

may be thought of as a grounded-cathode stage followed by a grounded-grid amplifier. The low input impedance of the second stage effectively eliminates feedback caused by the grid-plate capacitance of the first tube while retaining the low-noise feature of a triode. The grid-plate capacitance of V_2 is unimportant because the grid is effectively grounded for ac signals. The voltage divider R_1R_2 sets the grid voltage of V_2 while cathode bias is employed for V_1. The operating point is most easily found by a series of successive approximations starting with an assumed plate current and calculating the resulting V_1 grid potential. If this value does not correspond to the assumed current as given by the plate characteristics, a new current value is selected and the process repeated until a satisfactory match is obtained.

The pentode-like action of the cascode amplifier is illustrated by analyzing the ac equivalent circuit (Exercise 7-19). The gain of the circuit is given by

$$a = -\frac{\mu(\mu + 1)R_L}{R_L + (\mu + 2)r_p} \tag{7-35}$$

If $(\mu + 2)r_p \gg R_L$ and $\mu \gg 1$, Eq. (7-35) reduces to

$$a = -g_m R_L \tag{7-36}$$

which is identical to the gain of a pentode amplifier, Eq. (5-21).

The cascode amplifier is most often used at high frequencies where triode grid-plate capacitance is troublesome. Also, R_g and R_L can be replaced with parallel resonant circuits. Improved performance is obtained by connecting a variable inductance from grid to plate of V_1 and adjusting it for resonance with the grid-plate capacitance at the signal frequency. The high impedance of the resonant circuit further reduces the effect of the feedback capacitance.

7-14 Dc amplifiers

All the amplifier circuits discussed to this point have zero gain for dc signals because of the infinite reactance of the interstage coupling circuits at zero frequency. Amplification of dc or very slowly varying signals is achieved by eliminating the interstage coupling networks entirely. In addition to the dc response of such a *direct-coupled* amplifier, the high-frequency performance is also enhanced. Stray capacitances are reduced since fewer components are associated with the signal leads.

One of the problems of a direct-coupled amplifier is bringing the signal at the output of the first stage to the proper dc level for the next amplifier stage. This can be done, for example, with a Zener diode, as in the elementary dc amplifier of Fig. 7-40. The breakdown potential of the diode is selected so that the grid potential of the second stage is at the proper value. Since the voltage drop across the Zener diode is constant, variations in the plate voltage of V_1 resulting from a signal applied to the grid are transmitted to the grid of V_2. It is also possible to replace the Zener diode with a battery, but this introduces undesirable bulk.

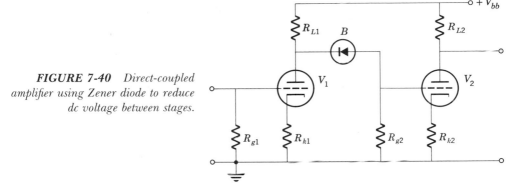

FIGURE 7-40   *Direct-coupled amplifier using Zener diode to reduce dc voltage between stages.*

This simple dc amplifier has a number of shortcomings. First, the output signal contains a quiescent dc voltage corresponding to the dc plate voltage of V_2. Second, any small change in the characteristics of V_1 is amplified by the second stage and is indistinguishable from a signal. The plate-supply voltage in all dc amplifiers must be stabilized to reduce *drift* in the circuit caused by slow changes of the electrode voltages. Drifts caused by variations in tube characteristics and supply voltages are minimized by using a balanced differential amplifier, Fig. 7-41. Changes in one side of

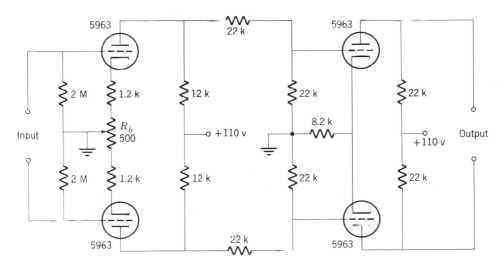

FIGURE 7-41   *Balanced dc amplifier.*

the circuit tend to be compensated by similar changes on the other side. Furthermore, the output terminals are at the same potential when the input signal is zero. The balance control R_b is included to adjust for any asymmetry in the circuit.

Interstage coupling in this amplifier uses a voltage divider to reduce the plate potential to a suitable value. This results in a signal loss, however, since the voltage divider acts on the signal voltage as well. Such amplifier circuits are commonly used in oscilloscopes where their dc response and good high-frequency performance are advantageous. It proves quite complicated to determine the quiescent conditions of such circuits because of the large number of interrelated voltages and currents involved. The method of successive approximations is most effective. The ac performance of the amplifier is analyzed by the equivalent-circuit technique in the usual fashion.

Direct-coupled transistor amplifiers are very susceptible to drift because of the temperature sensitivity of transistors. Differential circuits are most often used and careful temperature compensation is employed. Such circuits become fairly elaborate, but, nevertheless, quite successful designs are possible. One compensating feature of transistors is their ability to operate satisfactorily at collector potentials from a few tenths to many tens of volts; this permits a certain amount of flexibility in circuit design.

An elementary direct-coupled transistor amplifier employing *npn* and *pnp* transistors is shown in Fig. 7-42. The reversed-bias

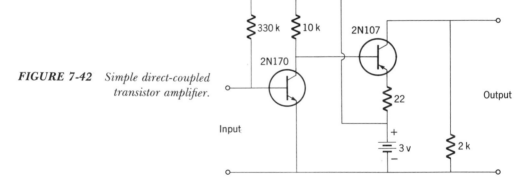

FIGURE 7-42 *Simple direct-coupled transistor amplifier.*

potentials inherent in the two transistor types is an example of the flexibility inherent in transistor circuits. This simple amplifier is useful to illustrate the principles of direct-coupled circuits but is not satisfactory for critical applications since no provision for compensation of drift caused by temperature changes, etc., is included. A more elaborate, practical version is considered in the next chapter.

7-15 Chopper amplifiers

To circumvent the drift and instabilities inherent in direct-coupled amplifiers, it is useful to convert the dc input signal to an ac voltage which can be amplified by a standard ac-coupled circuit. Subsequently, the amplifier output is rectified to recover the amplified dc input signal. The superior stability features of ac-coupled amplifiers provide much greater gains than are practical with dc amplifiers.

A convenient technique for converting a dc voltage to an ac signal is with a mechanical *chopper,* which is a rapidly vibrating switch driven by an electromagnet, Fig. 7-43. As the switch al-

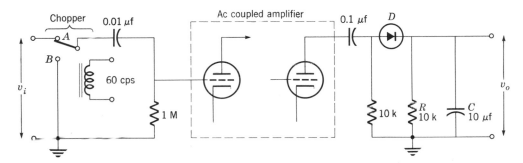

FIGURE 7-43   *Chopper amplifier using electromagnetically driven switch to convert input voltage to ac signal.*

ternately closes contact A and contact B, a square wave with an amplitude equal to the dc signal is produced. The frequency of the square wave corresponds to the chopping frequency. This is most often 60 cps, since it is convenient to drive the chopper from the power line. The amplifier is broadly tuned to the chopping frequency, which minimizes broad-band noise effects. A simple rectifier-filter combination attached to the amplified output results in a dc voltage corresponding to the amplified input signal.

Nonmechanical choppers employing diodes, transistors, vacuum tubes, SCRs, etc., are also used in various circuits. Consider, for example, the *balanced modulator* circuit, Fig. 7-44, which consists of four diodes arranged in a bridge. The chopping signal may be either a square-wave or a sine-wave signal at some convenient frequency. When the chopping voltage makes terminal A positive with respect to terminal B, diodes D_1 and D_2 are biased in the forward direction and diodes D_3 and D_4 are biased in the reverse direction. The small forward resistance of D_1 and D_2 means that the lower terminal of the input is effectively connected to the upper output terminal. On the alternate cycle of the chopping voltage, D_3 and D_4 conduct and the lower input terminal is connected to the lower output terminal. The result is a square wave with a peak-to-peak amplitude equal to twice the dc input signal.

In many applications the chopper amplifier must amplify a range of frequencies from dc to some high-frequency cutoff. The output voltage can then accurately reflect changes in the input signal. As a rule of thumb, the upper frequency limit of a chopper amplifier is about ¼ of the chopping frequency. Mechanical choppers are limited to 60 cps, although 400-cps units are occasion-

ally used.   Nonmechanical choppers, such as the balanced modulator, are useful because the chopping frequency can be much
higher.

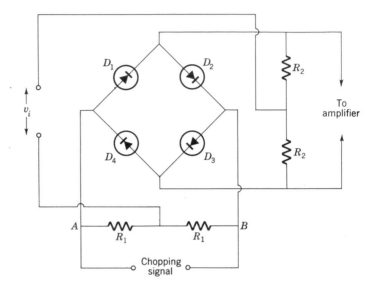

FIGURE 7-44   *Balanced modulator electronic chopper for use at high chopping frequencies.*

Mechanical choppers are most satisfactory for very-high-gain
dc amplification because they introduce minimum noise into the
circuit. Suppose, for example, that one of the four diodes of the
balanced modulator is slightly different from the other three. The
bridge is therefore slightly unbalanced and a portion of the
chopping signal appears at the amplifier terminals even when the
dc input signal is zero. This signal is amplified by the circuit and
appears as a noise voltage at the output. Similarly, other semiconductor and tube devices introduce switching noises to a greater
or lesser extent. The mechanical chopper has very small resistance
when the contacts are closed and very high resistance when the
contacts are open. It is nearly ideal in this respect. Nevertheless,
chopping noise limits the amplifier sensitivity at the very highest
gain applications. One source of noise is stray coupling between
the driving solenoid and the signal circuits.

A major advantage of chopper amplifiers is their very low effective internal random-noise level. The reason for this is the rectifier-filter combination in the output circuit. The output voltage
signal may be made as noise-free as desired by increasing the time
constant of the filter. In effect, the overall bandwidth of the system
is equal to the frequency interval from dc (zero cps) to $2/\pi\tau_0$,
where τ_0 is the filter time constant. If, for example, the time constant is 10 sec, the effective amplifier bandwidth is 0.016 cps, a very

small value indeed. Since the total noise voltage increases with bandwidth [compare Eqs. (7-22) and (7-27)], the total noise is very low. Of course, when τ_0 is 10 sec, a time interval of approximately 30 sec is required for the output voltage to reach its final value. Thus the amplifier responds very slowly to changes in the amplitude of the input signal. This reciprocity between bandwidth and response time is a general property of all electronic systems.

A major difficulty with the simple chopper amplifier is that the output voltage is independent of the polarity of the input signal. That is, the ac-coupled amplifier yields an ac output signal for either polarity of input voltage. This situation is corrected in chopper amplifiers which employ a second set of contacts to rectify the amplifier output, Fig. 7-45. The contacts are arranged to close

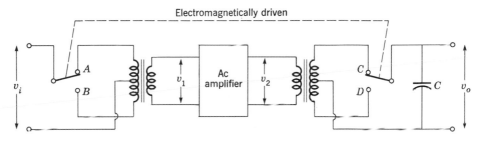

FIGURE 7-45 *Synchronous chopper amplifier preserves polarity of input voltage.*

synchronously so that as the input chopper converts the dc signal to a double-ended square wave, Fig. 7-46*a* and *b*, the output

FIGURE 7-46 *Waveforms in synchronous chopper amplifier: (a) dc input signal, (b) square-wave input to amplifier, (c) amplified square-wave output, and (d) rectified square wave produced by second chopper.*

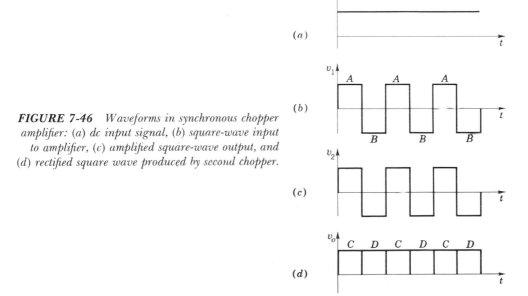

chopper reconverts the amplified square wave back to a dc signal, Fig. 7-46c and d. Comparing the waveforms in Fig. 7-46 shows that if v_i is positive, v_o is also positive. Similarly, if the input signal is negative, the output signal is also negative. Both sets of contacts are put on the same vibrating arm in practical synchronous choppers to assure that they open and close simultaneously. An electronic version of this *synchronous rectifier* is analyzed in the next section.

7-16 Lock-in amplifier

The principles of the synchronous chopper amplifier are employed in an electronic circuit which has found wide use in instrumentation systems. The version illustrated in Fig. 7-47 uses a

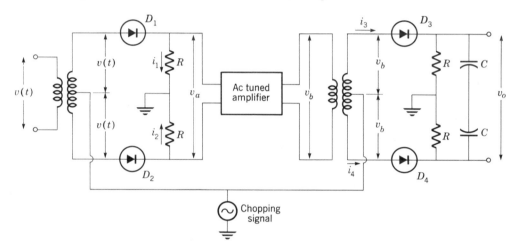

FIGURE 7-47 *Electronic synchronous chopper amplifier.*

diode modulator to convert the input signal to a form suitable for the amplifier and a diode demodulator to recover the amplified version of the input signal. For generality, we consider the input signal to be a slowly varying signal; if dc signals are important the input transformer can be replaced by a center-tapped resistor.

The input circuit is analyzed using techniques discussed in Chap. 4. It is assumed that the diode characteristic can be represented by a quadratic expression. Then the current in the diode D_1 is, from Eq. (4-37),

$$i_1 = a_1 v(t) + a_1 V_2 \sin \omega_2 t + a_2 v^2(t)$$

$$+ a_2 V_2^2 \sin^2 \omega_2 t + 2a_2 v(t) V_2 \sin \omega_2 t \qquad (7\text{-}37)$$

where a_1 and a_2 are constants related to the diode characteristic, $v_2 = V_2 \sin \omega_2 t$ corresponds to the chopping signal discussed earlier, and $v(t)$ is the input signal. An identical expression applies to the current in D_2, except that the polarity of $v(t)$ is reversed with respect to v_2. The voltage signal applied to the amplifier is

$$v_a = R(i_1 - i_2) \tag{7-38}$$

Substituting for i_1 and i_2, many terms cancel because of the reversed polarity of $v(t)$ in D_2. The result is

$$v_a = 2Ra_1v(t) + 4Ra_2v(t)V_2 \sin \omega_2 t \tag{7-39}$$

The first term in Eq. (7-39) is not transmitted by the amplifier since it is assumed that ω_2 is much larger than any of the frequency components associated with $v(t)$. Note that the second term is simply a modulated sine wave of frequency ω_2. The amplitude variations correspond to the input signal.

If the gain of the amplifier is k the signal applied to the demodulator circuit is

$$v_b = 4kRa_2v(t)V_2 \sin \omega_2 t \tag{7-40}$$

Ignoring the capacitors C for a moment, the current in D_3 is, again using Eq. (4-37),

$$i_3 = a_1v_b + a_1V_2 \sin \omega_2 t + a_2v_b{}^2 + a_2V_2{}^2 \sin^2 \omega_2 t + 2a_2v_bV_2 \sin \omega_2 t \tag{7-41}$$

The current in D_4 is similar except that the polarity of v_b with respect to v_2 is reversed. Consequently, the output voltage

$$v_o = R(i_3 - i_4) \tag{7-42}$$

reduces to

$$v_o = 2a_1Rv_b + 4a_2Rv_bV_2 \sin \omega_2 t$$
$$= 2a_1Rv_b + 16a_2{}^2kR^2v(t)V_2{}^2 \sin^2 \omega_2 t \tag{7-43}$$

Inserting the standard trigonometric identity $2 \sin^2 \omega t = 1 - \cos 2\omega t$,

$$v_o = 2a_1Rv_b + 8a_2{}^2kR^2V_2{}^2v(t)(1 - \cos 2\omega_2 t) \tag{7-44}$$

The filter capacitors eliminate the high-frequency terms in ω_2 and $2\omega_2$. Therefore, the filtered output signal is simply

$$v_o = (8a_2{}^2kR^2V_2{}^2)v(t) \tag{7-45}$$

According to Eq. (7-45) the output voltage is an amplified replica of the input signal.

The amplifier passband is conveniently peaked at ω_2 to minimize noise effects. Actually, however, the output filter circuit determines the effective bandwidth in the same way as for the chopper amplifier, and very-low-noise performance is possible. The minimum usable bandwidth depends upon the frequency components present in the signal $v(t)$.

In instrumentation applications it is often possible to produce the initial modulation in some way associated with the physical quantity being measured. For example, the infrared beam of an infrared spectrometer is chopped by means of a rotating shutter before it strikes the infrared detector. The amplified signal from the detector is demodulated by a circuit similar to Fig. 7-47 using a voltage v_2 derived from the shaft of the rotating shutter. The low-noise performance of the circuit permits extremely weak infrared signals to be detected. In this form the circuit is usually called a *lock-in amplifier*, since the detector is locked in step with the input signal. The system is also called a *phase-sensitive detector* because the circuit can recognize the phase of the input signal.

SUGGESTIONS FOR FURTHER READING

E. J. Angelo, Jr.: "Electronic Circuits," McGraw-Hill Book Company, New York, 1964.

Jack J. Studer: "Electronic Circuits and Instrumentation Systems," John Wiley & Sons, Inc., New York, 1963.

A. van der Ziel: "Noise," Prentice-Hall, Inc., Englewood Cliffs, N.J., 1954.

EXERCISES

7-1 Plot the frequency-response characteristics of the two-stage triode amplifier in Fig. 7-1. Assume $C_1 + C_3 = 50$ pf and $C_2 = 1.7$ pf. Use the small-signal parameters listed in Table 5-1.

7-2 Plot the frequency-response characteristics of the two-stage transistor amplifier in Fig. 7-3. Assume the output load resistance is 5000 Ω. The common-base h parameters for V_1 are: $h_{ib} = 50$ Ω, $h_{rb} = 300 \times 10^{-6}$, $h_{fb} = -0.99$, $h_{ob} = 0.2 \times 10^{-6}$ mho; for V_2: $h_{ib} = 11$ Ω, $h_{rb} = 600 \times 10^{-6}$, $h_{fb} = -0.99$, $h_{ob} = 0.72 \times 10^{-6}$ mho. Assume $C_1 + C_3 = 50$ pf and $C_2 = 8$ pf.

7-3 Plot the midband and high-frequency response of the first stage of the transistor amplifier of Fig. 7-3 if $C_{E1} = 5$ μf. Compare with the response when $C_{E1} = 50$ μf. Use h parameters given in Exercise 7-2 and assume the input impedance of V_2 is 1000 Ω.

7-4 Plot the midband and high-frequency response of the pentode amplifier in Fig. 7-13. Compare with the response of the amplifier without the inductance. Assume $C_1 + C_3 = 10$ pf and $g_m = 8 \times 10^{-3}$ mho.

7-5 Plot the low-frequency response of the transistor amplifier of Fig. 7-14. Compare with the response of the amplifier with R_3 and C_3 removed. Use values of h parameters given in Exercise 6-10.

7-6 Consider the class-A power amplifier, Fig. 7-16. Calculate the maximum power output for load resistances of 5, 10, 20, and 40 Ω, using the characteristic curves of Fig. 7-17. Calculate the power efficiency for each load.

7-7 Plot the dynamic transfer characteristic for each load resistance of the power amplifier studied in Exercise 7-6. Which load yields minimum distortion?

7-8 Determine the required reflected load impedance R'_L for a class-B push-pull power amplifier using 2N1415 type transistors if the output power is 0.3 watt and $V_{cc} = 6$ volts.   *Ans.*: 60 Ω

7-9 Plot the composite transfer characteristic of the amplifier of Exercise 7-8. Repeat if each transistor is biased to a quiescent base current of 0.2 ma.

7-10 Determine the composite transfer characteristics of the class-B power amplifier in Fig. 7-23. Assume that the quiescent current is 20 ma. Calculate the maximum power output. The characteristic curves of the 2N1719 are in Appendix 3.   *Ans.*: 6.1 watts

7-11 Plot the composite transfer characteristic of the push-pull pentode amplifier, Fig. 7-24. The characteristic curves are in Appendix 3. Calculate the maximum undistorted power output.

7-12 Sketch the equivalent circuit of the transistor tuned amplifier, Fig. 7-25. Calculate the peak gain assuming that the reactances of the tuned circuit are infinite at resonance. Use h parameters given in Exercise 6-10.   *Ans.*: 5.1×10^5

7-13 In the circuit studied in Exercise 7-12 comment on the relative Q value of L_1C_1 and L_3C_3 compared with that of L_2C_2 and L_4C_4. Plot the response characteristic of the amplifier assuming that the response is characterized principally by L_2C_2 and L_4C_4 and that $C_2 = C_4 = 200$ μf; $L_2 = L_4 = 5$ μh. Use the midband gain calculated in Exercise 7-12.

7-14 Draw the equivalent circuit of the pentode tuned amplifier, Fig. 7-30. Calculate the peak gain, assuming that the reactance of the tuned circuit is infinite at resonance. Take $r_p = 500$ kΩ and $g_m = 9500$ μmhos.   *Ans.*: 4.75×10^3

7-15 Suppose an amplifier with a bandpass from 10 cps to 100 kc and a gain of 10^5 uses a 1-MΩ input resistor. What is the rms noise output voltage?   *Ans.*: 4.1 volts

7-16 Determine the mean square noise voltage per unit bandwidth of two 100,000-Ω resistors in parallel. Repeat for a 10,000-Ω resistor in parallel with a 100,000-Ω resistor. Can you generalize on these results?

        Ans.: 8.26×10^{-16} volt^2/cycle; 1.5×10^{-16} volt^2/cycle

7-17 Repeat Exercise 7-15 if the input resistor is the carbon resistor of Fig. 7-33 and the direct current indicated is present.

        Ans.: 7.34 volts

7-18 With the aid of the equivalent circuit of Fig. 7-34 determine the minimum detectable input voltage (signal-to-noise ratio equal to unity) of the triode differential amplifier of Fig. 5-24. Assume the amplifier bandpass is 1 cps to 40 kc.   *Ans.*: 1.15×10^{-4} volt

7-19 Draw the equivalent circuit of the cascode amplifier, Fig. 7-39, and derive Eq. (7-35).

7-20 What is the minimum detectable input signal voltage of the chopper amplifier of Fig. 7-43, assuming chopper noise is negligible?

        Ans.: 1.62×10^{-7} volt

8
FEEDBACK AMPLIFIERS

The performance of transistor and vacuum-tube amplifiers is enhanced in many respects by returning a fraction of the output signal to the input terminals. This process is called feedback. The feedback signal may either augment the input signal or tend to cancel it. The latter, called negative feedback, is the primary concern of this chapter. Improved frequency-response characteristics and reduced waveform distortion are attained with negative feedback. In addition, amplifier performance is much less dependent upon changes in tube or transistor parameters caused by aging or temperature effects.

NEGATIVE FEEDBACK

The circuit alterations of a standard amplifier which return a portion of the output signal to the input may be analyzed by the techniques developed in previous chapters. It is more illustrative, however, to isolate the feedback portion of the circuit and treat it separately. Consider the feedback amplifier, Fig. 8-1, comprising

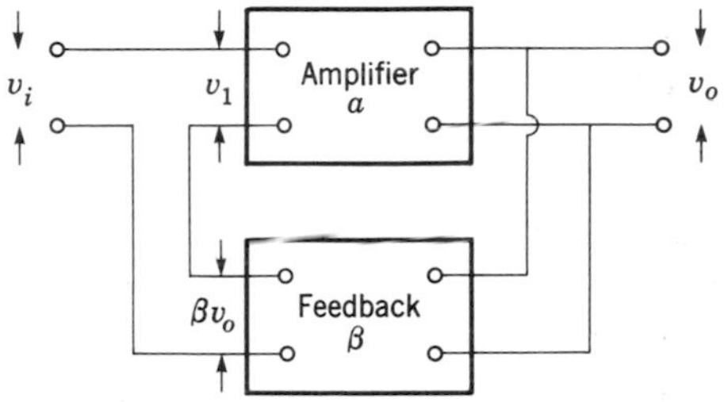

FIGURE 8-1 *Block diagram of feedback amplifier.*

a standard amplifier with a gain a and a feedback network indicated by the box marked β. According to this circuit, a voltage βv_o is added to the input signal v_i so that the total input signal to the amplifier is

$$v_1 = v_i + \beta v_o \tag{8-1}$$

Introducing the fact that $v_o = av_1$,

$$v_o = av_i + a\beta v_o \tag{8-2}$$

so that

$$v_o = \frac{a}{1 - \beta a} v_i \tag{8-3}$$

According to Eq. (8-3) the overall gain of the amplifier with feedback,

$$a' = \frac{a}{1 - \beta a} \tag{8-4}$$

may be greater or smaller than that of the amplifier alone, depending upon the algebraic sign of βa.

The condition of greatest interest in this chapter is *negative feedback*, when βa is a negative quantity. In this case, Eq. (8-4) shows that the overall gain is reduced because, in effect, the feedback voltage cancels a portion of the input signal. If the amplifier gain is very large, $a \gg 1$, the overall gain reduces to

$$a' = \frac{1}{\beta} \tag{8-5}$$

This shows that the gain depends only upon the properties of the feedback circuit. Most often, the feedback network is a simple combination of resistors and/or capacitors. Therefore, the gain is independent of variations in tube or transistor parameters in the amplifier. In addition to this desirable improvement in stability, the gain may be calculated from circuit values of the feedback network alone. Thus it is not necessary to know, for example, the *h* parameters of all transistors in the circuit.

Negative feedback is also effective in reducing waveform distortion in amplifiers. Waveform distortion results from a non-linear transfer characteristic, which may be interpreted as a smaller gain where the slope of the transfer characteristic is less, and as a larger gain where the slope of the transfer characteristic is greater. According to Eq. (8-5), however, the gain of an amplifier with feedback is essentially independent of variations caused by non-linearities in tube or transistor characteristics. Therefore, the transfer characteristic is more linear and distortion is reduced.

A quantitative measure of the reduction in distortion achieved with feedback is obtained by assuming that distortion signals can be represented by a voltage generator in the amplifier, Fig. 8-2.

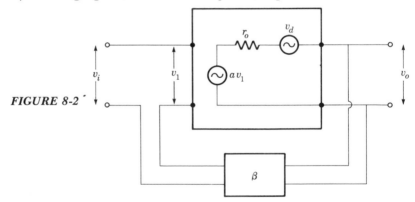

FIGURE 8-2

With this approximation the amplified signal av_1 is distortionless. As usual, r_o represents the internal impedance of the circuit as viewed from the output terminals of the amplifier. Under this condition, the output voltage

$$v_o = av_1 + v_d \qquad (8\text{-}6)$$

includes the distortion voltages v_d. Both the amplified signal and distortion voltages are fed back, so that the input to the amplifier is

$$v_1 = v_i + \beta(v_o + v_d) \qquad (8\text{-}7)$$

Introducing Eq. (8-7) into (8-6) and solving for output signal,

$$v_o = \frac{a}{1 - a\beta} v_i + \frac{1 + a\beta}{1 - a\beta} v_d \qquad (8\text{-}8)$$

The ratio of undistorted output signal to distortion voltages in the case of no feedback (where $v_1 = v_i$) is, from Eq. (8-6),

$$\left(\frac{S}{D}\right)_a = \frac{av_i}{v_d} \tag{8-9}$$

Including feedback, this ratio is, from Eq. (8-8),

$$\left(\frac{S}{D}\right)_f = \frac{a}{1 + a\beta} \frac{v_i}{v_d} \tag{8-10}$$

Comparing Eqs. (8-9) and (8-10),

$$\left(\frac{S}{D}\right)_f = \frac{1}{1 + a\beta} \left(\frac{S}{D}\right)_a \tag{8-11}$$

According to Eq. (8-11), feedback reduces the relative importance of distortion signals in the output by the factor $1 + a\beta$. Since $a\beta$ is a large number, this improvement is significant. In effect, feedback results in an amplified distortion signal that cancels the original distortion voltages to a large extent. This result is particularly useful in power amplifiers where transistors or tubes are used over the full range of their characteristics.

The benefits of negative feedback are obtained at the expense of reduced gain, according to Eq. (8-4). This is not a serious loss, however, because large amplifications are easily obtained in transistor and vacuum-tube circuits. In practice, the maximum usable gain is limited by random noise effects anyway and it is not difficult to achieve the maximum amplification that can be effectively used, even with feedback included.

The gain a and the feedback factor β are inherently complex numbers. That is, phase shifts associated with coupling capacitors and stray capacitance effects are present, particularly at frequencies outside of the passband of the amplifier. These phase shifts cause a departure from the 180° phase shift necessary for the feedback voltage to interfere destructively with the input signal. It can happen that the overall phase shift becomes zero (i.e., 360°) so that $a\beta$ is positive and the feedback voltage augments the input signal. This is called *positive feedback* and leads to serious instability effects in feedback amplifiers.

Note, particularly, that if $a\beta = +1$ the output voltage, Eq. (8-3), becomes very large, even in the absence of an input signal. This means that positive feedback may cause an amplifier to oscillate, as previously discussed in connection with the feedback effects of the grid-plate capacitance in triodes and the collector capacitance in transistors. Oscillation is deleterious in amplifiers since the output voltage is not a replica of the input signal. Positive feedback is, however, a useful condition in oscillator circuits, as discussed in the next chapter.

8-1 Voltage feedback

In the foregoing, a portion of the output voltage is returned to the input terminals, a condition referred to as *voltage feedback*. The two-stage transistor amplifier, Fig. 8-3, uses voltage feedback intro-

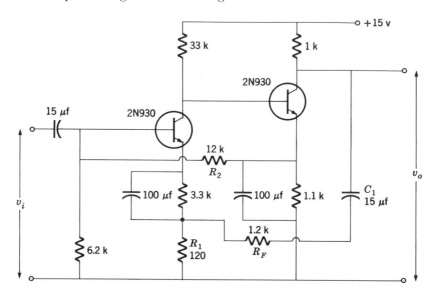

FIGURE 8-3 *Two-stage feedback amplifier. Feedback is determined by ratio R_1/R_F.*

duced by the resistor R_F connecting the output terminal with the input circuit of the first stage. The feedback voltage is introduced into the emitter circuit of the first stage because the output voltage of a two-stage amplifier is in phase with the input signal. The feedback factor is the result of the resistor divider made up of R_F and R_1, so that

$$\beta = \frac{R_1}{R_F + R_1} \cong \frac{R_1}{R_F} \qquad (8\text{-}12)$$

Capacitor C_1 isolates the dc components of the two stages. Also, note that dc interstage coupling is used in this amplifier, which is quite independent of negative-feedback considerations. Resistor R_2 sets the bias on the first stage and also provides a dc feedback effect which helps stabilize the dc-coupled amplifier against slow drifts. It is not part of the ac feedback circuit.

The effect of the feedback ratio on the frequency-response characteristic is illustrated in Fig. 8-4. Without feedback (resistor R_F removed) the midband gain of the amplifier is 1000 and the high-frequency cutoff is 100 kc. As feedback is increased by using smaller values of R_F the midband gain is reduced and the frequency response is extended to lower and higher frequencies. With a 1200-Ω feedback resistor the gain is 10 and the upper frequency cutoff is extended to 15 Mc. Under this condition β = 120/1200 = 0.1, so $a\beta = 100$. According to Eq. (8-5) the mid-band gain is $1/\beta$, in agreement with the experimental response

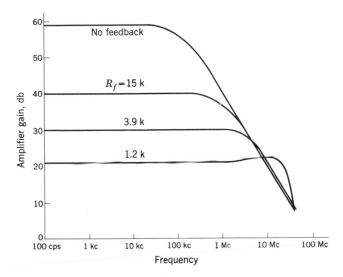

FIGURE 8-4 *Effect of feedback on response characteristic of amplifier in Fig. 8-3.*

curves, Fig. 8-4. Thus, a very stable wide-band amplifier is possible through the use of feedback.

Note that in Fig. 8-4 the gain increases at the extreme of the response curve when a large feedback ratio is used. This is a result of phase shift in the amplifier at these frequencies. In effect, the negative feedback is reduced since the feedback voltage is no longer exactly 180° out of phase with the input signal. The phase characteristic of feedback amplifiers at frequencies outside of the passband is very important. Such irregularities in the response curve should be small, particularly when large feedback ratios are employed. It is possible for the phase shifts to become great enough to cause positive feedback at the frequency extremes, a condition which must be avoided if the amplifier is to remain stable. This matter is considered further in a later section.

If the feedback circuit is frequency-selective, it is possible to develop a specific frequency-response characteristic for the amplifier. Consider, for example, an amplifier having a bridged-T feedback network in one stage, Fig. 8-5. In this circuit cathode followers are used to provide a high input impedance and a low output impedance so that the frequency-selective stage is isolated from disturbing influences of input and output loads. A difference amplifier is used in the first two stages to simplify coupling between stages in the presence of the feedback network.

Since the bridged-T filter is connected from plate to grid, the feedback voltage is 180° out of phase with the input signal, as required for negative feedback. According to the response curve of the bridged-T filter, Exercise 3-16, the feedback voltage is a minimum at the characteristic frequency of the filter. Accordingly, the

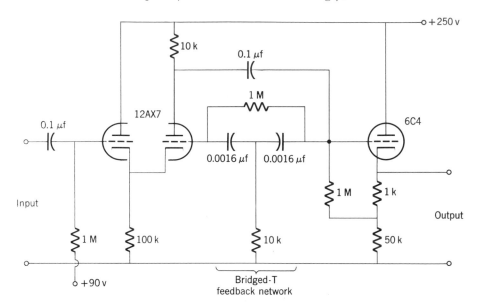

FIGURE 8-5 *Tuned amplifier using a frequency-selective feedback network consisting of bridged-T filter.*

amplifier gain is a maximum at this frequency and the result is a tuned amplifier. The feedback ratio β is a function of frequency because of the characteristics of the bridged-T filter, and the feedback effect considerably enhances the selectivity of the filter, as illustrated in Fig. 8-6.

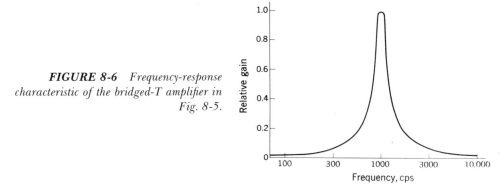

FIGURE 8-6 *Frequency-response characteristic of the bridged-T amplifier in Fig. 8-5.*

Feedback tuned amplifiers are commonly used at audio frequencies where high-Q inductances are difficult to construct because large values of inductance are required. Furthermore, it is a simple matter to tune the amplifier by making the resistors variable. This approach is also useful in integrated circuits where inductances are difficult to produce. Other frequency-selective feedback networks, such as the twin-T or Wien bridge, are also used in tuned feedback amplifiers.

Negative feedback alters the input and output impedance of an amplifier. To see how this comes about, replace the amplifier by its Thévenin equivalent, Fig. 8-7. The output impedance with feed-

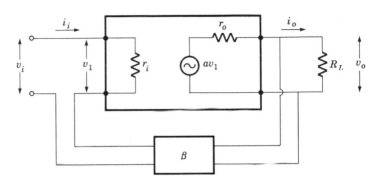

FIGURE 8-7 *Circuit to determine effective input and output impedance of amplifier with voltage feedback.*

back is determined from the ratio of the open-circuit output voltage to the short circuit output current. The open-circuit output voltage is, from Eq. (8-3),

$$(v_o)_{oc} = \frac{av_i}{1 - a\beta} \qquad (8\text{-}13)$$

The short-circuit output current is found by making $R_L = 0$ in Fig. 8-7,

$$(i_o)_{sc} = \frac{av_1}{r_o} = \frac{a(v_i + \beta v_o)}{r_o} = \frac{av_i}{r_o} \qquad (8\text{-}14)$$

where the fact that $v_o = 0$ has been used. Therefore, from Eqs. (8-13) and (8-14),

$$R_o = \frac{(v_o)_{oc}}{(i_o)_{sc}} = \frac{r_o}{1 - a\beta} \qquad (8\text{-}15)$$

According to this result, the effective output impedance is reduced by feedback by the same factor as the reduction in gain.

The effective input impedance is found from the ratio of the input voltage to the input current. Applying Kirchhoff's rule to the input circuit of Fig. 8-7,

$$v_i + \beta v_o - i_i r_i = 0 \qquad (8\text{-}16)$$

The output voltage with no load may be written as

$$v_o = av_1 = ar_i i_i \qquad (8\text{-}17)$$

Inserting Eq. (8-17) into Eq. (8-16) and solving for the ratio v_i/i_i yields

$$R_i = \frac{v_i}{i_i} = (1 - a\beta)r_i \qquad (8\text{-}18)$$

which shows that the effective input impedance is increased by the same factor as the decrease in output impedance.

Both changes, increased input impedance and reduced output impedance, are desirable improvements in amplifiers, as discussed previously. Feedback is often introduced to achieve these benefits alone. Actually, the cathode follower and emitter follower, in which the input impedance is large and the output impedance is small, may be considered to be feedback amplifiers (see Exercise 8-3). In this case the full output voltage across the emitter or cathode resistor is applied to the input and the feedback ratio is -1.

8-2 Current feedback

It is possible to develop a feedback signal proportional to the output current rather than to the output voltage, and this is called *current feedback*. Consider the current-feedback circuit, Fig. 8-8,

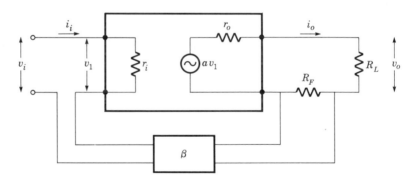

FIGURE 8-8 *Circuit to determine effective input and output impedance of amplifier with current feedback.*

in which the feedback signal results from the voltage drop across a resistor R_F in series with the load. Writing Kirchhoff's voltage equation around the output circuit,

$$-av_1 + i_o(r_o + R_F) + v_o = 0 \qquad (8\text{-}19)$$

and around the input circuit,

$$-v_1 + v_i + \beta i_o R_F = 0 \qquad (8\text{-}20)$$

Solving Eq. (8-20) for v_1 and inserting this into Eq. (8-19) results in

$$v_o = av_i - i_o[r_o + (1 - a\beta)R_F] \qquad (8\text{-}21)$$

Interpreting Eq. (8-21) in terms of a Thévenin equivalent circuit, the open-circuit voltage is av_i, which means, in effect, that the voltage gain of the amplifier is not affected by current feedback. On the other hand, the output impedance is increased, since, from Eq. (8-21),

$$R_o = r_o + (1 - a\beta)R_F \qquad (8\text{-}22)$$

Additionally, the input impedance is also increased, as can be shown by considering the input circuit as in the case of voltage feedback.

The output current is found from Eq. (8-21) by introducing $v_o = i_o R_L$ and solving for i_o,

$$i_o = \frac{av_i}{R_L + r_o + (1 - a\beta)R_F} \cong -\frac{v_i}{\beta R_F} \qquad (8\text{-}23)$$

where the approximation applies when the gain is large. Note that the output current is independent of the amplifier gain and transistor parameters. This equation is analogous to Eq. (8-5) for the case of voltage feedback. It indicates that current feedback minimizes distortion in the output current, rather than the output voltage.

Omitting the emitter or cathode bypass capacitor in power amplifiers is a commonly used form of current feedback. The load current in the emitter or cathode bias resistor introduces negative current feedback into the input circuit, with a consequent reduction in distortion (see Exercise 8-5). In this connection, the fact that bypass capacitors cannot be used in push-pull class-B power amplifiers, as mentioned in the previous chapter, is actually advantageous, except for the concomitant loss of gain.

Both voltage and current feedback can be employed in the same amplifier, Fig. 8-9. Voltage relations in the output circuit of Fig. 8-9 are identical to Eq. (8-19), so that

$$v_o = av_1 - i_o(r_o + R_F) \qquad (8\text{-}24)$$

Similarly, Kirchhoff's voltage equation for the input circuit yields

$$v_1 = v_i + \beta_v v_o + \beta_i i_o R_F \qquad (8\text{-}25)$$

Substituting Eq. (8-25) into Eq. (8-24) and solving for the output voltage,

$$v_o = \frac{a}{1 - a\beta_v} v_i - i_o \frac{r_o + (1 - a\beta_i)R_F}{1 - a\beta_v} \qquad (8\text{-}26)$$

Note that this expression incorporates both Eq. (8-3) for voltage feedback alone ($\beta_i = 0$) and also Eq. (8-21) for current feedback only ($\beta_v = 0$).

Combined current and voltage feedback permits a unique adjustment of the output impedance of the amplifier. The output impedance is given by the coefficient of i_o in Eq. (8-26) and can be made to vanish if

$$r_o + (1 - a\beta_i)R_F = 0$$

or

$$a\beta_i = 1 + \frac{r_o}{R_F} \tag{8-27}$$

If Eq. (8-27) is satisfied, the amplifier has zero internal impedance and therefore can deliver maximum power to any load impedance.

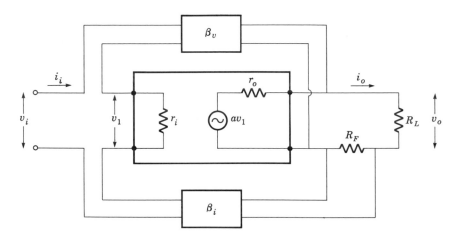

FIGURE 8-9 *Combined voltage and current feedback.*

Note that this requires positive current feedback, according to Eq. (8-27). Positive current feedback is permissible in this case because of the stabilizing effect of negative voltage feedback which is also present.

A practical amplifier employing both current and voltage feedback is illustrated in Fig. 8-10. Circuit-voltage feedback is taken from the secondary of the output transformer and applied to the input stage. The feedback ratio is determined by resistors R_f and R_k. Current feedback is provided by unbypassed cathode resistors in the output stage. Both current and voltage feedback effects in this circuit are negative.

Capacitor C_f shunting the feedback resistor R_f alters the feedback ratio and phase shift in order to eliminate positive-feedback effects at very high frequencies. Similarly, capacitor C_1 purposely reduces amplifier gain at frequencies beyond the normal bandpass of the amplifier (approximately 10 cps to 50 kc) to improve stability. Note that the pentode voltage amplifier is dc-coupled to the triode phase-inverter stage. This eliminates phase shift resulting from an interstage coupling network between these tubes, which also contributes to amplifier stability at low and high frequencies.

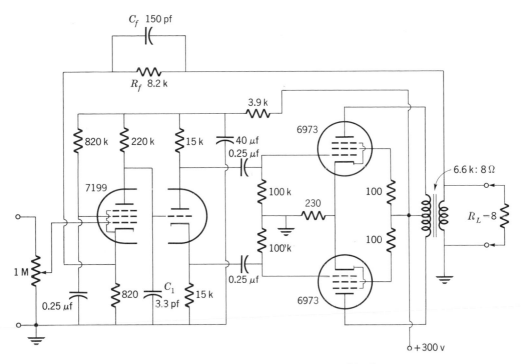

FIGURE 8-10 *Practical vacuum-tube amplifier using combined current and voltage feedback.*

8-3   Stability

Great care is taken in the design of feedback amplifiers to make them stable in the face of phase shifts leading to positive feedback at the frequency extremes of the amplifier bandpass. Fortunately there exists a rather straightforward criterion which can be applied to establish the stability of feedback amplifiers. According to Eq. (8-4), instability occurs if $a\beta$ is positive and equal to unity. It follows that if the absolute value of $a\beta$ drops below unity before the phase shift reaches $-360°$, the amplifier will be stable. It is convenient to plot the magnitude and phase of $a\beta$ as a function of frequency, Fig. 8-11, in order to establish the relative positions at which $a\beta = 1$ and the phase shift equals zero. By this standard, the amplifier with characteristics represented by Fig. 8-11 is stable.

In order to apply this criterion for stability, the amplifier must be stable in the absence of feedback. Also, there exist certain situations in which a feedback amplifier can be conditionally stable, that is, stable under some conditions of, say, loading, and not under others. For most practical circuit analysis, however, the stated condition is sufficient.

It is useful to consider the $a\beta$ characteristics of several amplifier types in the light of this stability requirement. Since in most cases the feedback ratio is independent of frequency, it is sufficient to examine the amplitude and phase characteristics of the amplifier gain separately. In the case of a single *RC*-coupled amplifier

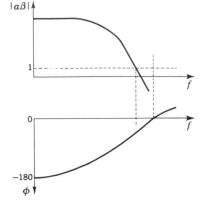

FIGURE 8-11 *Feedback amplitude and phase characteristics of stable amplifier.*

stage, Fig. 8-12*a* (compare Fig. 7-12), the phase shift never exceeds 90°. This means the phase of $a\beta$ is always less than $90 + 180 = 270°$. Since this is smaller than 360°, a single-stage feedback amplifier cannot be unstable.

Two identical *RC*-coupled stages in cascade have the ideal characteristic sketched in Fig. 8-12*b*. The phase shift reaches 180° at very low and very high frequencies, but the gain is very small at these extremes. Therefore, it is unlikely that $a\beta$ can be equal to unity, where the total phase shift is $180 + 180 = 360°$. Practical amplifiers always have stray capacitive effects that can introduce additional phase shift at high frequencies, however. It is possible that the additional phase shift caused by stray capacitances may result in unstable conditions at high frequencies if the gain is large.

The characteristics of three identical *RC*-coupled stages, Fig. 8-12*c*, are such that the extreme phase shift approaches 270°. Therefore, 180° phase shift is encountered at both low and high frequencies, and a three-stage feedback amplifier is certain to be unstable if the midband gain is large enough. It can be shown that the maximum value of $a\beta$ permitted at midband in this case is equal to 8, although even this value puts the amplifier on the verge of oscillation.

Many possibilities exist to remove this unfavorable difficulty other than minimizing the gain. For example, the bandwidth of two stages in a three-stage amplifier can be made very much greater than that of the remaining stage. This means that the phase characteristics are determined primarily by the single stage which is unconditionally stable. Alternatively, dc coupling can be used between two stages (as in Fig. 8-10) to eliminate the phase shift associated with one interstage coupling network. It is common practice to alter the feedback and gain characteristics, particularly at high frequencies, by including small capacitances to change the phase and gain characteristics in a way that improves stability. Usually such changes must be made empirically on the actual amplifier because of the unavoidable and unknown stray wiring capacitances.

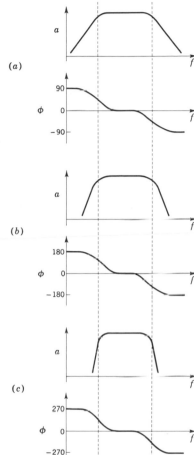

FIGURE 8-12 *Gain and phase characteristics of (a) one-stage amplifier, (b) two-stage amplifier, and (c) three-stage amplifier.*

OPERATIONAL AMPLIFIERS

8-4 Operational feedback

High-gain, dc-coupled feedback amplifiers can perform a number of operations such as multiplication, addition, and integration on an input signal. They are widely used in measurement and control applications as well as in electronic analog computers. Commercially available units have come to be known as *operational amplifiers*. In addition to dc coupling and high gain, operational amplifiers exhibit high input impedance and low output impedance and conventionally introduce a 180° phase shift between the input signal and the output voltage.

To illustrate the features of an operational amplifier, consider the feedback circuit, Fig. 8-13, in which negative voltage feedback is produced by the resistor R_f connected between the output and

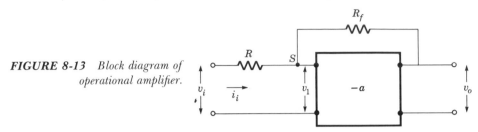

FIGURE 8-13 *Block diagram of operational amplifier.*

input. Note that the feedback is negative because of the phase inversion in the amplifier. The feedback ratio in *operational feedback* can vary from unity for a high-impedance source to $R/(R + R_f)$ for a low-impedance source since the feedback voltage is effectively connected in parallel with the input signal source. It is convenient to analyze the operational feedback circuit by applying Kirchhoff's current rule to the branch point S. Since the amplifier input impedance is large, the current in this branch is negligible, which means the current in R equals the current in R_f, or

$$\frac{v_i - v_1}{R} = \frac{v_1 - v_o}{R_f} \tag{8-28}$$

Introducing $v_1 = -v_o/a$ and rearranging,

$$v_o \left(1 + \frac{1}{a} + \frac{R_f}{aR}\right) = -\frac{R_f}{R} v_i \tag{8-29}$$

Since the gain is very large

$$v_o = -\frac{R_f}{R} v_i \tag{8-30}$$

which means that the output voltage is just the input signal multiplied by the constant factor $-R_f/R$. If precision resistors are used for R_f and R, the accuracy of this multiplication operation is quite good.

The branch point S has a special significance in operational amplifiers. This may be illustrated by determining the effective impedance between S and ground, which is given by the ratio of v_1 to the input current,

$$Z_s = \frac{v_1}{i_i} = \frac{v_1 R_f}{v_1 - v_o} = \frac{R_f}{1 - v_o/v_1} = \frac{R_f}{1 + a} \tag{8-31}$$

where the right side of Eq. (8-28) has been inserted for the input current. According to Eq. (8-31) the impedance of S to ground is very low if the gain is large. Typical values are $R_f = 100,000 \ \Omega$ and $a = 10^4$, so that the impedance is $10 \ \Omega$. The low impedance results from the negative feedback voltage, which cancels the input signal at S and tends to keep the branch point at ground potential. For this reason the point S is called a *virtual ground.* Although S is kept at ground potential by feedback action, no current to ground exists at this point.

The virtual ground at S shows immediately that the impedance viewed from the input terminals is equal to R. The output impedance is very low because an emitter-follower stage is used and this impedance is further reduced by feedback. For example, the output impedance of an emitter follower is typically about 200 Ω; if the feedback ratio, $R/(R + R_f)$ (for simplicity consider the input to be shorted), is about unity and the gain is 10^4, the effective output impedance is only 0.02 Ω.

Operational amplifiers are capable of responding to signal frequencies ranging from approximately 100 kc down to dc. Conventional chopper amplifiers are not used because the upper frequency limit of a chopper amplifier is only about $\frac{1}{4}$ of the chopping frequency. Accordingly, operational amplifiers are dc-coupled circuits with special design features to minimize slow drifts. Even minor drifts are significant in operational-amplifier applications because an output signal exists in the absence of an input signal.

The circuit of a typical transistorized operational amplifier, Fig. 8-14, includes three difference-amplifier stages together with an emitter-follower output stage. The inherently balanced circuitry of difference amplifiers minimizes drifting, as discussed in the previous chapter. The input stage is particularly significant in this connection; note that each base-bias resistor is returned to the collector of the opposite transistor in order to further stabilize the circuit. In this way any changes in one transistor are compensated by a corresponding shift of the bias on the other transistor. The input stage also employs a transistor in the common emitter lead to improve the ac balance of the stage. The reason for this is that a large emitter resistor improves balance [refer to Eq. (5-45) pertaining to a vacuum-tube difference amplifier], but a large resistance also means that the voltage drop is excessive. Introducing a transistor at this point means that the effective ac resistance is essentially equal to the collector resistance of the transistor. The dc potential drop is, however, only a few volts. In effect, transistor Q_3 is the emitter resistor for the difference amplifier comprising Q_1 and Q_2. Because of the large effective resistance of Q_3, the circuit is very well balanced.

The difference-amplifier input stage also presents two input terminals. One, called the *inverting,* or negative, input, is the normal input terminal and produces an output signal 180° out of phase with the input. The second, called the *noninverting,* or *positive,* input, results in an output signal in phase with signals applied to this terminal. Advantages of the noninverting input are discussed in a later section. The 100-Ω potentiometer in the

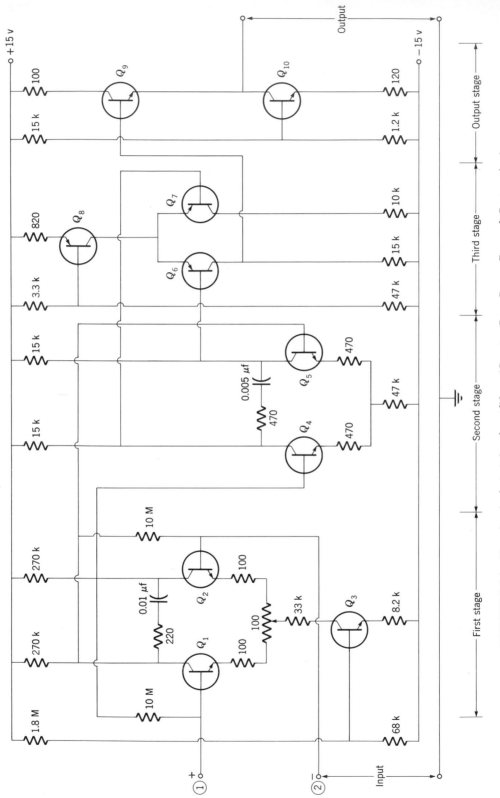

FIGURE 8-14 Transistorized operational amplifier. (Courtesy Burr-Brown Research Corporation.)

emitter circuit is a balance control which compensates for slight asymmetries in the overall amplifier and permits adjustment of the output voltage to zero in the absence of an input signal. An *RC* filter is connected between the collector of Q_1 and Q_2 in order to reduce the gain at high frequencies and thereby eliminate the possibility of high-frequency instabilities.

The second stage is a straightforward difference amplifier. Here again an *RC* filter connected between the collectors of Q_4 and Q_5 reduces the high-frequency gain. Transistors Q_6 and Q_7 form a third-stage difference amplifier, emitter-stabilized by Q_8 as in the input-stage circuit. Note that this stage uses *pnp* transistors, in contrast to *npn* devices in the first two stages. The reason for this is that the dc potential rise in a multiple-stage amplifier can be kept to reasonable limits since the *pnp* stage can be "inverted" insofar as the dc supply voltages are concerned. This is an example of the flexibility inherent in transistor circuitry resulting from the combination of *npn* and *pnp* transistors. The emitter-follower output stage, transistor Q_9, uses transistor Q_{10} as an emitter resistor. Here again the large effective ac collector resistance of Q_{10} means that the emitter-follower action of Q_9 is enhanced.

The overall gain of this amplifier is 30,000 and the bandwidth is from dc to 1 Mc. Nominally, the input impedance is 200,000 Ω, while the output impedance is only 100 Ω. The use of difference-amplifier circuitry reduces the drift rate to 50 μv per 24 hr. These characteristics result in a useful operational amplifier.

Even with very careful design and well-stabilized supply voltages, it is difficult to prevent drifts in dc amplifiers. Drift voltages at the amplifier output mean that operational feedback no longer keeps the branch point S at virtual ground and the error in the virtual ground is referred to as *offset*. Typically, offset voltages are of the order of 10 mv, which may be serious in critical applications. Improved performance is achieved by using a chopper amplifier to stabilize the virtual ground voltage, Fig. 8-15. Here, the chopper amplifier, which is drift-free because it is ac-coupled, measures the offset voltage at S and provides an amplified error signal to the positive input of the operational amplifier. This signal counteracts drifts in the operational amplifier and, in practice, offset can be reduced to about 0.1 mv.

Note that a capacitor is interposed between S and the operational amplifier so that offset is controlled only by the chopper amplifier. This prevents the operational amplifier itself from responding to dc signals, but the chopper amplifier does so and, in feeding its output signal to the operational amplifier, becomes part of the operational feedback circuit. In effect, the operational amplifier is now ac-coupled and handles the high-frequency signals, while the chopper amplifier handles the dc and

very-low-frequency signals. The dc gain is very large since it is
the product of the gains of both amplifiers. This means that the
overall response curve is nonuniform in that the low-frequency

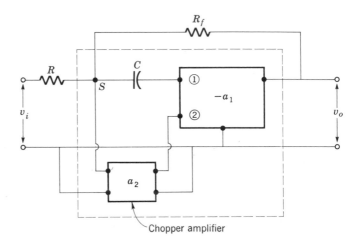

FIGURE 8-15 *Chopper-stabilized
operational amplifier.*

gain is larger than the gain at high frequencies. According to
Eq. (8-30) this is unimportant since by feedback action the gain
does not appear in the expression for the output signal, so long as
the gain remains large at all frequencies of interest.

The combination of an operational amplifier stabilized by a
chopper amplifier is often itself referred to as an operational
amplifier. Thus the dashed line in Fig. 8-15 encloses a chopper-
stabilized operational amplifier. In less critical applications where
chopper stabilization is unnecessary, the dc amplifier alone, such
as Fig. 8-14, is the operational amplifier. Chopper amplifiers
specifically designed for stabilizing operational amplifiers are also
available as separate units. A typical transistor circuit and a
vacuum-tube version are shown in Fig. 8-16a and b, respectively.
Both circuits are rather conventional ac-coupled amplifiers and
use a synchronous chopper to recover the dc signal. Note that
unbypassed emitter and cathode resistors provide current feedback to improve phase characteristics so that the synchronously
chopped output is in phase with the chopped input signal. In
fact, dc coupling is used for convenience in the transistor version
for the same reason. In this case, input and output capacitors
are present, so that the amplifier is actually ac-coupled.

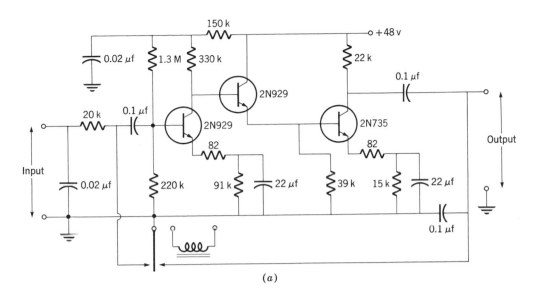

(a)

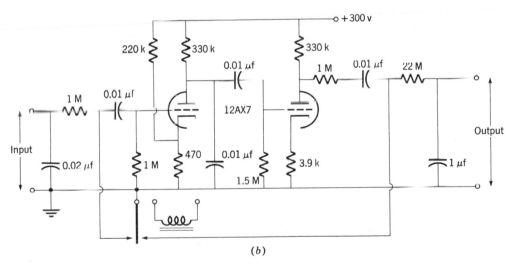

(b)

FIGURE 8-16 *Typical (a) transistor and (b) vacuum-tube chopper amplifiers.*

8-5 Mathematical operations

The operational feedback circuit, Fig. 8-13, multiplies the input signal by the constant $-R_f/R$. It is conventional to simplify the circuit diagram, as in Fig. 8-17, by not showing the ground terminals specifically. The operational amplifier is indicated by a triangle pointing toward the output terminal. It is understood that the simplified circuit diagram, Fig. 8-17, actually implies the corresponding complete circuit, Fig. 8-13. The operational ampli-

fier in Fig. 8-17 may actually be the combination of a dc amplifier
and a chopper amplifier, as explained previously.

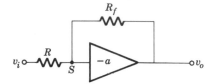

FIGURE 8-17   *Conventional circuit symbol for
operational amplifier.*

If $R_f = R$ in the multiplier circuit, the signal is simply multiplied by -1. This is often useful in obtaining a signal multiplied
by a positive constant wherein this operational amplifier precedes
one which determines the multiplier. Multiplicative factors ranging from -0.1 to -10 are possible, and the precision is determined
principally by the accuracy of the two resistors.

The operational amplifier can also be used to sum several signals
by connecting individual resistors to the branch point S, Fig. 8-18.

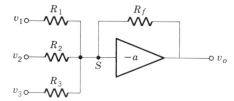

FIGURE 8-18   *Summing circuit using operational
amplifier.*

In this circuit, the sum of the currents in R_1, R_2, and R_3 equals the
current in R_f, since no current to ground exists at S. Furthermore,
S is at ground potential, so that [compare Eq. (8-28)]

$$\frac{v_1}{R_1} + \frac{v_2}{R_2} + \frac{v_3}{R_3} = -\frac{v_o}{R_f} \tag{8-32}$$

$$v_o = -R_f \left(\frac{v_1}{R_1} + \frac{v_2}{R_2} + \frac{v_3}{R_3} \right) \tag{8-33}$$

Many signals can be added in this way. There is no interaction between individual signal sources since S is a virtual ground. Because
the addition appears to take place at this point, S is commonly
called the *summing point*. Note that each signal may be multiplied
by the same factor (or -1), if $R_1 = R_2 = R_3$, etc., or that individual
factors may be selected, as convenient.

If the feedback resistor is replaced by a capacitor, Fig. 8-19, the
circuit performs the operation of integration. Using the fact that
S is at ground potential,

$$v_o = \frac{q}{C} = \frac{1}{C} \int_0^t i \, dt = -\frac{1}{RC} \int_0^t v_i \, dt \tag{8-34}$$

where Eq. (2-20) has been inserted for the voltage across a capacitor. According to Eq. (8-34) the output voltage is the integral of
the input signal. Note that there is no restriction placed on the

frequency components of the input signal, as in the case of the simple *RC* integrator discussed in Chap. 2. It is only necessary that the amplifier bandwidth be large enough to handle all signal fre-

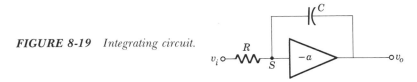

FIGURE 8-19   *Integrating circuit.*

quencies. The integral of the sum of several signals is obtained by introducing several input resistors, as in Fig. 8-18. Integrating circuits are particularly susceptible to offset voltages because, as Eq. (8-34) shows, a constant offset voltage results in an ever-increasing output signal. If this is not counteracted, the amplifier eventually is driven into saturation.

Interchanging *R* and *C*, Fig. 8-20, results in a differentiating cir-

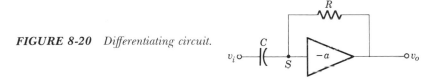

FIGURE 8-20   *Differentiating circuit.*

cuit which gives the time derivative of the input signal. Again equating currents at the summing point,

$$-\frac{v_o}{R} = \frac{dq}{dt} = \frac{d}{dt} Cv_i = C \frac{dv_i}{dt} \qquad (8\text{-}35)$$

$$v_o = -RC \frac{dv_i}{dt} \qquad (8\text{-}36)$$

The differentiator circuit is not affected by offset errors since, in effect, the capacitor makes the circuit ac-coupled. However, spurious noise pulses, which characteristically have a fast rate of change, may dominate in the output because of Eq. (8-36) and lead to a great deal of high-frequency noise.

8-6 Analog computers

The circuits of the preceding section can be assembled into *analog computers* to perform mathematical operations on voltages that are analogous to the numbers in a mathematical problem or equation. Although analog computers are not as accurate as their digital counterparts, they are much less expensive. The interconnection of operational amplifier circuits into a computer designed to solve the mathematical equation describing any physical system can be looked upon as simulating the actual system. In this way, the response of any system can be easily determined and the effect of changes in the system investigated by simply altering the values of electric components or potentials in the simulator.

Consider the analog-computer solution of the two simultaneous equations

$$a_1x + b_1y = c_1$$

$$a_2x + b_2y = c_2 \tag{8-37}$$

Solving for x and y,

$$x = \frac{c_1}{a_1} - \frac{b_1}{a_1} y$$

$$\tag{8-38}$$

$$y = \frac{c_2}{b_2} - \frac{a_2}{b_2} x$$

A summing amplifier solves each equation, Fig. 8-21. The output of the top amplifier is a voltage analogous to x and the output of

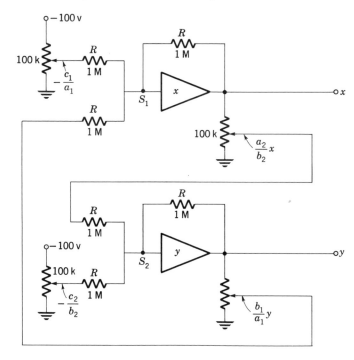

FIGURE 8-21 *Analog-computer circuit to solve simultaneous linear equations in Eqs. (8-38).*

the lower amplifier is a voltage analogous to y. A fraction b_1/a_1 of y is taken from the output of the lower amplifier by means of a variable potentiometer and summed with a voltage $-c_1/a_1$ derived from a potentiometer and a potential source. Applying Eq. (8-33) to the upper amplifier,

$$x = -R \left(\frac{-c_1/a_1}{R} + \frac{b_1/a_1}{R} y \right) = \frac{c_1}{a_1} - \frac{b_1}{a_1} y \tag{8-39}$$

which is just the upper equation in (8-38). A similar expression applies to the lower equation in (8-38) and the corresponding amplifier.

This analog computer thus presents a continuous solution for x and y of Eqs. (8-37). Desired values of the coefficients are selected by adjusting the potentiometers in the circuit, and the solutions are determined by measuring the voltages x and y with, say, two VTVMs. If, for example, c_1 varies with time, a voltage signal of the proper waveform is supplied to the summing point. In this case the solutions x and y are time-varying and can be measured with an oscilloscope or a chart recorder.

Actually, the simple analog circuit devised here is not convenient since each potentiometer involves two constants. By means of a slightly more complicated circuit than Fig. 8-21, it is possible to make each potentiometer relate to only one constant. This is useful since the parameters can then be adjusted individually with greater ease.

Many types of differential equations can also be solved by analog computers. Consider the mechanical vibrations of a body of mass m on the end of a spring of force constant k in the presence of viscous damping described by the damping constant b and driven by an arbitrary force $F(t)$. The differential equation for the position x of the body is

$$m \frac{d^2x}{dt^2} + b \frac{dx}{dt} + kx = F(t) \tag{8-40}$$

Rearranging,

$$\frac{d^2x}{dt^2} = -\frac{b}{m}\frac{dx}{dt} - \frac{k}{m}x + \frac{1}{m}F(t) \tag{8-41}$$

The design of an analog computer to solve this equation begins by assuming a voltage signal corresponding to d^2x/dt^2 is available. This is integrated to yield $-dx/dt$, where for convenience the RC time constant in Eq. (8-34) is made equal to unity. Next, $-dx/dt$ is integrated again to obtain x. A fraction b/m of $-dx/dt$ is obtained from a voltage-divider potentiometer across the output of the first integrator; this is inverted and added to the fraction k/m of x from the output of the second integrator and to a voltage signal corresponding to $(1/m)F(t)$ (Fig. 8-22). The sum is equal to d^2x/dt^2, according to Eq. (8-41), and is returned to the input, where the second derivative signal was assumed to be originally. This computer, therefore, continuously solves the original differential equation (8-40) and voltages corresponding to x and, if desired, dx/dt can be measured at appropriate points in the circuit.

It is necessary to set voltages corresponding to dx/dt, and x for their initial values at the time when the solution begins, as in solving any differential equation. This is most effectively accomplished by opening switches s_1 and s_2 at $t = 0$. The voltages across the inte-

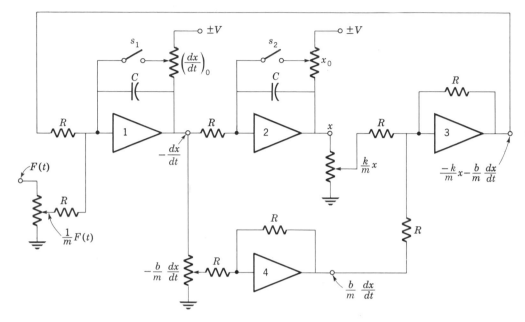

FIGURE 8-22   *Analog computer for vibrating-mass problem.*

grating capacitors represent the velocity and displacement at all times, as can be seen by the fact that the summing points are at ground potential. These switches must be opened simultaneously with the beginning of $F(t)$ and in practice this is most often done with electronic switches such as diodes.

Note that Eq. (8-40) has the same form as Eq. (3-28) for the current in an RLC circuit. This means that the analog computer in Fig. 8-22 also can be used to investigate, say, resonance effects in this simple circuit. Although the computer is much more complicated than the circuit it simulates, study of the circuit is facilitated by the ease with which circuit parameters can be altered. Furthermore, the computer can be rewired to simulate other circuits as the need arises.

8-7   Measurement and control

The operational amplifier is a useful tool in measurement and control of electrical quantities. For example, according to Eq. (8-30), the output voltage of an amplifier with operational feedback is

$$v_o = -R_f i_i \qquad (8\text{-}42)$$

where i_i is the input current. Thus by eliminating the input resistor R in Fig. 8-17 the operational amplifier becomes a very sensitive ammeter. If R_f is 1 MΩ, Eq. (8-42) shows that the output voltage is 1 volt for each microampere of input current. Also the resistance introduced into the circuit is the impedance between S and ground, which may be of the order of 10 Ω, according to Eq. (8-31). Currents as low as 10^{-11} amp can be measured with very large values of R_f although care must be exercised to take into account stray leakage currents at this sensitivity.

A modified operational feedback circuit which uses both inputs, Fig. 8-23, is known as a *voltage follower* because the output voltage

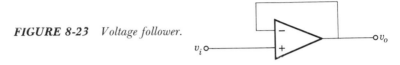

FIGURE 8-23 *Voltage follower.*

is equal to the input signal. Since the full output voltage is returned to the input, the feedback ratio β is -1 and the gain equals, from Eq. (8-4), $a/(1 + a) \cong 1$. The voltage follower has very high input impedance and very low output impedance, of the order of 100 MΩ and 0.1 Ω, respectively, for a typical vacuum-tube amplifier. Obviously, very effective isolation between the voltage source and output circuit is achieved.

Conventional operational feedback can control the current in an impedance (Fig. 8-24). According to Eq. (8-28) the current in the

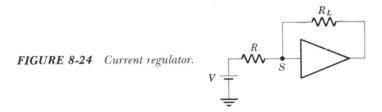

FIGURE 8-24 *Current regulator.*

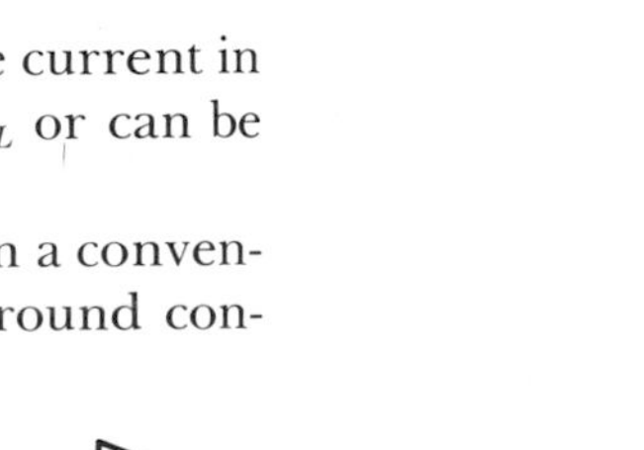

arbitrary impedance R_L is equal to V/R. In this way the current in R_L can be kept constant independent of changes in R_L or can be adjusted by altering V or R.

The high-gain dc operational amplifier can be used in a conventional voltage feedback circuit, Fig. 8-25, where the ground con-

FIGURE 8-25 *Voltage stabilizer.*

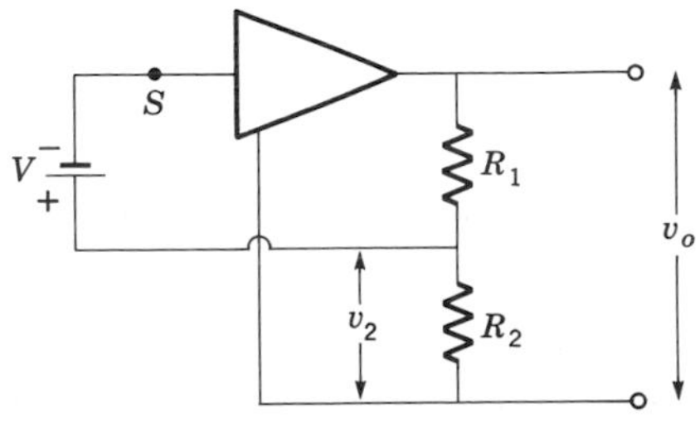

nection is shown explicitly to enhance comparison with Fig. 8-1. Since the feedback ratio is $-R_2/(R_1 + R_2)$, the output voltage is controlled by the amplifier to be, from Eq. (8-5),

$$v_o = -\frac{R_1 + R_2}{R_2} V \tag{8-43}$$

Suppose V is a constant reference voltage, such as a standard battery or the breakdown voltage of a Zener diode. Then the output voltage is controlled at the value given by Eq. (8-43) independent of the current in a load connected to the output terminals. Practical circuits of this type are considered in greater detail in the next section.

Note also that the feedback voltage v_2 is

$$v_2 = \frac{R_2}{R_1 + R_2} v_o = \frac{R_2}{R_1 + R_2} \left(-\frac{R_1 + R_2}{R_2} V \right) = -V \tag{8-44}$$

This means that the voltage across R_2 is controlled to be equal to the standard voltage, independent of the values of R_1 and R_2. Therefore, the voltage at any point in a complex network can be maintained at the reference potential regardless of the other circuit connections to R_2.

VOLTAGE REGULATORS

It is often desirable to stabilize the voltage output of a rectifier power supply to a greater extent than is possible using the simple Zener-diode or *VR*-tube circuits described in Chap. 4. Feedback amplifiers are widely used in this application. Control over the dc supply voltage is maintained in the face of changes in load and also in ac line voltage. Such *voltage regulators* are essential in power supplies for operational amplifiers to minimize drifts and in other similar critical circuits.

8-8 Series regulator

The output voltage of a power supply is conveniently controlled by introducing a power transistor in series with the rectifier-filter and the load, Fig. 8-26. This circuit is equivalent to that of Fig. 8-25 with the addition of the power transistor, which enables the regulator to control larger currents. Actually, the combination of the dc amplifier and the control transistor may be considered to be an operational amplifier equivalent to Fig. 8-25. The output voltage is stabilized at $V_o = -V(R_1 + R_2)/R_2$, according to Eq. (8-43). In effect, the voltage-regulator circuit compares a fraction of the dc output voltage with the reference voltage V and adjusts the control transistor to maintain V_o constant.

The stabilizing effect of the regulator is determined by analyzing the control transistor separately from the dc amplifier.   Variations in the supply voltage are assumed to arise from an ac generator v_i

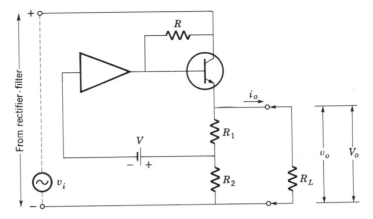

FIGURE 8-26   *Series voltage regulator.*

in Fig. 8-26 and result in a variation v_o in the output voltage. The control transistor is essentially an emitter-follower amplifier and the appropriate equivalent circuit (using Fig. 6-17b) is shown in Fig. 8-27.   Since we want to determine the output voltage conditions,

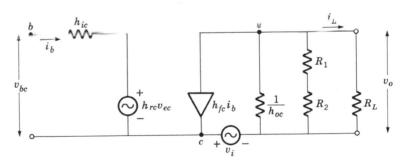

FIGURE 8-27   *Equivalent circuit of control transistor in Fig. 8-26.*

begin by writing an expression for the output current. Considering the currents at point e and neglecting the minor current drain in the feedback divider $R_1 R_2$,

$$h_{fc} i_b + i_L + \frac{v_o - v_i}{1/h_{oc}} = 0 \tag{8-45}$$

where the third term is the current in $1/h_{oc}$.   The base current is found by considering the voltages in the input circuit,

$$i_b = \frac{v_{bc} - h_{rc} v_{ec}}{h_{ic}} = -\frac{a\beta v_o + v_i + h_{rc} v_{ec}}{h_{ic}} \tag{8-46}$$

where the input voltage v_{bc} is v_i less the amplified feedback voltage

$-a\beta v_o$, as may be best seen from Fig. 8-26. Finally, v_{ec} is determined by writing Kirchhoff's rule around the output circuit,

$$v_{ec} - v_o + v_i = 0 \tag{8-47}$$

Equations (8-47) and (8-46) are substituted into Eq. (8-45),

$$i_L = v_i \left[h_{oc} + \frac{h_{fc}(1 - h_{rc})}{h_{ic}} \right] - v_o \left[h_{oc} - \frac{h_{fc}(h_{rc} + a)}{h_{ic}} \right]$$

Solving for the output voltage,

$$v_o = v_i \frac{h_{ic}h_{oc} + h_{fc}(1 - h_{rc})}{h_{ic}h_{oc} - h_{fc}(h_{rc} + a\beta)} - i_L \frac{h_{ic}}{h_{ic}h_{oc} - h_{fc}(h_{rc} + a\beta)} \tag{8-48}$$

This expression has the form of the Thévenin equivalent of the regulated power supply in that the first term is the internal voltage generator and the second term is the voltage drop resulting from the load current in the equivalent internal resistance.

Before considering Eq. (8-48) further, it is useful to simplify the expression by considering the relative magnitudes of the h parameters. When this is done (Exercise 8-14), Eq. (8-48) reduces to

$$v_o = v_i \frac{h_{ic}}{r_c(1 + a\beta)} - i_L \frac{h_{ic}(1 - \alpha)}{1 + a\beta} \tag{8-49}$$

which is sufficiently accurate for all practical purposes. According to Eq. (8-49) input voltage variations are reduced by a large factor through the feedback action of the regulator. Typical values of the power-transistor parameters in Eq. (8-49) are $h_{ic} = 1000 \ \Omega$, $r_c = 10,000 \ \Omega$, $a = 50$, and $\beta = 0.3$, so that input voltage changes are reduced by a factor of 160 at the output terminals.

Additionally, the effective internal impedance of the regulated power supply, which is the coefficient of i_L in Eq. (8-49), is very small. Taking $1 - \alpha = 0.05$, the internal resistance is only 3.1 Ω. This means that changes in load current cause only minor changes in the regulated supply voltage. It is apparent that this simple regulator is effective against both input-voltage and output-current variations.

The control transistor in this regulator circuit must be capable of withstanding the full supply voltage without collector breakdown. Higher voltage regulators conventionally employ vacuum tubes as the control element because of their higher operating voltages. The circuit is identical to Fig. 8-26 with the transistor replaced by a triode or pentode. Analysis of the vacuum-tube regulator proceeds the same as that for the transistor version (see Exercise 8-15). The expression corresponding to Eq. (8-48) for the variation in output voltage is

$$v_o = \frac{v_i}{1 + \mu(1 + a\beta)} - i_L \frac{r_p}{1 + \mu(1 + a\beta)} \tag{8-50}$$

Typical values for the control tube in a regulator are $\mu = 10$ and $r_p = 2000\ \Omega$. Therefore, input voltage variations are reduced by a factor of 160 and the equivalent internal resistance is 12.5 Ω, if the amplifier gain and feedback ratio are the same as in the transistor circuit.

Note that the factor by which input voltage variations are reduced at the output terminals applies to ripple voltages as well as to other voltage changes. Therefore output voltage ripple is very small in a regulated power supply. Both the reduction factor and the effective internal resistance can be improved by increasing the gain of the dc amplifier, according to Eqs. (8-49) and (8-50). In many critical applications the gain is made large enough that residual variations in the regulated voltage reflect the stability of the reference potential.

The series control transistor or tube must be capable of dissipating the heat generated by the entire load current without overheating. Power tubes and transistors are often used. It is feasible to employ two or more identical units connected in parallel, if this is necessary to carry the maximum load current.

Although the series regulator is most popular, it is also possible to connect the control transistor in parallel with the load, much as in the case of a simple Zener-diode regulator, Fig. 4-26. The current through the transistor is controlled so that the voltage drop across the series resistor is the same independent of load-current changes. Effective voltage stabilization is obtained by such a *shunt regulator*, but the circuit suffers from the additional power loss in the series resistor. On the other hand, it is only necessary for the control transistor to carry a fraction of the full load current, which is a considerable advantage in high-current power supplies (see Exercise 8-18).

8-9 Practical circuits

A complete regulated power supply is illustrated in Fig. 8-28. The dc amplifier is a single grounded-emitter transistor stage and the reference voltage is provided by an 18-volt Zener diode. The Zener diode is placed in the emitter circuit of the amplifier, rather than in series with the feedback signal, so that one terminal of the diode can be grounded. The 33-kΩ resistor provides reverse potential for the diode. Note that the feedback ratio is adjustable. This enables the output voltage to be set at any desired value, within limits dictated by the operating conditions of the transistors. In this circuit, the output voltage can be adjusted over the range 40 to 50 volts, while maintaining good regulation. The 1500-μf capacitor across the output terminals provides a very low effective internal impedance for ac signals.

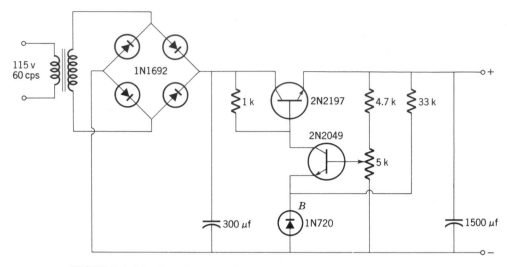

FIGURE 8-28 *Complete 40-volt 500-ma regulated power supply.*

A very precisely regulated voltage is obtained with the more elaborate vacuum-tube version in Fig. 8-29. A two-stage dc amplifier is used to increase the factor a in Eq. (8-50), and the pentode

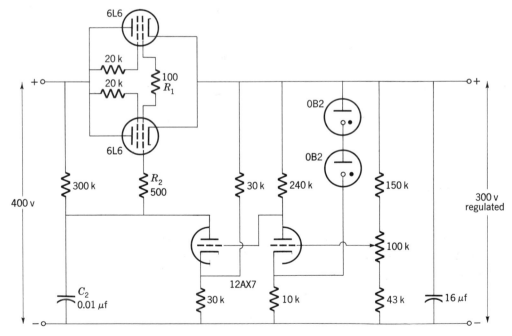

FIGURE 8-29 *Vacuum-tube voltage regulator.*

regulator tubes have a large μ. Both improvements result in excellent regulation (see Exercise 8-17). Two regulator tubes are used in parallel in order to permit a greater current to be drawn from the power supply without exceeding the rated current of the type 6L6 tube.

Note that the reference voltage is developed across two VR tubes in series. The difference between the regulated voltage and the reference potential is introduced into the cathode circuit of the dc amplifier. This is done to achieve negative feedback since the output of a two-stage amplifier is in phase with the input. The purpose of R_2 and C_2 is to reduce the amplifier gain at high frequencies and thus eliminate the possibility of positive feedback. Similarly, resistor R_1 is included to reduce the tendency of parallel-connected tubes to oscillate as a result of stray capacitances and inductances.

SERVOS

It is often useful to control the mechanical position or motion of a device in accordance with an electric signal. To assure that the desired motion takes place, a voltage feedback signal corresponding to the mechanical motion is developed. This voltage is compared with the input signal. When the two are equal, mechanical motion ceases since the mechanism has then responded to the actuating signal. Feedback systems incorporating a mechanical link in the feedback network are called *servomechanisms*, or *servos*, from the Latin word for "slave," since the mechanical motion is the slave of the input signal. Servos are widely used in control applications, from laboratory chart recorders to ballistic-missile guidance systems.

8-10 Mechanical feedback

Consider the servo system sketched in block-diagram form in Fig. 8-30. The amplifier drives a mechanical actuator as, for example, a dc motor. Suppose the motor moves a mechanical arm to a position x and that the feedback voltage is proportional to

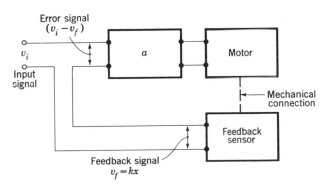

FIGURE 8-30   *Block diagram of servo system.*

the position of the arm and equal to kx. So long as the *error signal*, which is the difference between the input and feedback voltages, is not equal to zero, the amplified error signal continues to drive the motor. When the feedback signal equals the actuating signal, the error is zero, and motion ceases. Thus

$$v_i - v_f = v_i - kx_0 = 0 \tag{8-51}$$

so that

$$x_0 = \frac{v_i}{k} \tag{8-52}$$

According to Eq. (8-52), the equilibrium position of the mechanical motion x_0 is directly proportional to the input signal.

The servo cannot respond instantaneously to rapid changes in the input signal because of mechanical inertia and friction. According to the above discussion, the motive force from the motor is proportional to the error signal. This force is opposed by the inertial and frictional forces (which are assumed to be proportional to the velocity), so that

$$Ka(v_i - v_f) = m\frac{d^2x}{dt^2} + b\frac{dx}{dt} \tag{8-53}$$

where K is the motor constant, a is the amplifier gain, m is the mass of the moving parts, and b is a friction constant. Inserting Eq. (8-52), the differential equation for the response of the system is

$$m\frac{d^2x}{dt^2} + b\frac{dx}{dt} + (Kak)x = (Kak)x_0 \tag{8-54}$$

This equation can be solved by the methods used in Chap. 3 or by analog-computer methods (compare Eq. 8-40). In fact, the

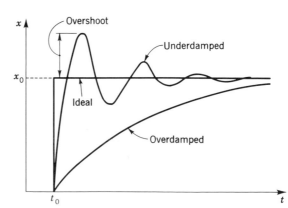

FIGURE 8-31 *Characteristic responses of servo to sudden input signal.*

equation is identical in form to the one for an *RLC* circuit, Eq. (3-28). Based on the discussion in Chap. 3, a ringing effect is anticipated. Actually, the solutions are of two general kinds. If the system is *underdamped*, i.e., the frictional force is small compared with the driving force, a damped oscillation results, Fig. 8-31. On the other hand, if the frictional force is large, the system is *overdamped* and requires an excessively long time to reach the equilibrium position. Most servo systems are designed so they are slightly underdamped because this minimizes the response time. This results in a small *overshoot*, Fig. 8-31. If desirable, additional damping may be introduced by including an *RC* filter in the input circuit. Thus, the servo is never subjected to a signal change faster than the time constant of the filter.

8-11 The recording potentiometer

A common laboratory instrument based on servo principles is the *recording potentiometer*. This is a self-balancing dc potentiometer in which the balance position is marked on a moving paper strip or chart producing a continuous record of the input voltage. The heart of the system, Fig. 8-32, is the slide-wire R_S, in which there

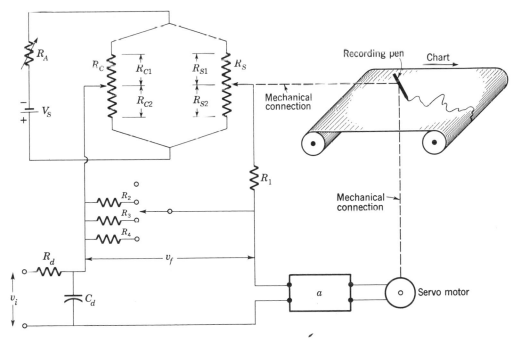

FIGURE 8-32 *Recording-potentiometer servo.*

is a calibrated current supplied by the battery V_S and variable resistor R_A. The current is standardized by comparison with a standard battery, as described in Chap. 1. If less accuracy is satisfactory, V_S may be a mercury battery which supplies a relatively constant current.

The potentiometer in parallel with the slide-wire resistance forms a bridge circuit which is balanced when, from Eq. (1-69),

$$\frac{R_{C1}}{R_{C2}} = \frac{R_{S1}}{R_{S2}} \tag{8-55}$$

Under this condition the feedback voltage v_f is zero. In the absence of an input signal, the adjustable contact on the slide-wire is moved by the servomotor until balance is achieved. The recording pen mechanically attached to the slide-wire contact continuously records the balance position on the chart. This means that the zero position ($v_i = 0$) may be placed anywhere on the chart by adjusting R_C.

When an input voltage is applied, an initial signal $v_i - v_f$ is fed to the amplifier. The servomotor drives the slide-wire contact to a new equilibrium position where the unbalanced bridge voltage equals the input voltage, and $v_i - v_f = 0$. The displacement of the sliding contact is a linear function of the input voltage, as can be shown in the following way. Using Eq. (1-81), the unbalance voltage from the bridge is

$$v_f = V \left(\frac{R_{C1}}{R_{C1} + R_{C2}} - \frac{R_{S1}}{R_{S1} + R_{S2}} \right) \tag{8-56}$$

where V is the voltage across the bridge. If the slide-wire is uniform, and the zero position, $x = 0$, is taken to be at the center,

$$R_{S1} = \frac{R_S}{2} - mx$$

$$R_{S2} = \frac{R_S}{2} + mx \tag{8-57}$$

where m is a constant of the slide-wire. Introducing Eqs. (8-57) into Eq. (8-56) and noting that $R_{C1} = R_{C2}$ since the zero position is at the center,

$$v_f = V \left(\frac{1}{2} - \frac{R_S/2 - mx}{R_S/2 - mx + R_S/2 + mx} \right)$$

$$= V \left(\frac{1}{2} - \frac{1}{2} + \frac{mx}{R_S} \right) = \frac{V}{R_S} mx \tag{8-58}$$

Therefore, according to Eq. (8-52),

$$x_0 = \frac{1}{mI_S} v_i \tag{8-59}$$

where $I_S = V/R_S$ is the standardized current in the slide-wire. Equation (8-59) shows that the deflection of the slider, and hence of the recording pen, is proportional to the input signal. It is common practice to select m and the standard current I_S such that the full chart width is an integral voltage such as 100 mv.

Resistors R_1 through R_4 in Fig. 8-32 constitute a voltage divider for changing the sensitivity of the potentiometer. When the divider is in the circuit, only a fraction of the unbalance voltage is available as the feedback signal and the sensitivity is increased correspondingly. The combination of R_d and C_d is a damping filter at the input to optimize the response time of the recorder.

The recording potentiometer is a very versatile instrument in the laboratory. It combines high sensitivity for dc signals and the inherently high input impedance of a potentiometer circuit with automatic operation and a permanent record. It is widely used as part of other instruments, such as optical spectrometers, X-ray diffractometers, and gas chromatographs, or as a separate unit.

8-12   Servo amplifiers

Amplifiers used in servo systems are of several types, depending upon the application and the kind of servomotor used. Simple systems may use a dc motor, so that a dc amplifier and power amplifier are required. This approach is subject to the drift prob lems of dc amplifiers and requires that the entire power of the servomotor come from the amplifier. Most often, two-phase ac motors are used in which one phase is supplied by the ac line volt- age. An ac power amplifier controlled by the servo amplifier feeds the second-phase winding of the motor. Thus only a frac- tion of the total power of the motor is required from the amplifier.

In this case a chopper amplifier develops an ac voltage corre- sponding to the dc input signal. This is followed by a conventional ac amplifier and a push-pull class-B power amplifier to drive the motor. Chopping frequencies of 60 and 400 cps are standard, although the latter is preferred as it permits a faster response.

Since the amplifier need only handle signals of the chopping fre- quency, it is permissible to employ a rectified but unfiltered collec- tor supply voltage of the chopping frequency, Fig. 8-33. The efficiency of the power amplifier is greater than that of a conven- tional class-B amplifier using a dc collector supply voltage. The reason for this is that the pulsating collector supply reduces the average power dissipation in each transistor. It is conventional to drive the servomotor directly without an output transformer, al- though this requires a center-tapped motor winding. The other phase winding of the motor is fed directly from the ac line through a phase-shifting capacitor C_2. This provides a 90° phase shift be- tween the currents in the two windings, as required by a two-phase motor. Capacitor C_1 resonates the motor winding at the chopping frequency so that the motor presents a resistive load to the ampli- fier. The circuit of Fig. 8-33 is a grounded-collector push-pull amplifier using diodes for temperature compensation of the base bias, as described in the previous chapter. Grounded-emitter and common-base circuits are also used for servo amplifiers.

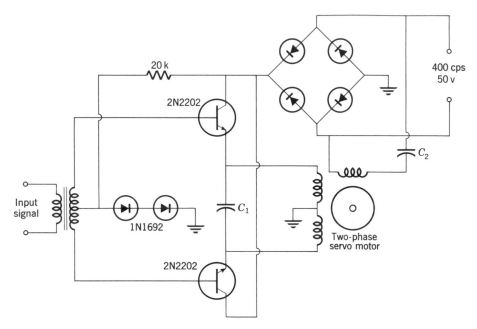

FIGURE 8-33   *Push-pull servo power amplifier.*

The increased efficiency accompanying an unfiltered collector supply is analyzed in the following way. Each transistor is con-sidered a switch with internal resistance R_T which depends upon the magnitude of the input signal. The internal resistance is very large for a small input signal and reaches a lower limit called the collector saturation resistance for large values of input signal. The internal resistance of the transistors determines the magnitude of the supply voltage that is delivered to the load. This analysis is epitomized by an equivalent circuit consisting of R_T in series with the load resistance R_L and a voltage generator $V_p/\sqrt{2}$ for each tran-

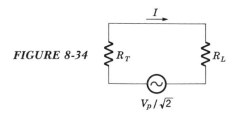

FIGURE 8-34

sistor. V_p is the peak value of the rectified collector supply poten-tial, Fig. 8-34.

Using this equivalent circuit, the average power delivered to the load by each transistor is

$$P_L = \frac{1}{2} I^2 R_L = \frac{V_p^2 R_L}{4(R_L + R_T)^2} \tag{8-60}$$

where the factor $1/2$ results from the fact that each transistor is active for only one-half of the input cycle because of the class-B operation of the power amplifier. Similarly, the power dissipated in each transistor is

$$P_T = \frac{1}{2} I^2 R_T = \frac{V_p^2 R_T}{4(R_L + R_T)^2} = \frac{V_p^2}{4R_L} \frac{R_T/R_L}{(1 + R_T/R_L)^2} \tag{8-61}$$

The power efficiency is, from Eqs. (8-60) and (8-61),

$$\eta = \frac{P_L}{P_L + P_T} = \frac{R_L}{R_L + R_T} = \frac{1}{1 + R_T/R_L} \tag{8-62}$$

which indicates that the efficiency approaches 100 percent when $R_T \ll R_L$. Although this ideal is not achieved in practical amplifiers, efficiencies greater than those of conventional class-B stages can be attained.

Note that according to Eq. (8-61) the power dissipated in each transistor is small when R_T is large, that is, when the input signal is zero. Transistor dissipation is also small when maximum power is delivered to the load ($R_T \ll R_L$) corresponding to a large input signal. This means that the power lost in the power amplifier is smallest not only when the servo is quiescent, but also when the servo is striving to attain a new stable position corresponding to a change in the input signal. These two conditions are predominant in normal servo applications. This analysis shows that deleterious heating effects caused by transistor dissipation are minimized by the use of an unfiltered collector supply voltage.

SUGGESTIONS FOR FURTHER READING

E. J. Angelo, Jr.: "Electronic Circuits," McGraw-Hill Book Company, New York, 1964.

H. V. Malmstadt, C. G. Enke, and E. C. Toren, Jr.: "Electronics for Scientists," W. A. Benjamin, Inc., New York, 1963.

R. D. Middlebrook: "Differential Amplifiers," John Wiley & Sons, Inc., New York, 1963.

EXERCISES

8-1 Draw the equivalent circuit of the bridged-T feedback amplifier, Fig. 8-5. Plot the characteristic curve of the filter alone, that is, the frequency variation of β, and determine the response curve of the feedback amplifier. Use small signal parameters given in Chap. 5.

8-2   Consider the transistor bias circuit, Fig. 6-21, as a feedback amplifier and calculate β. Derive an expression for the gain and compare with the results of Exercise 6-6.   *Ans.:* 1.4×10^{-3}, 262

8-3   Consider the emitter follower, Fig. 6-30, as a feedback amplifier.
Derive an expression for the gain corresponding to Eq. (5-31).

8-4   Calculate the input and output impedance of the transistor feedback amplifier in Fig. 8-3. The h parameters are $h_{ie} = 3600 \ \Omega$,
$h_{fe} = 150$, $h_{re} = 3 \times 10^{-3}$, $h_{oe} = 1.4 \times 10^{-4}$ mho.

Ans.: $3.56 \times 10^6 \ \Omega$, $7.6 \ \Omega$

8-5   Analyze the circuit of Fig. 6-25 as an amplifier with current feedback if the emitter bypass capacitor is omitted. Calculate β and the
gain and compare with the corresponding expression for a vacuum-
tube amplifier, Eq. (5-26).   *Ans.:* 1, 3.3

8-6   Derive an expression for the input impedance of a feedback amplifier with both voltage and current feedback. Use this expression to
show that both current and voltage negative feedback increase the
input impedance. Using Eq. (8-27) find the expression for the input impedance when the output impedance is zero.

8-7   Determine β_v and β_i of the push-pull amplifier, Fig. 8-10. The un-
fedback gain is 14,000, $r_p = 73,000 \ \Omega$ for a type 6973 tube, and the
gain of the push-pull stage is 12. Calculate the midband gain with
feedback and the output impedance.   *Ans.:* 0.1, 1, 10, 0.1 Ω

8-8   Explain qualitatively the purpose of each resistor and capacitor in
the transistor chopper amplifier, Fig. 8-16a.

8-9   Explain qualitatively the purpose of each resistor and capacitor in
the vacuum-tube chopper amplifier, Fig. 8-16b.

8-10   Design an analog computer to solve the falling-body problem, for
which the equation is

$$\frac{d^2x}{dt^2} = mg \tag{8-63}$$

where m is the mass of the body and g is the acceleration due to
gravity.

8-11   Simplify the analog computer of Fig. 8-22 by eliminating one
operational amplifier. *Hint:* Consider an alternative way of carrying out the summing operation of amplifier 3.

8-12   Compute the input and output impedance of the operational
amplifier, Fig. 8-14, connected as a voltage follower. The nominal
input and output impedance of the amplifier are 200,000 Ω and
100 Ω, respectively, and the gain is 30,000.

Ans.: $6 \times 10^9 \ \Omega$; $3.3 \times 10^{-3} \ \Omega$

8-13   Consider resistor R_1 in Fig. 8-25 to be an arbitrary load and show
that the circuit controls the current in the load. Is any current
drawn from the standard battery?

8-14   Starting with Eq. (8-48) for a regulated power supply, reduce it
to Eq. (8-49) by introducing T-equivalent parameters from Table
6-3 and considering the magnitude of the parameters.

8-15 Draw the equivalent circuit of a vacuum-tube voltage regulator analogous to Fig. 8-26 and derive Eq. (8-50).

8-16 Determine the regulation factor and internal resistance of the transistor regulated power supply, Fig. 8-28. Assume properties of the control transistor given in the text and that the h parameters of the 2N2049 are the same as those given in Exercise 6-10.

Ans.: 4.5×10^{-4}; $2.3 \ \Omega$

8-17 Calculate the approximate regulation factor and internal resistance of the vacuum-tube regulator, Fig. 8-29. Use the small signal parameters given in Chap. 5 for the 12AX7 and assume $g_m = 6000 \times 10^{-6}$ mho, $r_p = 22,500 \ \Omega$ for the 6L6. Note that the plate resistances of the two control tubes are in parallel.

Ans.: 7.1×10^{-6}; $0.16 \ \Omega$

8-18 Analyze the simple shunt regulator in Fig. 8-35 to determine the

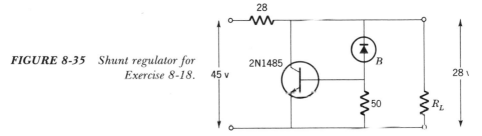

FIGURE 8-35 *Shunt regulator for Exercise 8-18.*

effective internal resistance and regulation factor. The h parameters are $h_{ie} = 100 \ \Omega$, $h_{re} = 10^{-4}$, $h_{fe} = 60$, $h_{oe} = 175 \times 10^{-6}$ mho.

Ans.: 5.9×10^{-2}; $1.6 \ \Omega$

8-19 What are the output voltage extremes of the regulated power supply in Fig. 8-29 obtainable by adjusting the 100,000-Ω potentiometer? Assume that the tubes in the circuit are neither saturated nor cut off at these extremes. *Ans.:* 436 volts, 264 volts

8-20 Show that the method of connecting the reference potential in the circuit of Fig. 8-29 is equivalent, with respect to the voltage polarities involved, to Fig. 8-28.

9
OSCILLATORS

Electronic circuits can generate ac signals of a variety of waveforms over a wide range of frequencies. In fact, transistor and vacuum-tube oscillators are the only convenient way of generating high-frequency voltages. They are widely used in radio and TV transmitters and receivers, for dielectric and induction heating, and in electronic instruments for timing and testing purposes. An oscillator, in effect, converts power delivered by the dc supply voltages into ac power having the desired characteristics. In addition to the frequency and waveform of the oscillations, the conversion efficiency and frequency stability are important in the design of oscillator circuits.

POSITIVE FEEDBACK

Oscillation is achieved through positive feedback which produces an output signal without any input signal. According to Eq. (8-4), the gain of a feedback amplifier is given by

$$a' = \frac{a}{1 - a\beta} \qquad (9\text{-}1)$$

If circuit conditions are arranged so that

$$a\beta = 1 \qquad (9\text{-}2)$$

the gain becomes infinite, which means that an output signal exists even when the input signal is zero. For sinusoidal oscillations the feedback network is designed so that Eq. (9-2), called the *Barkhausen criterion*, is satisfied at only one frequency, and the circuit oscillates at that frequency. The Barkhausen criterion requires that the overall phase shift of the feedback signal be 360°, and this is the significant factor in determining the frequency of oscillation. In addition, the amplifier gain must be large enough to assure that the $a\beta$ product is equal to unity, in order for the oscillations to persist.

The amplitude of oscillation is determined indirectly by Eq. (9-2). The gain of any amplifier is reduced at large signal amplitudes because of cutoff and saturation conditions in the transistors or vacuum tubes. Accordingly, the quiescent amplitude is such that the absolute value of gain is $1/\beta$. Since the feedback network is most often a passive circuit, the amplitude depends primarily upon amplifier characteristics.

It is not necessary to supply an input signal in order to initiate oscillations. Random noise voltages or transients accompanying application of the supply voltages are sufficient to start the feedback process. Since the amplitude of the feedback signal depends upon amplifier gain, the rapidity with which the oscillations reach the steady-state magnitude increases when the gain is large. It is usually desirable for the small-signal gain to be significantly larger than required by the Barkhausen criterion. This produces strong oscillations unaffected by minor circuit changes. On the other hand, if the gain is very great, nonsinusoidal oscillations may result from nonlinearities accompanying large signal amplitudes.

RC OSCILLATORS

9-1   Phase-shift oscillator

A simple but useful oscillator circuit employing a conventional amplifier stage and an *RC* feedback network is the *phase-shift oscillator*, Fig. 9-1.   The grounded-emitter stage has an inherent phase

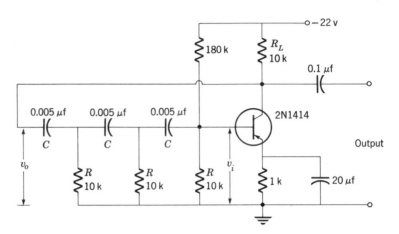

FIGURE 9-1   *Phase-shift oscillator.*

shift of 180°, so the three cascaded *RC* circuits shift the phase an additional 180° in order to satisfy the Barkhausen criterion.   At some particular frequency the phase shift in each *RC* section is 60°, so the total phase shift in the feedback network is 180° and the circuit oscillates at this frequency, provided the amplification is great enough.   Note that the maximum phase shift in one *RC* section is limited to 90°.   This means that a two-section feedback network is not possible because it would require an infinite gain to overcome the attenuation in the feedback network at a total phase shift of 180°.   Conversely, there is no particular advantage to having more than three *RC* sections in the feedback network, although it is possible to design such an oscillator.

The phase-shift oscillator is analyzed by first ignoring the loading effect of the amplifier upon the network.   Considering that a voltage v_o is applied to the feedback network, the signal v_i applied to the transistor can be calculated by straightforward network analysis (Exercise 9-1).   The result is

$$\beta = \frac{v_i}{v_o} = \frac{1}{1 - 5/(\omega RC)^2 + j[1/(\omega RC)^3 - 6/\omega RC]} \tag{9-3}$$

In order for the phase shift of the feedback network to be 180°, the imaginary part of Eq. (9-3) must vanish, or

$$\frac{1}{(\omega_0 RC)^3} = \frac{6}{\omega_0 RC} \tag{9-4}$$

The oscillation frequency is found by solving for $f_0 = \omega_0/2\pi$,

$$f_0 = \frac{1}{2\pi\sqrt{6}} \frac{1}{RC} \tag{9-5}$$

Inserting Eq. (9-5) into Eq. (9-3), $\beta = 1/(1 - 5 \times 6) = -1/29$, which means that the gain must be

$$a = \frac{1}{\beta} = -29 \tag{9-6}$$

in order to satisfy the Barkhausen criterion. According to this result the amplification must be at least 29 or the circuit cannot oscillate.

Actually the amplifier gain must be somewhat larger than 29 in order to assure stable oscillations in the face of circuit losses and component aging effects. The amplitude of oscillations increases until limited to a value of 29 by nonlinearities in the transistor. Most often, the onset of cutoff at the peak of the wave is the limiting factor, and a peak signal amplitude nearly equal to the quiescent collector potential is expected.

In a practical circuit the loading of the amplifier upon the feedback network cannot be ignored. For example, consider the

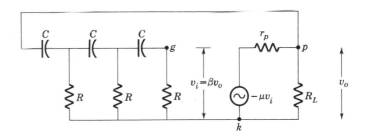

FIGURE 9-2 *Equivalent circuit of vacuum-tube phase-shift oscillator.*

equivalent circuit of a vacuum-tube phase-shift oscillator, Fig. 9-2. Using Eq. (5-16) for the gain of a vacuum-tube amplifier,

$$v_o = \frac{-\mu v_i}{1 + r_p/Z_L} = \frac{-\mu \beta v_o}{1 + r_p/Z_L} \tag{9-7}$$

where Z_L is the parallel combination of the plate load resistor R_L with the input impedance of the feedback network, Z_i. Solving for β,

$$\beta = -\frac{1}{\mu}\left(1 + \frac{r_p}{Z_L}\right) = -\frac{r_p}{\mu}\left(\frac{1}{r_p} + \frac{1}{Z_L}\right) \tag{9-8}$$

$$\beta = -\frac{1}{g_m}\left(\frac{1}{r_p} + \frac{1}{R_L} + \frac{1}{Z_i}\right) \tag{9-9}$$

This result, together with Eq. (9-6), determines the characteristics of the vacuum tube necessary for the circuit to oscillate. Note that the impedance of the feedback network is included in Eq. (9-9). A similar result applies to the transistor phase-shift oscillator except that the loading effect of the transistor input impedance must also be taken into account (see Exercise 9-2).

The simplicity of the phase-shift oscillator makes it attractive for noncritical applications, particularly at medium and low frequencies down to about 1 cps. The frequency stability is not as good as can be obtained with other RC oscillators, however. In addition, in order to change frequency it is necessary to vary all three capacitors (or the three resistors), and this is inconvenient.

9-2 Wien-bridge oscillator

The frequency-selective properties of the Wien bridge discussed in Chap. 3, Fig. 3-14, are very appropriate for the feedback network of an oscillator. The *Wien-bridge oscillator*, Fig. 9-3, is widely

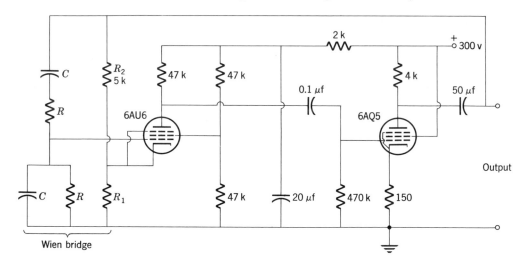

FIGURE 9-3 *Wien-bridge oscillator.*

used for variable-frequency laboratory instruments called *signal generators*. A conventional two-stage amplifier provides positive feedback at the resonant frequency of the bridge, where, according to Eq. (3-77), the phase shift in the feedback network is zero. The characteristic frequency is, from Eq. (3-73),

$$f_0 = \frac{1}{2\pi RC}. \tag{9-10}$$

The output voltage of the Wien bridge is zero at exact balance when $R_2 = 2R_1$ (refer to Fig. 3-15), so it is necessary to unbalance the bridge slightly by adjusting the ratio R_2/R_1. This provides sufficient feedback voltage to maintain stable oscillations, since the feedback ratio is determined by the relative values of R_1 and R_2. It is common practice to use a small tungsten-filament lamp bulb for R_1 in order to stabilize the amplitude of the oscillations. The way this comes about is as follows. The tungsten lamp-bulb filament has a positive temperature coefficient of resistance. If the output of the amplifier increases for any reason, the greater current through the lamp increases the filament temperature and therefore its resistance. Accordingly, the feedback voltage is decreased and the amplitude of oscillation returns to nearly the original value.

The excellent frequency stability of the Wien-bridge oscillator compared with the phase-shift oscillator is a result of the rapid change of phase of the feedback voltage with frequency. The feedback ratio is, from Eq. (3-77),

$$\beta = \frac{v_o}{v_i} = \frac{1}{3 + j(\omega/\omega_0 - \omega_0/\omega)} - \frac{1}{1 + R_2/R_1} \tag{9-11}$$

The phase shift is found by rationalizing Eq. (9-11) and computing the tangent of the phase angle. For frequencies near to the resonant frequency, the result is

$$\tan \theta \cong \frac{1 + R_2/R_1}{9 - 3(1 + R_2/R_1)} \left(\frac{\omega}{\omega_0} - \frac{\omega_0}{\omega} \right) \tag{9-12}$$

If, for example, $R_2 = 1.9R_1$, the coefficient of the frequency term in Eq. (9-12) is equal to 9.7. By comparison, the corresponding expression for the phase-shift oscillator is, after rationalizing Eq. (9-3),

$$\tan \theta \cong -\frac{\sqrt{6}}{5} \left(\frac{\omega}{\omega_0} - \frac{\omega_0}{\omega} \right) \tag{9-13}$$

where Eq. (9-5) has been used to introduce ω_0. The numerical factor in Eq. (9-13) is only 0.49, which is smaller by a factor of 20 than in the case of the Wien bridge.

This comparison is illustrated more clearly in Fig. 9-4 where the phase angle of the feedback signal is plotted as a function of ω/ω_0 for both oscillators. The phase angle changes much more rapidly with frequency in the Wien-bridge feedback circuit. This means that the oscillation frequency is quite stable since only feedback signals with a near-zero phase angle are effective.

The excellent frequency stability together with the relative ease in changing frequency (only the two capacitors need be variable) makes the Wien-bridge oscillator popular. In most practical circuits the variable capacitors provide a frequency range of about

10 to 1. In addition, fixed decade values of the resistors are selected by a switch so that a wide frequency range can be covered
in a single instrument. A typical commercial Wien-bridge oscillator can have a frequency range extending from 5 cps to 1 Mc
in decade steps.

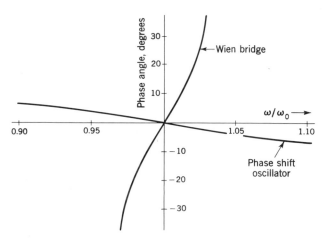

FIGURE 9-4 *Phase-shift characteristics
near resonant frequency for two RC
oscillators.*

RESONANT CIRCUIT OSCILLATORS

9-3 *LC* oscillators

Resonant *LC* circuits are often used in the feedback network of
oscillators to select the frequency of oscillation. Consider the so-
called *Hartley oscillator,* Fig. 9-5, in which a parallel resonant cir-

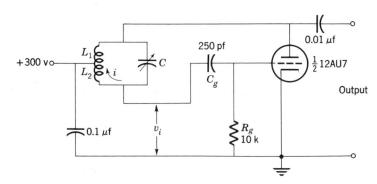

FIGURE 9-5 *Hartley oscillator.*

cuit is connected between grid and plate. The inductance is
tapped so that, in effect, the portion L_1 is part of the plate load

while the remainder L_2 is in the grid circuit. The resonant frequency involves the series inductance of L_1 and L_2, so that, as in Chap. 3,

$$\omega_0 = \frac{1}{\sqrt{(L_1 + L_2)C}} \tag{9-14}$$

The feedback ratio is determined by first calculating the feedback voltage across L_2,

$$v_i = ij\omega L_2 = \frac{v_0 j\omega L_2}{j\omega L_2 + 1/j\omega C} \tag{9-15}$$

Introducing the resonance condition $\omega_0(L_1 + L_2) = 1/\omega_0 C$,

$$v_i = v_0 \frac{\omega_0 L_2}{-\omega_0 L_1} \tag{9-16}$$

so that the feedback ratio is just

$$\beta = -\frac{L_2}{L_1} \tag{9-17}$$

Note that the ratio is negative, which means that the additional 180° phase shift of the amplifier produces positive feedback as required. Equation (9-17) and the Barkhausen criterion specify the gain of the amplifier needed to sustain oscillations.

The bias conditions in the Hartley oscillator are worthy of note. Operating bias is supplied by the $R_g C_g$ combination in the grid circuit. When oscillations start, the grid bias is zero. As oscillations build up, the grid-cathode diode rectifies the feedback signal, thereby charging C_g to nearly the peak value of the input signal. The $R_g C_g$ time constant is much longer than the period of oscillation so that the voltage across C_g is constant and represents the necessary dc grid bias. In effect, the grid is clamped at ground potential (compare Figs. 4-37 and 4-38). The grid bias therefore automatically adjusts itself to the amplitude of the feedback signal and this action stabilizes the amplitude of oscillation.

This form of bias means that the circuit operates as a class-C amplifier. The large impedance of the resonant circuit allows only the fundamental component of the output signal to have any appreciable amplitude, however, so that the output waveform is sinusoidal. Another way of explaining the action of the resonant circuit is to say that the circuit is excited by periodic pulses from the class-C amplifier and that a continuous wave is produced by ringing in the resonant circuit. These two explanations are equivalent.

The *Colpitts oscillator,* Fig. 9-6, is similar to the Hartley circuit except that the feedback ratio is determined by the relative values of C_1 and C_2 (see Exercise 9-9). Base bias in this circuit is such that the transistor operates as a class-A amplifier, but class-C opera-

tion equivalent to the Hartley oscillator is equally possible.   The
output load is coupled to the resonant circuit with a secondary
winding L_o, which is particularly useful in feeding low-impedance
loads.

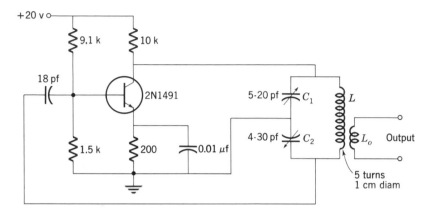

FIGURE 9-6   *70-Mc Colpitts oscillator.*

Another way to develop feedback voltage is by including a secondary winding, or *tickler* winding, coupled to the inductance.
Consider, for example, the grounded-base oscillator, Fig. 9-7a.

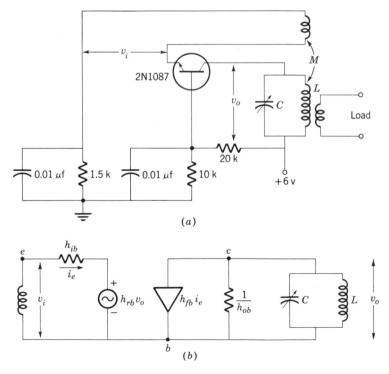

FIGURE 9-7   (a) *Grounded-base tickler oscillator*
and (b) *equivalent circuit.*

Mutual inductance between L and the tickler winding induces a feedback signal of the proper amplitude and phase to sustain oscillations. From the definition of mutual inductance in Chap. 2, the feedback voltage is just the ratio of the mutual inductance M between coils to the total inductance L times the voltage across L [see Eqs. (2-89) and (2-70)]. Therefore

$$v_i = \frac{M}{L} v_o \qquad (9\text{-}18)$$

or

$$\beta = \frac{v_i}{v_o} = \frac{M}{L} \qquad (9\text{-}19)$$

The equivalent circuit of the oscillator, Fig. 9-7b, is analyzed in the following way. The impedance of the parallel resonant circuit is very large at resonance, so the gain of the grounded-base amplifier is, from Eq. (6-48),

$$a = \frac{-1}{h_{ib}h_{ob}/h_{rb} - h_{ib}} = \frac{1}{r_e/\alpha r_c + r_b/r_c}$$

$$= \frac{\alpha r_c}{r_e + \alpha r_b} \cong \frac{r_c}{r_b} = \frac{1}{h_{rb}} \qquad (9\text{-}20)$$

Applying the Barkhausen criterion, the condition for oscillation is obtained by comparing Eqs. (9-20) and (9-19),

$$h_{rb} = \frac{M}{L} \qquad (9\text{-}21)$$

In a good-quality transistor h_{rb} is of the order of 10^{-4}, which means that the mutual inductance may be quite small. Accordingly, a tickler winding consisting of only a few turns is sufficient. This is fortunate since the small input impedance of the amplifier is best matched with a large turns ratio between L and the feedback winding.

A major advantage of the tickler feedback circuit is that the amplitude of the feedback voltage can be easily adjusted by choosing the number of turns on the feedback winding. The proper phase is obtained by interchanging the leads of the winding, if necessary, to obtain positive feedback. Thus, although Fig. 9-7 is a grounded-base circuit, the grounded-emitter and grounded-collector configurations are equally useful. Furthermore, the resonant circuit can be put in the emitter or base circuits as well. The specific configuration illustrated by Fig. 9-7 is particularly appropriate for good frequency stability, as discussed below.

Class-C operation of transistor oscillators is often used in circuits designed to develop appreciable power at high frequencies. Figure 9-8 is the circuit diagram of a typical power oscillator. The overall power efficiency of an oscillator is not as good as that of a class-C amplifier. Input circuit losses must be supplied by the oscillator itself, but even so, efficiencies of the order of 70 percent

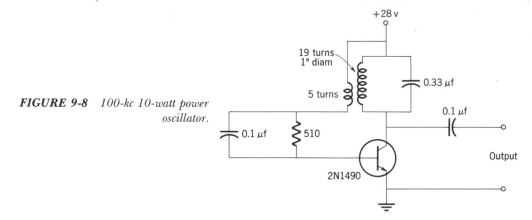

FIGURE 9-8   *100-kc 10-watt power oscillator.*

are possible. In this circuit, base bias is developed by the resistor-capacitor combination in the base-emitter circuit analogous to the action in the Hartley vacuum-tube oscillator.

9-4 Crystal oscillators

The frequency stability of *LC* oscillators is determined primarily by the *Q* factor of the resonant circuit. The resonance curve is sharply peaked and the rate of change of phase with frequency is rapid when the *Q* is large, and both factors contribute to frequency stability of the oscillator. In this connection, any equivalent resistance connected in parallel with the resonant circuit lowers the effective *Q*. Therefore, the loading effect on the resonant circuit should be minimized to improve frequency stability. According to the discussion in Chap. 6, the output impedance of the grounded-base amplifier is larger than for any other configuration. This is why the grounded-base oscillator with the resonant combination in the collector circuit is the most satisfactory transistor oscillator configuration. Correspondingly, vacuum-tube oscillators most often have the resonant circuit in the grid circuit. In either case, practical values of *Q* from 100 to 500 can be obtained, and quite stable oscillations result.

Many applications require a higher order of frequency stability than can be obtained with *LC* resonant circuits, and *crystal oscillators* are widely used to fill this need. Certain crystalline materials, most notably quartz, exhibit piezoelectric properties, that is, they deform mechanically when subjected to an electric field. Piezoelectricity also implies that the inverse is also true: when the crystal is forcibly deformed, an electric potential is developed between opposing faces of the crystal. As a result of this piezoelectric property, a thin plate of quartz provided with conducting electrodes vibrates mechanically when the electrodes are connected to an alternating voltage source. The vibrations, in turn, produce electrical signals which interact with the voltage source. The vibrations and electrical signals are a maximum at the natural mechanical resonant frequency of the crystal.

The equation for the motion of a vibrating body has already been written in Eq. (8-40),

$$m \frac{dx^2}{dt^2} + b \frac{dx}{dt} + kx = F(t) \tag{9-22}$$

where in the present case m is the mass of the crystal, b is the internal mechanical loss coefficient, and k is the elastic constant of the crystal. As has already been noted, this expression is identical in form with that for the current in a series resonant circuit, Eq. (3-28),

$$L \frac{d^2i}{dt^2} + R \frac{di}{dt} + \frac{1}{C} i = F(t) \tag{9-23}$$

Comparing Eqs. (9-22) and (9-23) it can be seen that the vibrating mass is analogous to inductance, mechanical losses are equivalent to resistance, and the elasticity corresponds to the reciprocal of capacitance. Because of the identical form of the two equations, mechanical resonance is expected, and it is useful to define a mechanical Q factor by analogy with Eq. (3-54),

$$Q = \frac{\omega m}{b} \tag{9-24}$$

It turns out that the internal losses in quartz crystals are very small and that Q values reaching as high as 100,000 can be achieved. Furthermore, the elastic constants are such that resonant frequencies ranging from 10 kc to several tens of megacycles are possible, depending upon the mechanical size and shape of the crystal.

The piezoelectric properties of quartz result in electrode potentials corresponding to the mechanical vibrations. This suggests that the electrical characteristics can be represented by an equivalent circuit. Comparing Eqs. (9-22) and (9-23), the appropriate circuit is a series combination of a resistance, inductance, and capacitance. To this must be added the electric capacitance resulting from the parallel-plate capacitance of the electrodes with the crystal as a dielectric. Therefore, the complete equivalent circuit of a quartz crystal is the series-parallel combination shown in Fig. 9-9a. In this equivalent circuit L, C, and R are related to the properties of the quartz crystal and C' is the electrostatic capacitance of the electrodes. Appropriate values for a 90-kc crystal are $L = 137$ henrys, $C = 0.0235$ pf, $R = 15,000\ \Omega$, and $C' = 3.5$ pf. The conventional circuit symbol for a crystal is a parallel-plate capacitor with the crystal between the plates, Fig. 9-9b.

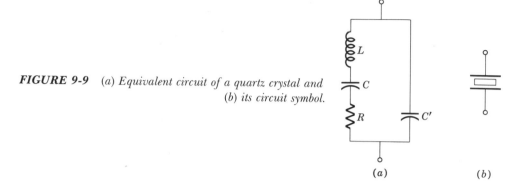

FIGURE 9-9 (a) Equivalent circuit of a quartz crystal and (b) its circuit symbol.

(a) (b)

The series-parallel equivalent circuit of a quartz crystal shows that there will be a series resonant frequency (zero impedance) and a parallel resonant frequency (infinite impedance). The frequency of a series resonance is $\omega_S = 1/\sqrt{LC}$. The parallel resonance occurs when the reactance of C' equals the net inductive reactance of the combination of L and C, $\omega_P = \sqrt{1/L(1/C + 1/C')}$. Accordingly, the parallel resonant frequency is always greater than the series resonant frequency, although, since $C' \gg C$, the two are very close. The reactance is capacitive both below and above the resonant frequencies, Fig. 9-10.

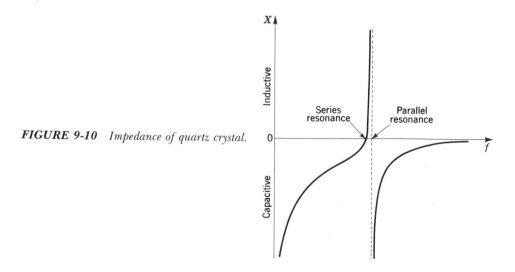

FIGURE 9-10 *Impedance of quartz crystal.*

Extremely stable oscillator circuits are possible with the large Q of a quartz resonator, and a variety of circuits have been designed.

Either the series or parallel resonance frequency may be used, although parallel resonance is more common. Consider, for example, the *Pierce oscillator,* Fig. 9-11, in which the crystal is connected between base and collector. This circuit is identical to

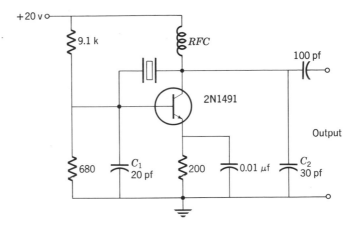

+20 v

9.1 k

RFC

100 pf

2N1491

Output

680

C_1
20 pf

200

0.01 µf

C_2
30 pf

FIGURE 9-11   *Quartz-crystal oscillator.*

the Colpitts oscillator, Fig. 9-6, with the crystal replacing the resonant circuit. The feedback ratio is determined by the relative values of C_1 and C_9. The inductance RFC (for *radio frequency choke*) in the collector lead is a useful way of applying collector potential without shorting the collector to ground at the signal frequency. It can be replaced by a 10,000-Ω resistor with some loss in circuit performance. A parallel resonant LC combination can also be used with attendant gain in circuit performance. In the latter case the resonant circuit is merely a convenient collector load impedance and does not determine the oscillation frequency.

Quartz is almost universally used in crystal oscillators because it is hard, reasonably strong, and has a small temperature coefficient of expansion. Suitable orientation of the plane faces with respect to the crystalline structure makes the resonant frequency independent of temperature over a reasonable range. As a result, frequency stability of the order of 100 ppm can be achieved. Even greater accuracy is obtained by placing the crystal in a temperature-controlled oven and evacuating the crystal holder to reduce air damping forces on the vibrating crystal. It is also common practice to stabilize the temperature of the remainder of the circuit and to employ a regulated power supply for the oscillator. Amplifier stages are used to isolate the oscillator from variations in load. Such carefully designed crystal oscillators provide an extremely precise standard of time which can be accurate to 1 part in 100 million.

RELAXATION OSCILLATORS

Oscillator circuits discussed to this point can be analyzed in terms of linear elements. Circuits which employ nonlinear active elements are termed *relaxation oscillators* for reasons which become clear in the following discussion. Very often relaxation oscillators are based upon negative resistance properties of the active element. Although, as discussed in connection with the tunnel-diode oscillator in Chap. 4, it is possible to generate a sinusoidal waveform using a negative-resistance characteristic, relaxation oscillators characteristically produce nonsinusoidal signals.

9-5 Sawtooth generators

Consider the neon-tube relaxation-oscillator circuit in Fig. 9-12. The operation of this circuit can be understood after examining

FIGURE 9-12   *Neon-tube relaxation oscillator.*

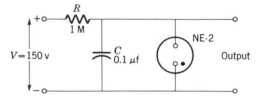

the current-voltage characteristic of a neon tube, Fig. 9-13. The neon tube is a gas-discharge device similar to a VR tube. Voltage V_b required to initiate the discharge is larger than V_m, which main-

FIGURE 9-13   *Current-voltage characteristic of neon glow-discharge tube.*

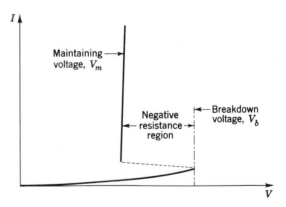

tains the discharge once it has been started. Therefore, as the voltage across the tube is increased from zero, the terminal voltage suddenly drops from V_b to V_m as soon as the discharge starts. The dashed line in Fig. 9-13 is a negative-resistance region of the characteristic since the current increases as the voltage decreases. Typical values for V_b and V_m are 90 and 70 volts, respectively, for the NE-2 type neon tube.

The neon-tube oscillator, Fig. 9-12, operates as follows: Capacitor C charges through resistor R and the voltage across C increases exponentially (refer to Exercise 3-18) until the breakdown potential V_b is attained. At this point gas discharge begins and the voltage immediately drops to V_m. The resistor R is too large to supply sufficient current to maintain the discharge, the tube turns off, and the capacitor begins to recharge. The output waveform, Fig. 9-14, is a series of RC charging curves with a peak-to-peak

FIGURE 9-14 *Waveform of neon-tube relaxation oscillator.*

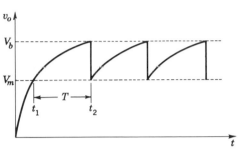

amplitude equal to $V_b - V_m$. Note that following every charging period the circuit "relaxes" back to the starting point. This is the origin of the terminology for this type of oscillator.

The period of oscillation is found from the expression for the capacitor voltage in a simple RC circuit,

$$v = V(1 - e^{-t/RC})$$

The voltage reaches V_m at t_1,

$$V_m = V(1 - e^{-t_1/RC}) \tag{9-25}$$

Solving for t_1

$$t_1 = -RC \ln (1 - V_m/V) \tag{9-26}$$

Similarly, the voltage reaches V_b at t_2, so that

$$t_2 = -RC \ln (1 - V_b/V) \tag{9-27}$$

The period of the oscillation is just $t_2 - t_1$, or

$$T = RC \ln \frac{V - V_m}{V - V_b} \tag{9-28}$$

According to Eq. (9-28) the oscillation frequency depends upon the properties of the neon tube and magnitude of the supply voltage, as well as upon the circuit time constant. This equation assumes that the discharge time is zero, which is not true in practical neon tubes. Because of the finite discharge time, neon-tube relaxation oscillators are limited to frequencies less than about 50 kc.

The frequency stability of relaxation oscillators is inherently, and characteristically, very poor. The initiation of a gas discharge is a probabilistic phenomenon, which means that the discharge does not always start exactly at the potential V_b. Furthermore, the rate of change of the capacitor voltage is comparatively slow. This means that the exact instant at which the discharge is initiated varies slightly from cycle to cycle. In many applications, however, the poor frequency stability is an advantage since the oscillations can be *triggered,* or *synchronized* by an external signal.

Suppose, for example, that a synchronizing signal comprising a series of sharp voltage pulses is applied across the resistor. The

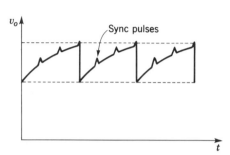

FIGURE 9-15   *Synchronizing the frequency of a relaxation oscillator.*

capacitor voltage then includes these pulses, Fig. 9-15. The sharp voltage rise of one of the pulses causes the capacitor voltage to exceed V_b at some point and the neon tube is triggered into conduction. This repeats on successive cycles with the result that the frequency of oscillation is synchronized to the period of the pulse signal. Note that the period of the relaxation oscillator is a multiple or submultiple of the period of the pulses. In this way a relaxation oscillator acts as a frequency multiplier or divider. Frequency division by a factor as large as 10 or so is easily possible.

The free-running frequency of the relaxation oscillator must be reasonably close to a multiple or submultiple of the sync frequency. Since, however, the frequency stability of a relaxation oscillator is poor, the disparity may be as large as 20 percent or so without loss of synchronization. Triggering by a sinusoidal synchronizing voltage is also possible. Sharp pulses are more effective, however, since the time at which the breakdown voltage is attained is more definite.

The waveform of a neon-tube oscillator is a crude approximation to a sawtooth wave. A more accurate sawtooth waveform can be obtained in several ways. The simplest technique is to restrict the oscillation to a very small portion of the RC charging cycle. Note that if the equation for the voltage across the capacitor is expanded in a series,

$$v = V[1 - 1 - (-t/RC) - (-t/RC)^2/2 + \cdots] \tag{9-29}$$

$$v = \frac{V}{RC} t - \frac{V}{2} \left(\frac{t}{RC}\right)^2 + \cdots \tag{9-30}$$

The second term is negligible if the charging time is much smaller

than the RC time constant. Then the voltage increases linearly
with time, as in a sawtooth wave. The period of oscillation is
small compared with the time constant when the dc supply voltage
is very large. Using Eq. (9-28), if $V \gg V_m$ and $V \gg V_b$,

$$\frac{T}{RC} = \ln\frac{V}{V} = \ln 1 = 0 \qquad (9\text{-}31)$$

which means $T \ll RC$ and the waveform is a sawtooth. Any
departure from linearity can be calculated by computing the
second term in Eq. (9-30).

   The current-voltage characteristic of an SCR, Fig. 4-29, is similar
in form to that of the neon tube. However, the breakdown voltage
is easily adjusted by varying the gate current. This means that
the amplitude and frequency of oscillation can be changed in a
relaxation oscillator. Furthermore, synchronizing signals can be
introduced into the gate circuit to take advantage of the inherent
amplification of the SCR.

   A useful relaxation oscillator employing an SCR is shown in
Fig. 9-16. The gate potential is determined by the variable volt-

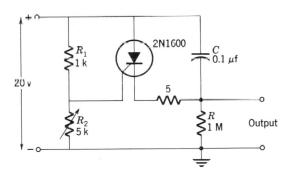

FIGURE 9-16 *SCR relaxation oscillator.*

age divider comprising R_1 and R_2. Initially, when C is uncharged,
the cathode of the SCR is at a potential of 20 volts with respect
to ground, so the gate is biased in the reverse direction. As the
capacitor voltage increases, the SCR remains switched off until
the cathode potential becomes slightly less positive than the gate.
At this point the SCR switches on, the capacitor is discharged, and
the cycle repeats. The purpose of the 5-Ω resistor in series with
the cathode is to limit the discharge current to a safe value for the
SCR. This is necessary because the internal resistance of the SCR
in the on state is so small that the peak current can be destructive.

   A convenient way of generating a true sawtooth waveform is to
replace the series charging resistor in a relaxation oscillator by a
constant-current transistor, Fig. 9-17. Since the charging current
is constant, the capacitor voltage increases linearly with time according to

$$v = \frac{q}{C} = \frac{I}{C}t \qquad (9\text{-}32)$$

where I is the current value and t is the time measured from when the capacitor voltage is zero.

A transistor is an excellent constant-current source since the collector current is essentially equal to the emitter current quite

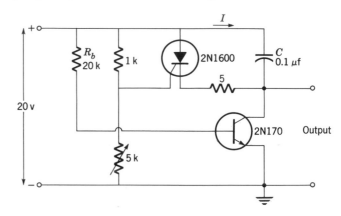

FIGURE 9-17   *Relaxation sawtooth generator.*

independent of the collector potential (refer to typical collector characteristics, Fig. 6-11). The emitter current is determined by the base bias resistor R_b. It can be made adjustable in order to vary the charging current and consequently the period of oscillation. The use of a constant-current source means that the peak amplitude of the sawtooth is nearly as large as the dc supply voltage, which is advantageous in most applications.

Another form of relaxation oscillator is exemplified by the tunnel-diode circuit, Fig. 9-18. Note that the current-voltage char-

FIGURE 9-18   *Tunnel-diode relaxation oscillator.*

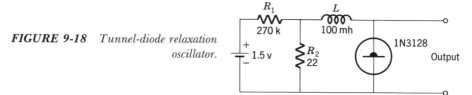

acteristic of a tunnel diode, Fig. 9-19, is inherently different from those of a neon tube or SCR, although both types exhibit negative-resistance regions. The difference between the two may be identified by noting that a line through the negative-resistance region parallel to the voltage axis in Fig. 9-19 intercepts the characteristic curve at another point. By contrast, the line must be parallel to the current axis if it is to intercept the curve in Fig. 9-13 or Fig. 4-29. The shape of the tunnel-diode curve is often called an *N-type* negative-resistance characteristic and the neon tube or SCR curve is called an *S-type* negative-resistance characteristic, because of the relative shapes of the two types.

The operation of the tunnel-diode relaxation oscillator is as follows. Resistors R_1 and R_2 bias the diode to the negative-resistance region between the peak and valley potentials. The current initially increases from zero along segment 1, Fig. 9-19, at a

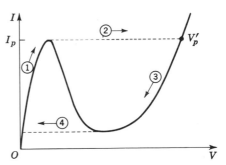

FIGURE 9-19 *Path of diode voltage in tunnel-diode relaxation oscillator.*

rate determined by the series inductance L. When the current reaches I_p it cannot increase further and the diode potential suddenly changes to V'_p. Now the diode potential is greater than the bias voltage, so the current decreases along segment 3, again at a rate fixed by the inductance. When the valley point is reached there is no way for the current to increase back up the curve, so the potential immediately drops back to nearly zero and the cycle repeats. Oscillation in the circuit depends upon the negative resistance properties of the tunnel diode and the fact that current in an inductance cannot change rapidly, in close analogy with the capacitor and neon-tube oscillator.

9-6   Blocking oscillator

A widely used circuit to generate pulse waveforms is the *blocking oscillator,* so called because the circuit cuts itself off, or *blocks,* periodically. The circuit of a blocking oscillator, Fig. 9-20a, looks similar to a feedback oscillator, except that the inductances are not tuned. In addition, the feedback ratio is very large, which means the feedback signal overdrives the transistor. Suppose the collector current is increasing; the positive feedback voltage further increases the collector current until the transistor is driven into saturation and the collector current no longer changes. The feedback is through a transformer so that when the rate of change of current stops, the feedback signal becomes zero. Simultaneously, the base capacitor, which was charged during the current pulse, discharges and gives a negative signal to the base. The collector current begins to decrease, again producing a feedback signal which rapidly decreases the collector current. The capacitor is charged and biases the transistor to cutoff. When the capacitor charge has drained away, the cycle repeats. The net result is a pulselike waveform, Fig. 9-20b.

In effect, the blocking-oscillator circuit tries to oscillate at its natural resonant frequency, but the strong feedback signal alternately drives the transistor into saturation and cutoff. The

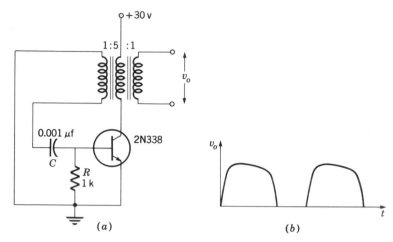

FIGURE 9-20   (a) *Blocking-oscillator circuit and*
(b) *output waveform.*

rise and decay times of the pulses are given essentially by the natural resonant frequency. This is purposely made high by minimizing stray capacitances so the rise and fall is rapid. The pulse length is determined by the effective inductance in the collector circuit, and the pulse-repetition frequency depends upon the RC time constant in the base circuit.

In some blocking oscillators dc base bias is used such that the transistor is cut off under quiescent conditions. A trigger voltage introduced across the base resistor starts the collector current and one output pulse is produced as described above. At the end of the output pulse the transistor remains cut off until another trigger signal arrives. Thus, the circuit produces an output pulse of specified amplitude and waveform whenever it is triggered into action. This form of blocking oscillator is often used as a pulse generator in digital-computer circuits.

SPECIAL CIRCUITS

9-7   Converters and inverters

It is often necessary to convert from a low dc supply voltage to one of a higher voltage (for example, in portable operation of vacuum-tube circuits from a low-voltage storage battery). Typically, vacuum tubes perform best at plate potentials above 100 volts while a commercial storage battery, as in an automobile, may have a terminal voltage of only 12 volts. There is no simple device analogous to a transformer for increasing dc potentials; instead *converters* perform this function. A converter is basically an oscillator that changes the dc input voltage to an ac signal which can be increased by transformer action and subsequently rectified to provide a higher dc potential. Most converters are designed to handle appreciable power; ratings from 10 watts to several hundred watts are common.

Converter oscillators are designed to produce square waves since in this way the conversion efficiency is maximized. A square waveform means the oscillator transistors are alternately cut off or saturated and internal power dissipation is a minimum. Furthermore, full-wave rectification of a square wave results in a dc output having a minimum of ripple, and this simplifies the filtering required. Oscillation frequencies are usually of the order of a few hundred to a thousand cycles per second; high frequencies are desirable to further simplify filtering, but transformer losses become significant if the frequency is too great.

Most often, converters are push-pull relaxation oscillators, Fig. 9-21, employing a special magnetic core transformer to develop

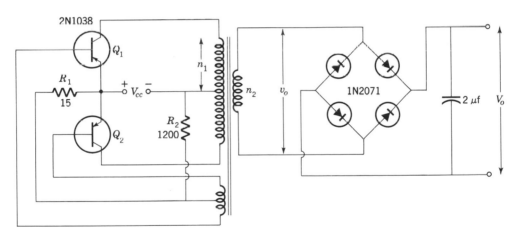

FIGURE 9-21 *15-watt converter.*

square-wave output. The magnetic core has a so-called *square-loop* hysteresis characteristic, Fig. 9-22. The essential feature is that magnetic flux in the core saturates suddenly as the current in the winding increases. In particular, the inductance of windings on the core is small when the core is saturated and large when the flux is changing along the vertical portion of the hysteresis loop. This can be confirmed by referring to the definition of inductance, Eq. (2-69).

The performance of such a *saturated-core oscillator* can be described in the following way. Start by assuming that, say, transistor Q_1 in Fig. 9-21 is conducting. The feedback signal is very strong, so

Q_1 is driven into saturation, while transistor Q_2 is cut off since the polarity of the feedback voltage applied to Q_2 is in the opposite direction. Since Q_1 is saturated, the emitter-collector voltage is

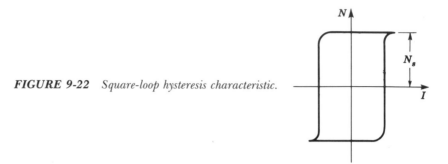

FIGURE 9-22 *Square-loop hysteresis characteristic.*

small and the entire collector supply voltage V_{cc} is equal to the induced voltage across the transformer winding. Therefore, from Eqs. (2-69) and (2-70),

$$V_{cc} = L\frac{di}{dt} = n_1 \frac{dN}{dt} \qquad (9\text{-}33)$$

where L is the inductance of one-half of the primary winding consisting of n_1 turns, i is the current in the winding, and N is the magnetic flux in the core. According to Eq. (9-33) the rate of change of current and of magnetic flux are constant during this portion of the cycle, which corresponds to the vertical segment of the hysteresis loop in Fig. 9-22.

The current in Q_1 continues to increase at a constant rate until the core saturates. At this point the magnetic flux ceases to change and the feedback signal becomes zero. Since Q_1 no longer has an input signal, its collector current begins to decrease. This means that the core comes out of saturation and a positive feedback signal is generated which drives Q_1 into cutoff and at the same time forces Q_2 into saturation. The current in Q_2 now increases linearly according to Eq. (9-33) until the core is magnetically saturated in the reverse direction. At this point the cycle repeats. Thus, through the combined action of strong positive feedback and saturation of the transformer, each transistor is alternately fully conducting or cut off.

The current and flux waveform in the transformer primary is a triangular wave, Fig. 9-23a, since the current changes linearly on each half-cycle according to Eq. (9-33). The output voltage of the secondary is constant during each half-cycle, since

$$v_o = n_2 \frac{dN}{dt} = \frac{n_2}{n_1} V_{cc} \qquad (9\text{-}34)$$

where Eq. (9-33) has been used, and n_2 is the number of turns on the secondary winding. The output waveform, Fig. 9-23b, is a square wave since the flux alternately increases and decreases. Full-wave rectification of the square wave results in a dc output voltage, Fig. 9-23c. Note that the magnitude of the output voltage is much larger than V_{cc} if $n_2 \gg n_1$, according to Eq. (9-34).

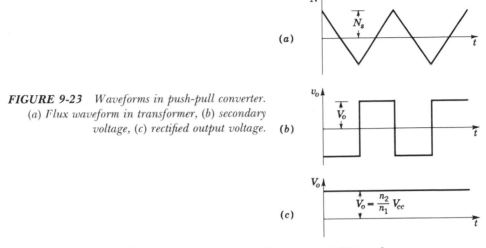

FIGURE 9-23 *Waveforms in push-pull converter.*
(a) Flux waveform in transformer, (b) secondary voltage, (c) rectified output voltage. (b)

The frequency of oscillation is determined from Eq. (9-33) and the flux waveform, Fig. 9-23a,

$$V_{cc} = n_1 \frac{dN}{dt} = n_1 \frac{2N_s}{T/2} = 4n_1 N_s f \qquad (9\text{-}35)$$

$$f = \frac{V_{cc}}{4n_1 N_s} \qquad (9\text{-}36)$$

where N_s is the saturation flux density of the core. According to Eq. (9-36), the frequency is controlled primarily by the transformer characteristics.

It is usually desirable to include a filter capacitor, Fig. 9-21, in order to remove spurious switching transients associated with the transition of conduction from one transistor to the other. Additionally, it is common practice to connect a junction diode in parallel with each transistor to protect the transistors against voltage transients that might exceed the collector breakdown potential. Bias resistors R_1 and R_2 are useful in providing a small base bias to improve starting characteristics when the circuit is first turned on. Once oscillations begin, bias is unnecessary since the transistors are either fully conducting or cut off.

A saturated-core oscillator followed by a conventional power amplifier increases the power capability of the converter. Also, SCRs are used in place of transistors with some improvement in power efficiency. This is so because of the very low internal resistance characteristic of SCRs. Since the main function of the transistors is to provide a switching action, the use of SCRs in this connection is quite appropriate.

The unrectified output of a converter can be used as a source of alternating current to power ac devices such as motors or electronic circuits designed to be operated from the power mains. In this application the unit is called an *inverter* since it provides an ac output from a dc source, which is just the inverse of a conventional rectifier circuit. Inverters are also used to generate 400-cps power suitable for use with servo systems because of the improved performance of servo systems at 400 cps compared with the standard 60-cps power-line frequency. Here, the 60-cps power-main voltage is rectified and filtered to power the inverter, which supplies 400-cps power. Thus the inverter may be looked upon as a power-frequency converter.

Usually it is desirable for the inverter frequency to be reasonably close to a specified value, generally either 60 cps or 400 cps, depending upon the application. A saturated-core oscillator is sufficiently stable for this use except for the change in frequency associated with any drop in the dc supply voltage under load, as given by Eq. (9-36). To compensate for the change in frequency from this effect, a voltage-regulator circuit is commonly included, as in the block diagram of a typical inverter, Fig. 9-24. Most often,

FIGURE 9-24 *Block diagram of dc-to-ac inverter.*

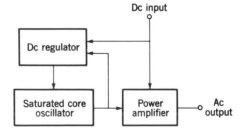

the regulator senses the output signal of the oscillator and adjusts the dc supply voltage to maintain the oscillator output at a constant level. This assures that the frequency of the oscillator remains substantially constant.

A conventional class-B push-pull power amplifier is used to provide the necessary power output. If necessary, the power input to the amplifier can also be regulated to hold the output voltage constant. In many applications this refinement is not required, however. The inverter output is a square wave rather than sinusoidal and this may interfere with the proper operation of some devices. A low-pass *LC* output filter can be used to deliver a sinusoidal output waveform in this case.

9-8   Regenerative and superregenerative detectors

According to Eq. (9-1), the gain of an amplifier can be increased markedly through the use of positive feedback if the feedback ratio is adjusted so that βa is very close to unity. This is not often used because the feedback adjustment is so critical that instabilities are likely to result and large gains are attainable by cascading stages anyway. Nevertheless, where it is desirable to achieve maximum amplification with a minimum number of stages, positive feedback, or *regeneration,* is attractive.

Consider the *regenerative-detector* circuit, Fig. 9-25, which is a

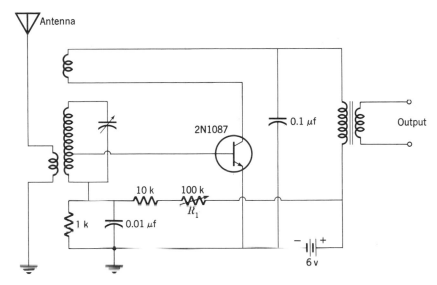

FIGURE 9-25   *Regenerative detector.*

sensitive detector of modulated waveforms (refer to Chap. 4) useful in radio communications. In this circuit feedback is provided by a tickler winding and the transistor gain is adjusted by resistor R_1, which alters the base bias. The amplified signal is detected by the rectifying action of the emitter junction and the modulation signal appears as variations in collector current. In effect, the circuit combines very high gain at the carrier frequency (because of regeneration), diode detection, and amplification of the demodulated signal. The result is a very large overall gain with a minimum number of circuit components. Actually, a regenerative detector makes a simple and useful one-transistor radio receiver.

In order to achieve good amplification, the circuit is adjusted to the threshold of oscillation, which makes the performance rather unstable and adjustments quite critical. A useful modification, called the *superregenerative detector,* removes some of these disadvantages. In this circuit, Fig. 9-26, the feedback signal is made large enough so oscillations result. Note that the circuit is basically a Colpitts oscillator with a feedback ratio of ½. The purpose of the 22-μh inductance in the emitter lead is to prevent shorting ac signals to ground. This also provides a convenient place to insert the input signal from the pickup antenna, which is indicated schematically by the triangle.

Oscillations in the superregenerative detector are periodically quenched by the action of the base bias resistor and capacitor R and C. This comes about through voltage developed across the

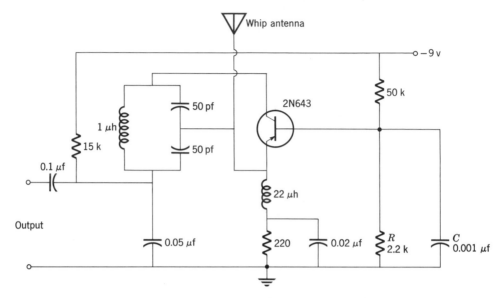

FIGURE 9-26 *Superregenerative detector for use at 27 Mc.*

capacitor which cuts off the transistor, quite analogous to the action in a blocking oscillator. After the transistor is cut off the charge on the capacitor is dissipated through the resistor and the process is repeated. The RC time constant determines the rate at which oscillations start and are quenched, which, conventionally, is of the order of 20 to 200 kc.

Since the circuit is oscillatory, the apparent gain is very large. The feedback adjustment is not as critical as in the case of the regenerative detector since the detector is allowed to break into oscillation. Therefore, a variable feedback adjustment is often unneeded. The effect of an input signal is to alter the initiation and quenching of oscillations in accordance with the amplitude of the signal. This is reflected in the average voltage of the base capacitor, and the demodulated signal appears as variations in the collector current.

Superregenerative detectors are useful as simple high-frequency detectors in the range from 1 to 100 Mc. They represent about the ultimate in gain that can be attained in a single stage, of the order of several million. For this reason the circuit is employed where simplicity and small size are of paramount importance. Improved operation is always attained in multistage circuits, however, wherein the design of each stage can be optimized.

SUGGESTIONS FOR FURTHER READING

Jacob Millman: "Vacuum-tube and Semiconductor Electronics," McGraw-Hill Book Company, New York, 1958.

Joseph A. Walston and John R. Miller (eds.): "Transistor Circuit Design," McGraw-Hill Book Company, New York, 1963.

"The Radio Amateur's Handbook" (published annually by the American Radio Relay League, West Hartford, Conn.).

EXERCISES

9-1 Derive Eq. (9-3) for the feedback network of a phase-shift oscillator. *Hint:* Use the technique of loop currents and solve for the current in the last resistor by determinants.

9-2 Draw the h-parameter equivalent circuit of the phase-shift oscillator, Fig. 9-1, and derive a relation analogous to Eq. (9-9) for the vacuum-tube oscillator.

$$Ans.: \beta = h_{re} - [(Z_i + h_{ie})/h_{fe}](h_{oe} + 1/R_L + 1/Z_i)$$

9-3 Using the results of Exercise 9-2, show that the circuit of Fig. 9-1 does oscillate. The h parameters of the 2N1414 are $h_{ie} = 1260\ \Omega$, $h_{re} = 3 \times 10^{-4}$, $h_{fe} = 44$, and $h_{oe} = 2.7 \times 10^{-5}$ mho. What is the frequency of oscillation?   *Ans.:* 1300 cps

9-4 Design a 400-cps vacuum-tube phase-shift oscillator using a type 12AX7 vacuum tube. Use the second triode section for a cathode-follower output stage.

9-5 What is the value of R_1 in the Wien-bridge oscillator, Fig. 9-3, if the amplifier gain is 10? Repeat for gains of 100 and 1000.

Ans.: 1520 Ω, 2390 Ω, 2490 Ω

9-6 Considering Eq. (9-12) and the results of Exercise 9-5, should the amplifier gain in the Wien-bridge oscillator be large or small, if frequency stability is important?   *Ans.:* Large

9-7 Based on the results of Exercise 9-6, what effect does an output load have on a Wien-bridge oscillator?

Ans.: Reduces frequency stability

9-8 What factors are important in determining the low-frequency limit of a Wien-bridge oscillator? The high-frequency limit? Suggest improvements in the circuit of Fig. 9-3 that can increase the upper frequency limit.

9-9 Derive an expression for the feedback ratio of a Colpitts oscillator, Fig. 9-6. Compare with the corresponding relation for the Hartley oscillator, Eq. (9-17).

9-10 By inspection, determine the voltage output of the power-oscillator circuit in Fig. 9-8.   *Ans.:* 19.8 volts

9-11 Develop an expression analogous to Eq. (9-13) for the phase of the feedback voltage as a function of frequency in a tickler LC oscillator. Show that a resonant circuit with a large Q is desirable for maximum frequency stability.

9-12 Sketch the circuit of a vacuum-tube tickler oscillator with the resonant circuit in the grid circuit and using class-C bias. Draw the equivalent circuit and derive an expression giving the condition for oscillation corresponding to Eq. (9-21).

9-13 Neglecting the resistance in the equivalent circuit of a quartz crystal, determine the equivalent impedance as a function of frequency. With the component values given in the text, plot Fig. 9-10.

9-14 Including the resistance in the equivalent circuit of a quartz crystal, obtain an expression for the phase angle of the impedance near the parallel resonant frequency. Plot the phase angle as a function of frequency and compare with a plot of an *LC* resonant circuit having a *Q* of 200. Use the results of Exercise 9-11.

9-15 Plot the waveform of the neon-tube oscillator of Fig. 9-12. What are the peak-to-peak voltage and frequency of the output signal?
Ans.: 20 volts, 34.2 cps

9-16 Repeat Exercise 9-15 if the dc supply voltage is 1500 volts.
Ans.: 672 cps

9-17 Find the period and amplitude of the output signal from the SCR relaxation oscillator, Fig. 9-16, if $R_2 = 1000\ \Omega$ and the gate voltage required for turn-on is 3 volts. Plot the output voltage waveform.
Ans.: 13 volts, 0.105 sec

9-18 Repeat Exercise 9-17 for the SCR sawtooth oscillator, Fig. 9-17. Assume $h_{fe} = 20$.　　　　　　　*Ans.*: 6.3 volts, 3.16×10^{-5} sec

9-19 In the blocking-oscillator circuit of Fig. 9-20a, what is the peak-pulse output voltage, if the turns ratio between collector winding and output winding is $5:1$. Also, what is the approximate pulse-repetition frequency?　　　　　*Ans.*: 6 volts, 500 kc

9-20 What is the approximate quench frequency of the superregenerative detector, Fig. 9-26?　　　　　　　*Ans.*: 72 kc

10
PULSE
AND
DIGITAL
CIRCUITS

Most circuits discussed in preceding chapters are designed for dc or sinusoidal signal waveforms. Signals which consist of a series of rapid transitions from one voltage magnitude to another, for example, a square wave, are of equal importance. Although such pulse waveforms may be resolved into their sinusoidal harmonic components using the method of Fourier analysis discussed in Chap. 2, it is usually more convenient to consider the signal pulses themselves. Circuits specifically designed to be used with pulses are discussed in this chapter.

Electric signals from many physical phenomena, most notably reactions in nuclear physics, are inherently pulses. In addition, modern communication techniques, such as radar, television, and data telemetry, involve the transmission of pulses from the transmitter to the receiver. In these applications the size and relative timing of the pulses represent an encoding of the information transmitted.

Furthermore, numerical digits can be represented by waveforms which are a time sequence of pulses having only two voltage magnitudes, zero and some finite value. In this situation only the presence or absence of a pulse is significant and the magnitude is relatively unimportant. Therefore, such digital circuits need have only two stable states represented, for example, by a transistor fully conducting or completely cut off. Such circuits are inherently more reliable than conventional analog circuits, which must handle a continuous range of signal levels. Any given number can be represented by a digital waveform, so accuracy is not limited by the inherent uncertainty and change of circuit parameters. The advantages of reliability and accuracy were first attained in digital-computer circuits but now find application in a wide range of instrumentation and measuring circuits.

PULSE AMPLIFIERS

10-1   Rise time

The pulse size and shape representing a physical effect carry the information that describes the phenomenon.   For example, the voltage pulse from a Geiger counter which has detected a nuclear disintegration may be characterized by the exact time of onset of the pulse, its magnitude, and its duration.   Since the output of many detectors is small, it is often necessary to amplify the pulse signal before measurement.   Vacuum-tube and transistor ampli- fiers are used for this purpose.   An ideal pulse amplifier introduces no change in the pulse shape other than increasing its amplitude, and practical circuits can come close to this performance.

The important characteristics of pulse amplifiers, gain, fre- quency response, stability, and distortion are similar to those already discussed in Chaps. 7 and 8 in connection with conven- tional amplifiers.   To illustrate, in particular, the significance of frequency response, consider the ideal square pulse shown in Fig. 10-1 and the nonideal pulse shape resulting from passing this

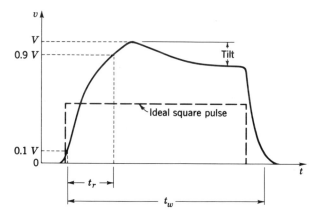

FIGURE 10-1   *Comparison of ideal square voltage pulse with amplified, nonideal pulse.*

waveform through a practical amplifier.   Note that the amplified pulse does not rise instantaneously to the maximum value.   This is a result of the high-frequency cutoff of the amplifier caused by shunt capacitance.   Consider the case of a single-stage transistor or vacuum-tube amplifier, which can be represented for present

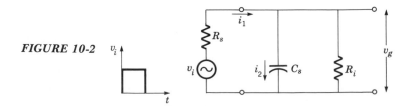

FIGURE 10-2

purposes by the input circuit of Fig. 10-2, in which C_s represents the total shunt capacitance (compare Fig. 7-11), R_i is the input impedance, and R_s is the output impedance of the preceding stage. The waveform of the output pulse v_g due to a square voltage pulse v_i starting at $t = 0$ is found by analyzing the circuit using techniques described in Chap. 3. The voltage and current equations of the circuit are

$$v_i = R_s i_1 + v_g$$

$$0 = \frac{1}{C_s} \int i_2 \, dt - v_g \tag{10-1}$$

$$i_1 = i_2 + \frac{v_g}{R_i}$$

Upon differentiating the second equation and substituting for i_1 and i_2 from the remaining expressions, the differential equation of the circuit is just

$$C_s \frac{dv_g}{dt} + \left(\frac{1}{R_s} + \frac{1}{R_i} \right) v_g = \frac{v_i}{R_s} \tag{10-2}$$

The solution to Eq. (10-2) is

$$v_g = \frac{v_i}{1 + R_s/R_i} (1 - e^{-t/\tau}) \tag{10-3}$$

where

$$\tau = \frac{C_s}{1/R_s + 1/R_i} \tag{10-4}$$

is the time constant of the circuit.

According to Eq. (10-3) the output voltage rises exponentially to its final value at a rate determined by the circuit time constant. It is desirable to make the time constant as small as possible for minimum distortion of the leading edge of the pulse.

At the end of the input pulse, the output voltage decays back to zero at a rate again determined by the circuit time constant. Note, however, that the preceding stage may be completely cut off at the end of the pulse, so that $R_s \cong \infty$ and $\tau = R_i C_s$ at the trailing edge. In vacuum-tube amplifiers $R_s \ll R_g$ during conduction and the time constant at the onset of the pulse is $\tau = R_s C_s$. This means that the rise and fall of the amplified pulse are likely to have different time constants. The rise time is usually the faster. By contrast, $R_i \ll R_s$ in transistor amplifiers and the time constant for both rise and fall is simply $R_i C_s$.

It is convenient to define the *rise time* t_r of a pulse as the time required for the voltage to go from 10 to 90 percent of its final value, as indicated in Fig. 10-1. A useful approximate expression for t_r may be developed by introducing

$$v_g = 0.9 \, \frac{v_i}{1 + R_s/R_i} \tag{10-5}$$

into Eq. (10-3). The result is solved for t_r,

$$0.9 \, \frac{v_i}{1 + R_s/R_i} = \frac{v_i}{1 + R_s/R_i} \, (1 - e^{-t_r/\tau}) \tag{10-6}$$

$$0.1 = e^{-t_r/\tau}$$

$$t_r = \tau \ln 10 \tag{10-7}$$

Introducing the upper cutoff frequency $2\pi f_0 = 1/\tau$ of the amplifier from Eq. (7-12),

$$t_r = \frac{\ln 10}{2\pi f_0} \cong \frac{1}{3 f_0} \tag{10-8}$$

According to Eq. (10-8) an amplifier with a good high-frequency response is necessary if the pulse rise time is short. For example, if the pulse rise time is 1 μsec, the amplifier bandwidth must extend to 370 kc. In this connection it should be remembered that the bandwidth of a multiple-stage amplifier is always poorer than that of any individual stage. Inverse feedback is commonly used in pulse amplifiers to improve high-frequency characteristics.

10-2 Tilt

A second form of pulse distortion is departure of the top of the pulse from a constant value, called *tilt*, in Fig. 10-1. This is a result of low-frequency cutoff of the amplifier. In effect, the pulse length represents a dc signal of short duration. Therefore, the appropriate single-stage equivalent circuit, Fig. 10-3, includes the inter-

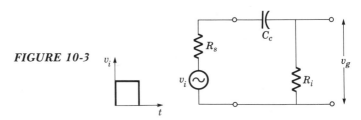

FIGURE 10-3

stage coupling capacitor C_c (compare Fig. 7-5). The output voltage accompanying a square-wave input v_i beginning at $t = 0$ is found immediately from Eq. (3-97),

$$v_g = v_i e^{-t/\tau} \tag{10-9}$$

where

$$\tau = (R_i + R_s) C_c \tag{10-10}$$

Clearly, the circuit time constant τ must be long for minimum decay of output voltage during the pulse. This means that a large value of C_c is required.

The tilt is small in most practical situations, so Eq. (10-9) can be approximated by the first two terms of a series expansion,

$$v_g = v_i \left(1 - \frac{t}{\tau} \right) \tag{10-11}$$

The percentage tilt $P = \Delta v_g / v_i$ at the end of the pulse duration t_w is then

$$P = \frac{\Delta v_g}{v_i} = \frac{t_w}{\tau} \tag{10-12}$$

Introducing the low-frequency cutoff $2\pi f_0 = 1/\tau$ from Eq. (7-4),

$$t_w = \frac{P}{2\pi f_0} \tag{10-13}$$

Notice that a long pulse requires an amplifier with an excellent low-frequency response. For example, suppose that tilt distortion must be less than 1 percent. Then the low-frequency cutoff of an amplifier required to handle 1-msec pulses must extend down to 1.6 cps.

10-3 Square-wave testing

The results of the two previous sections provide a convenient technique for determining response characteristics of amplifiers. A square wave is applied to the input, and the output waveform is displayed on an oscilloscope. The frequency of the square wave is reduced until tilt is measurable in the output waveform and the low-frequency cutoff determined using Eq. (10-13). Similarly, the square-wave frequency is increased until the rise time of the amplified pulse is observed on the oscilloscope. Then Eq. (10-8) gives the high-frequency cutoff of the amplifier. Of course, it is assumed that the square-wave signal source and the response characteristics of the oscilloscope are sufficiently good so that they introduce negligible pulse distortion.

Such *square-wave testing* is particularly advantageous in adjusting amplifiers for optimum response because the results of any changes are immediately apparent in the output pulse waveform. This makes repeated laborious determinations of the sine-wave frequency-response characteristic unnecessary. Waveforms similar to those of Figs. 3-27 and 3-29 are often seen, depending upon the relative values of the square-wave frequency and amplifier cutoff frequency.

MULTIVIBRATORS

10-4   Astable multivibrators

Two-transistor or two-tube regenerative circuits called *multi-vibrators* find extensive application in pulse circuits. In one or another of its many modifications a multivibrator can be used to generate nonsinusoidal waveforms, to discriminate between pulses of different amplitudes, and to count the number of pulses in a signal. The multivibrator is a basic building block in pulse and digital circuits.

It is easiest to begin with a study of the so-called astable multi-vibrator, Fig. 10-4, the terminology for which will become clear as

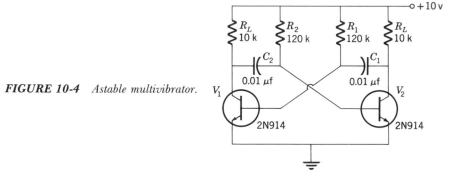

FIGURE 10-4   *Astable multivibrator.*

we proceed. This circuit can be recognized as a two-stage RC amplifier with the output coupled back to the input. The feedback ratio is unity and positive because of the 180° phase shift in each stage so the circuit oscillates. Because of the very strong feedback signals, the transistors are driven into either cutoff or saturation, and nonsinusoidal oscillations are generated.

Suppose that at some instant the feedback voltage drives V_1 into cutoff; this implies that V_2 is conducting because of the relative phase shift between the two stages. The voltage drop across the collector resistor of V_2 puts the collector at nearly ground poten-tial, and C_1 charges through R_1 toward the collector supply poten-tial. When the voltage across C_1 increases sufficiently to bias the emitter junction of V_1 in the forward direction, V_1 begins to con-duct. The collector voltage of V_1 drops and V_2 is driven into cutoff through coupling capacitor C_2. Now, C_2 charges through R_2 until V_2 becomes forward-biased and the cycle repeats. These actions will be illustrated graphically when voltage waveforms in the cir-cuit are considered.

Notice that the circuit alternates between a state in which V_1 is conducting and simultaneously V_2 is cut off and a state in which V_1 is cut off and V_2 is conducting. The transition between these two states is rapid because of the strong feedback signals. The time in each state depends upon the coupling capacitor–bias resistor time constant. Since each transistor is driven alternately into cutoff and saturation, the voltage waveform at either collector is essentially a square wave with a peak amplitude equal to the collector supply voltage.

This picture is confirmed by actual collector voltage waveforms, Fig. 10-5. The triangular base voltage waveforms illustrate the

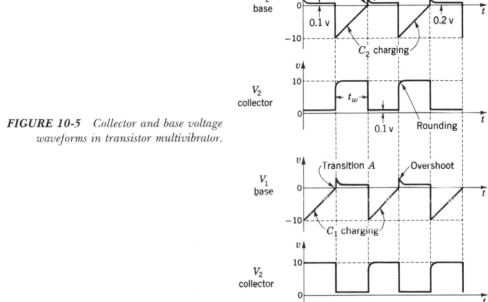

FIGURE 10-5 *Collector and base voltage waveforms in transistor multivibrator.*

alternate charging and discharging of the coupling capacitors. Of particular interest is the very low voltage drop across the transistors when saturated (≈ 0.1 volt) and the fact that the transition from one state to another is initiated when the base voltage of the cutoff transistor just slightly exceeds zero. Note, too, that there is a small voltage spike, or *overshoot*, in the base voltage waveform at the transition from one state to the other. The reason for the overshoot may be seen by focusing attention on capacitor C_2 when V_1 goes from conducting to cutoff. Consider that portion of the circuit shown in Fig. 10-6a where the on-to-off transition of V_1 is represented by a switch. Further simplification in the circuit is effected by ignoring R_2 since $R_L \ll R_2$; in addition, the forward-biased emitter junction of V_2 is represented approximately by a simple resistor r, Fig. 10-6b. According to the waveforms of Fig. 10-5, V_1 switches from saturation to cutoff at transition B when the base voltage of V_2 (and hence the voltage across C_2) is essentially zero. Thus, when the switch in the circuit of Fig. 10-6b opens, C_2

begins to charge through R_L and r and the charging current results in an overshoot voltage drop across the emitter junction resistance. From Fig. 10-6b the peak value of this voltage is

$$v_{\text{overshoot}} = \frac{V_{cc}}{R_L + r} r \qquad (10\text{-}14)$$

while the time constant of the overshoot spike is

$$\tau_{\text{overshoot}} = (R_L + r)C_2 \qquad (10\text{-}15)$$

The charging current through R_L also prevents the collector voltage of V_1 from rising immediately to V_{cc}. This is the source of the

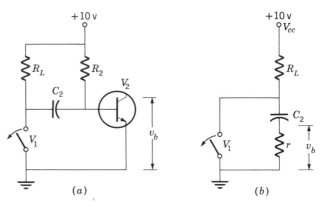

FIGURE 10-6 *Equivalent circuits of the V_2 portion of Fig. 10-4 showing the origin of overshoot.*

rounding of the collector waveform pulse edge shown in Fig. 10-5. A typical value for r is 200 Ω, so that the peak overshoot in the multivibrator of Fig. 10-4 is $10(200/10,200) = 0.2$ volt. This small value, plus the relatively short time constant, Eq. (10-15), means that overshoot introduces only a minor departure from a square collector waveform.

The pulse width in a multivibrator depends upon the time constant of C_1 (or C_2) charging through R_1 (or R_2). A value for t_w can be written down immediately from the expression for the period of a relaxation oscillator derived in the previous chapter, Eq. (9-28). Comparing the waveforms in Fig. 10-5 with those of Fig. 9-14,

$$t_w = R_1 C_1 \ln \frac{V_{cc} - (-V_{cc})}{V_{cc} - 0}$$

$$t_w = R_1 C_1 \ln 2 \qquad (10\text{-}16)$$

When $R_1 = R_2$ and $C_1 = C_2$ the waveform is a square wave of frequency $f = 1/2t_w$. It is equally possible to generate asymmetrical waveforms by choosing nonequal values for, say, the coupling capacitors.   The result is alternating pulses of widths given by Eq. (10-16) for each time constant.

A typical vacuum-tube multivibrator circuit, Fig. 10-7, is similar to the transistor version and the mode of operation is identical. Voltage waveforms in the vacuum-tube multivibrator, Fig. 10-8,

FIGURE 10-7   *Vacuum-tube multivibrator.*

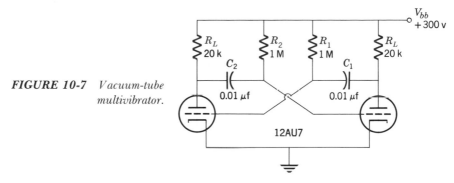

vary from those of the transistor circuit because of the difference in control characteristics between vacuum tubes and transistors. Thus, the transition in which V_2 changes from cutoff to saturation, point A in Fig. 10-8, occurs when the grid voltage is -22 volts, rather than very near zero as in the transistor case.   One result of

FIGURE 10-8   *Voltage waveforms in vacuum-tube multivibrator.*

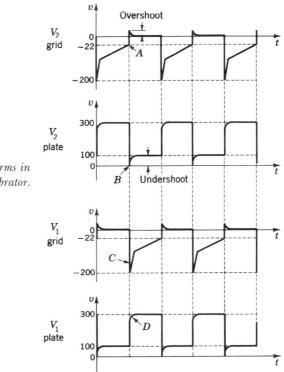

this is the jump in grid voltage to a positive value (because of over-shoot) at the transition point A. Overshoot occurs for exactly the same reason as in the transistor case. The magnitude is considerably greater (typically several volts), however, because the effective resistance of the grid-cathode diode of V_2 is comparatively large.

The second important waveform difference comes about because the plate current in a vacuum tube continues to increase as the grid voltage is increased positively from zero. For this reason, the plate voltage *undershoots* its final saturated value during grid overshoot. This is indicated at point B on the plate voltage waveform. The undershoot voltage spike is transmitted to the grid of V_1 by capacitive coupling through C_1 and appears at point C. Finally, the plate voltage pulse of V_1 is rounded, point D, as in the transistor case.

Waveforms in a vacuum-tube multivibrator are determined by first finding the saturated plate current. This is done by plotting the load line on the plate characteristics in the usual fashion and noting the plate current at the intersection of the load line with the zero grid bias curve. If the plate current is known, the drop across R_L, and hence the plate voltage, can be calculated. The negative grid bias for which conduction starts is estimated from the plate characteristics by noting the grid bias which just gives zero plate current at the full plate supply voltage. Next, the grid overshoot is calculated using Eq. (10-14) except that V_{cc} is replaced by the sum of the saturated plate voltage plus the grid cutoff voltage just determined, since this is the net voltage applied to the coupling capacitor at the transition point. A value for r can be estimated from the positive grid current characteristic, if available. If not, a value of $1000 \ \Omega$ is a reasonably good estimate for most common tubes. The overshoot time constant is given by Eq. (10-15). Plate-current undershoot is now determined from the plate characteristics using the known positive grid overshoot. This voltage spike is also the undershoot in the grid voltage waveform. Finally, the period is determined by the $R_1 C_1$ time constant. Usually the charging curve can be approximated by a straight line drawn backward from point A with a slope $V_{bb}/R_1 C_1$, as discussed in connection with Eq. (9-30).

Astable multivibrators are relaxation oscillators and can therefore be synchronized by application of external signals, as considered in the previous chapter. Positive synchronizing pulses can be applied to either plate (or collector in the transistor version) to trigger the other tube into conduction. Multivibrators are often used in this way as frequency dividers. The circuit is also a useful square-wave generator, and, in conjunction with a differentiating circuit, yields sharp, spike waveforms.

10-5   The binary

A dc-coupled multivibrator can exist in either of its two states indefinitely. It can be caused to make a transition from one state to the other by an external trigger pulse. Because of its two stable states, a multivibrator with dc coupling is called a *binary*. A binary is also commonly referred to as a *flip-flop*, although this descriptive term more properly applies to all forms of multivibrators.

Consider the typical transistor binary in Fig. 10-9. Note that

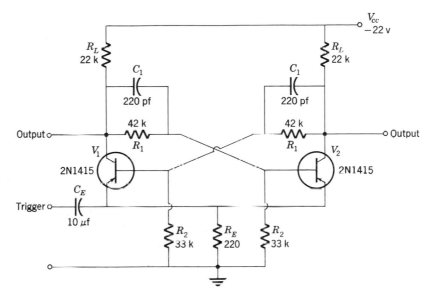

FIGURE 10-9   *Binary circuit is dc-coupled multivibrator.*

conventional dc coupling using resistors R_1 and R_2 is used. In other respects the circuit is similar to the ac-coupled, astable multivibrator. Trigger pulses are introduced across the emitter resistor R_E. The purpose of capacitors C_1 is to improve triggering action, as will be discussed subsequently. Output is conventionally taken from either, or both, collectors.

It is important to verify that a stable state of the binary exists when one transistor is cut off and the other is saturated. To begin, assume that V_1 in Fig. 10-9 is cut off so that its collector current is negligible. Collector current in the saturated transistor V_2 is found by drawing a load line corresponding to the total load resistance $R_L + R_E$ on the collector characteristics. The intersection of this load line with the current axis gives the collector current, 9.3 ma, and also shows that a base current of 125 μa is needed to reach saturation. The bias on V_1 may now be calculated using the portion of the circuit shown in Fig. 10-10a, where the emitter voltage $V_e = i_cR_E = 9.3 \times 10^{-3} \times 220 = 2.1$ volts.   The emitter-collector voltage of V_2 is taken to be 0.1 volt when saturated.

Actually, a more accurate value for the emitter-collector voltage may be determined from transistor manufacturer's data, but it is usually small enough to be ignored in any event. Using Fig. 10-10a, the emitter base voltage of V_1 is

$$V_{eb} = V_e \frac{R_1}{R_1 + R_2} = 2.1 \frac{42}{42 + 33} = 1.2 \text{ volts}$$

This value of reverse bias at the emitter junction is much more than required to keep V_1 cut off, as assumed.

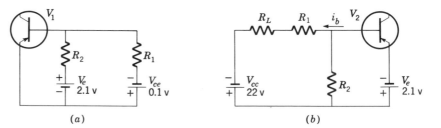

(a)   (b)

FIGURE 10-10 *Equivalent circuits of transistor binary used to show that binary has only two stable states.*

To show that V_2 is biased to saturation, focus attention on that portion of the circuit shown in Fig. 10-10b. The resistance R_2 may be ignored in comparison with the resistance of the emitter junction, and the current through V_1 is negligible because it is cut off. Therefore,

$$i_b = \frac{V_{cc} - V_e}{R_L + R_1} = \frac{22.5 - 2.1}{2.2 + 42} 10^{-3} = 460 \ \mu a$$

This is much greater than the 125 μa needed to keep V_2 in saturation. Thus, it is established that V_1 is cut off and V_2 is saturated. Because of the symmetry of the circuit, it is obvious that an equally stable state is the one in which V_1 is saturated and V_2 cut off. When the binary switches from one configuration to the other the collector voltage changes from essentially the emitter potential in the saturated condition to a voltage equal to V_{cc} less the drop across R_L resulting from the base bias current. Therefore the output signal is

$$v_o = (22.5 - 2.2 \times 10^3 \times 460 \times 10^{-6}) - 2.1 = 19.4 \text{ volts}$$

The circuit is triggered into switching from one state to the other by a positive voltage pulse applied across the emitter resistor. This drives the saturated transistor out of saturation and also tends to turn on the cutoff transistor. As current in the saturated transistor decreases, the collector signal is coupled to the cutoff transistor, further turning it on. Once initiated, the circuit flips itself over because of the strong regenerative feedback. Each successive trigger pulse causes the binary to assume its alternate state. The trigger-pulse amplitude must be somewhat greater than the quiescent voltage across R_E in order to initiate the transfer; in the circuit of Fig. 10-9, a positive pulse of 2.5 volts is sufficient.

It is of interest to inquire if the binary has any other stable states than the two considered so far. According to the above analysis, it is not possible for both transistors to be cut off simultaneously, for then the base bias conditions on one transistor would be inappropriate. Similarly, both transistors cannot be saturated at the same time. A state in which equal, but not saturation, currents are in each transistor is possible in principle, but this is a state of unstable equilibrium. Any slight departure from exact balance upsets the equilibrium and the circuit reverts to one of the stable states. Suppose, for example, that a random noise voltage decreases the current in V_1 slightly. The signal at the collector of V_1 tends to increase the current in V_2, and the collector signal of V_2 further reduces the current in V_1. This regenerative action continues until V_1 is cut off and V_2 is saturated. We conclude that the only two stable states of a binary are with one transistor cut off and the other saturated, and vice versa. Note that minor noise voltages cannot cause a transition out of one of the stable states because the transistors are cut off and saturated. Therefore, the amplifier gain is very small and regeneration is not effective.

The vacuum-tube binary, Fig. 10-11, is exactly analogous to the transistor circuit and is examined in the same fashion. The analysis is slightly more complicated by the fact that the voltage

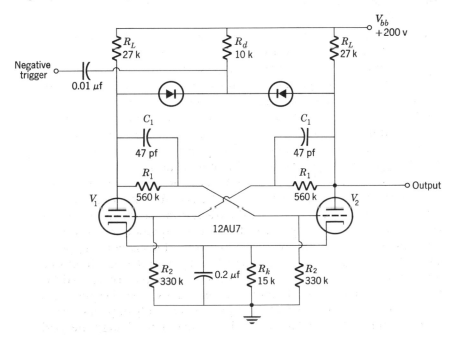

FIGURE 10-11 *Vacuum-tube binary with steering diodes for triggering.*

drop across the saturated tube cannot be taken equal to zero, but in other respects it is identical to that for the transistor binary (Exercise 10-6). It turns out that the grid voltage of the cutoff tube is several volts below cutoff while the grid bias of the saturated tube is just slightly positive. In fact, the grid of the conducting tube is essentially at cathode potential for all practical purposes. The 0.02-μf capacitor shunting the cathode resistor maintains the cathode voltage constant during the transition from one state to the other when cathode triggering is not used.

The triggering scheme illustrated in Fig. 10-11 makes use of *steering diodes* to transmit negative trigger pulses to the grid of the saturated tube. The negative pulse reduces current in this tube and the circuit flips to the other state as a result of regenerative feedback. The on grid is at cathode potential while the off grid is many volts below cutoff. Therefore, the negative trigger that must be applied to the on grid to initiate the transition is smaller than the positive pulse that must be applied to the off grid. Note that the diodes of Fig. 10-11 are returned to V_{bb} through resistor R_d. This means that the diode connected to the on plate is reverse-biased and represents a high resistance, while the diode connected to the off plate is unbiased. A negative trigger pulse is therefore "steered" through the low forward resistance of this diode to the off plate (hence to the on grid), where it initiates the transition. Other forms of triggering, including cathode triggering, Fig. 10-9, are also used, depending upon the particular application. Conversely, steering diodes are often used in transistor binary circuits.

For certain applications triggering is accomplished by pulses fed directly to only one or the other grid (or base). In this case a negative pulse induces a transition only when the tube it is impressed on is in the on state. Such *unsymmetrical* triggering is useful when a binary is to be triggered from two separate sources, one applied to each grid. Thus the output of the binary is a square wave of duration equal to the time interval between a pulse presented to the grid of V_1 and a pulse presented to the grid of V_2. Other applications are discussed in later sections.

The speed with which a binary makes the transition from one state to the other limits the trigger pulse rate for reliable switching. Stray shunt capacitances reduce the transition speed, and the same considerations that apply to the high-frequency response of amplifiers are important in binary circuits. This is not surprising since during the transition the circuit really operates as a feedback amplifier. In particular, the total shunt capacitance from grid (or base) to ground is the limiting factor. This is so because this capacitance must be charged through the relatively high resistance of R_1 (refer to Figs. 10-9 and 10-11) in order to change the grid (base) voltage corresponding to one state to that of the other state. The time required to charge the input capacitance is reduced by shunting both R_1 resistors with small capacitances C_1, called *commutating capacitors*. In the steering-diode triggering method the commutating capacitors assure that the trigger pulse is delivered to the on grid with minimum attenuation. When commutating capacitors are used, the time between states is reduced to essentially that required for C_1 to charge through the parallel combination of R_1 and R_2. Thus, the resolving time of the vacuum-tube binary of Fig. 10-11 is

$$t = \frac{C_1}{1/R_1 + 1/R_2} = 47 \times 10^{-12} \frac{560 \times 330}{890} \times 10^3 = 9.7 \ \mu sec$$

This means that the binary can respond reliably to sequential trigger pulses only if they are separated by about 10 μsec. With special design and additional circuit complications binaries having resolving times of the order of 0.1 μsec are possible.

A useful binary circuit called the *Schmitt trigger* (after its inventor) results if one collector-to-base coupling is omitted and replaced by feedback through a common-emitter resistor, Fig. 10-12. This

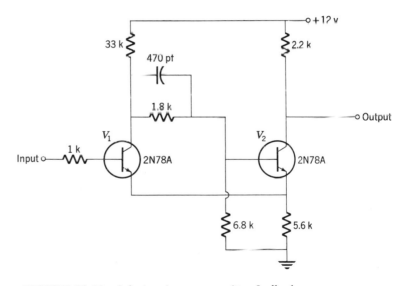

FIGURE 10-12 *Schmitt trigger uses emitter feedback.*

circuit has two stable states and the magnitude of the input voltage determines which of the two is possible. Suppose the input voltage is zero and assume that V_1 is cut off while V_2 is conducting but not saturated. Since V_1 is cut off, the quiescent current of V_2 is found by determining the operating point. The voltage drop across the emitter resistor is large enough to cut off V_1, as initially assumed. In the circuit of Fig. 10-12, for example, the emitter bias is 6.6 volts. Thus, the normal state of the Schmitt trigger has V_1 cut off and V_2 conducting.

Suppose now the input voltage in Fig. 10-12 is increased from zero.   Nothing happens until the input voltage just exceeds the base bias, 6.6 volts, at which point V_1 begins to conduct. The bias on V_2 is reduced and the emitter bias voltage decreases; this, in turn, increases current in V_1. Regenerative action continues until V_1 is conducting and V_2 is cut off. This state is maintained so long as the input voltage is greater than 6.6 volts. As the input voltage is decreased, the circuit does not regain its original state until an input voltage significantly smaller than 6.6 volts is attained. The reason for this is that the base bias on V_2 is much lower in this state than previously because the collector of V_1 is at a lower potential. Therefore the current in V_1 must be considerably reduced before the smaller emitter voltage and increased collector potential of V_1 combine to increase the base current of V_2 and it begins to turn on. In the circuit of Fig. 10-12 it is necessary to reduce the input voltage to 5.2 volts before regeneration returns the circuit to the original state.

An interesting application of the Schmitt trigger is as a pulse regenerator or *squaring circuit*, illustrated in Fig. 10-13. The input

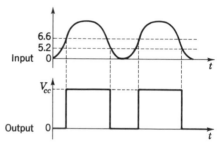

FIGURE 10-13   *Waveforms in Schmitt trigger used as squaring circuit.*

signal, a series of degraded pulse waveforms, is converted to a square pulse output as the circuit is triggered back and forth between its two states by the input waveform. Note that even a sinusoidal signal may be converted to a square wave in this way.

The Schmitt trigger is also useful as a *pulse height discriminator* to measure the voltage pulse amplitudes of an input signal. Each time an input pulse exceeds the trigger threshold the circuit generates an output pulse. Thus, by varying, say, a dc voltage in series with the input signal, the range of pulse sizes in a signal can be determined.   A precision of the order of 0.1 volt is possible with this circuit. Note that the output pulses are all of uniform amplitude, independent of the input trigger pulse. This is useful in that subsequent circuits need not be capable of handling a wide range of pulse sizes.

10-6   Monostable multivibrators

A final form of multivibrator is the partial combination of a binary and an astable multivibrator. Both dc and ac coupling are employed, Fig. 10-14. As might be anticipated, this circuit has only one stable state: with V_1 cut off and V_2 saturated. When triggered out of this state by a negative pulse applied to the grid of V_2, V_1 becomes conducting and V_2 is cut off. This state lasts for a

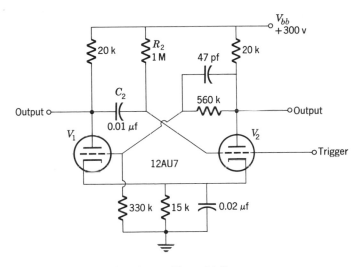

FIGURE 10-14 *Monostable multivibrator uses both ac and dc coupling between stages.*

time determined by the R_2C_2 time constant, after which the circuit reverts spontaneously to the stable configuration. Because of this action the circuit is called a *one-shot* or *monostable* multivibrator. This completes the roster of multivibrator types: the binary, which has two stable states and is therefore bistable; the mono-stable multivibrator with its one stable state; and the astable circuit which is a free-running oscillator having no stable states.

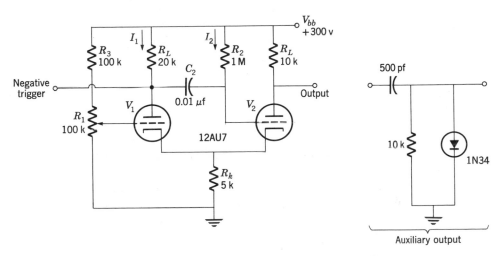

FIGURE 10-15 *Cathode-coupled monostable multivibrator. Auxiliary circuit produces negative output pulses similar to input trigger pulses but delayed by multivibrator.*

A useful version of the monostable multivibrator uses cathode feedback for dc coupling as in the Schmitt trigger. In this circuit, Fig. 10-15, the time that V_1 spends in the conducting state is easily varied by changing the bias using potentiometer R_1. This action can be understood by focusing attention on the voltage waveform at the grid of V_2, Fig. 10-16. In the stable state with V_2 conducting,

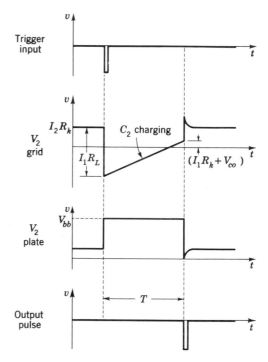

FIGURE 10-16 *Waveforms in monostable multivibrator used as variable time delay. Delay time T is adjusted by changing I_1.*

the grid voltage is essentially at cathode potential I_2R_k because of the positive grid voltage applied through R_2. This bias causes a small forward current in the grid-cathode diode and the resulting drop across R_2 places the grid just slightly positive with respect to the cathode. When the circuit is triggered, V_1 conducts and the grid voltage drops momentarily by the amount I_1R_L because of coupling through C_2. Now C_2 begins charging through R_2 until the grid-cathode potential of V_2 reaches cutoff V_{co}. The grid voltage with respect to ground at this time is the sum of the cathode potential I_1R_k plus the cutoff potential V_{co} at the given plate voltage. When the grid reaches this potential, V_2 begins to conduct and the circuit returns to its stable state.

The time T that the circuit remains in its second state can be determined from the expression for the period of a relaxation oscillator, Eq. (9-28). Comparing the waveforms of Fig. 9-14 with those of Fig. 10-16,

$$T = R_2C_2 \ln \frac{V_{bb} - (I_2R_k - I_1R_L)}{V_{bb} - (I_1R_k + V_{co})}$$

$$T = R_2 C_2 \ln \frac{1 - (I_2 R_k - I_1 R_L)/V_{bb}}{1 - (I_1 R_k + V_{co})/V_{bb}} \tag{10-17}$$

Expanding the log term in a series and retaining only the first term is equivalent to assuming that the portion of the exponential charging characteristic is linear. Thus, Eq. (10-17) becomes

$$T = R_2 C_2 [(I_1 R_L - I_2 R_k)/V_{bb} + (I_1 R_k + V_{co})/V_{bb}]$$

$$T = R_2 C_2 \frac{R_L + R_k}{V_{bb}} I_1 + \frac{R_2 C_2}{V_{bb}} (V_{co} - I_2 R_k) \tag{10-18}$$

The first term in Eq. (10-18) increases with I_1, while the second term is a constant set by the circuit design. The current I_1 in V_1 during conduction is determined by the grid bias of V_1, which can be adjusted by the potentiometer. Actually, because of the cathode-follower action of V_1, the current is very nearly a linear function of the dc grid bias. Thus, the conduction period can be altered simply by changing the grid bias on V_1 and, in practice, T varies linearly with bias to an accuracy of about 1 percent.

The output voltage waveform, Fig. 10-16, is a square pulse of duration T. If this waveform is differentiated and the positive peaks clipped (refer to Fig. 10-15), the result is a negative output pulse delayed by a time T from the negative input trigger pulse. Therefore, this cathode-coupled monostable multivibrator is a convenient circuit for introducing a time delay in pulse circuits. The duration of the delay is adjusted by varying the grid bias on the input tube.

WAVEFORM GENERATORS

Several techniques for generating nonsinusoidal waveforms have been discussed. These include blocking oscillators, SCR relaxation oscillators, and multivibrator circuits. The output signals from these generators can be further modified through the use of diode clippers and clamps to select a portion or set the dc level of a waveform. Also, integrating and differentiating circuits can be used to modify waveforms in specific ways. A number of additional waveform generators which further illustrate the variety of waveshapes of interest in pulse circuits are described in this section.

10-7 The diode pump

Consider the action of the so-called *diode-pump* circuit, Fig. 10-17, in response to negative-going signal pulses. On each negative pulse, diode D_1 conducts and C_1 charges to the peak value of the input pulse. Since the input pulse biases D_2 in reverse, no charge reaches C_2. Thus the charge on C_1 is

$$Q_1 = C_1 v_i \qquad (10\text{-}19)$$

During the time that the input voltage is zero, the voltage on C_1 biases D_2 in the forward direction and C_2 becomes charged. Since

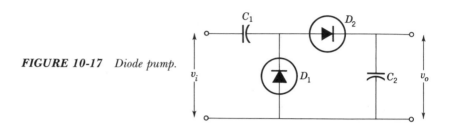

FIGURE 10-17 *Diode pump.*

the two capacitors are now effectively connected in parallel, the charge on C_2 is

$$Q_2 = C_2 v_o = C_2 \frac{Q_1}{C_1 + C_2}$$

or

$$Q_2 = \frac{Q_1}{1 + C_1/C_2} \qquad (10\text{-}20)$$

If $C_2 \gg C_1$, $Q_2 = Q_1$ and the charge has effectively been pumped from the source to C_1 and then to C_2. Note that under this condition C_1 is essentially discharged and the process can be repeated on the next cycle.

The output voltage after the first cycle is

$$v_o = \frac{Q_2}{C_2} = \frac{v_i}{1 + C_2/C_1} \cong \frac{C_1}{C_2} v_i \qquad (10\text{-}21)$$

where Eqs. (10-19) and (10-20) have been used. On each subsequent cycle a voltage increment given by Eq. (10-21) appears across C_2 as long as the total voltage remains small compared with the input pulse amplitude. The result is a *staircase* waveform, Fig. 10-18. In most applications the voltage across C_2 is rapidly discharged by an auxiliary circuit after a finite number of steps and the staircase waveform then repeats.

The diode pump is also a convenient frequency meter when the output capacitor is shunted by a resistance which discharges C_2 on each cycle. Suppose the resistance is that of a d'Arsonval meter connected across C_2. The current through the meter can be calculated from the fact that a charge Q_2 is pumped through the meter once each cycle. If f is the frequency of the input signal, the meter current is

$$I = Q_2 f = \frac{Q_1 f}{1 + C_1/C_2} = \frac{C_1 v_i f}{1 + C_1/C_2} \cong C_1 v_i f \qquad (10\text{-}22)$$

The meter current is directly proportional to the signal frequency as long as the pulses are of uniform amplitude and the frequency is low enough so that C_2 discharges on each cycle. Most often, a

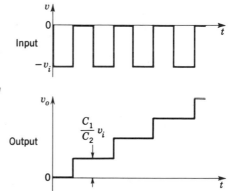

Input

Output

FIGURE 10-18 *Staircase waveform produced by diode pump when input is negative square wave*

squaring circuit such as a Schmitt trigger precedes the diode pump to convert the input signal to a train of uniform pulses. The meter scale can be calibrated directly in terms of frequency and the input signal may have any arbitrary waveform.

10-8 Ramp generators

A voltage that increases linearly with time, called a *ramp,* is widely used for the horizontal sweep voltage in oscilloscopes. Recurring ramps such as those produced by the SCR relaxation oscillators discussed in Chap. 9 are referred to as *sawtooth* waves, Fig. 2-25. Other ramp generators are designed to produce a single ramp waveform when triggered by an external signal.

Figure 10-19a is the circuit diagram of a ramp generator called the *Miller sweep,* which yields a linear ramp with a peak amplitude nearly equal to the dc supply potential. Actually the circuit is basically an operational-amplifier integrator, Fig. 8-19, in which V is the amplifier and the input signal, applied through resistor R, is the constant voltage V_{bb}. Since the integral of a constant increases linearly, the output voltage is a ramp.

With the switch closed a negative grid bias V_{cc} is applied such that V conducts slightly. Opening the switch allows the capacitor to charge through R. As the plate current increases, the drop across R_L results in a negative-going ramp at the output. When the switch is closed again the circuit is returned to the initial condition and is set for a subsequent excursion.

A practical version of the Miller sweep, Fig. 10-19b, uses a pentode amplifier. The increased gain of the pentode results in better integration and yields a more linear sweep than a simple triode stage. Furthermore, it is convenient to start and stop the

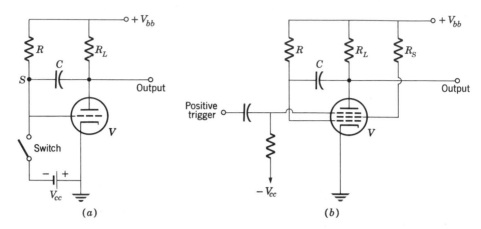

FIGURE 10-19 *(a) Miller sweep ramp generator and (b) practical pentode version.*

integration by means of suppressor grid control. Normally the suppressor grid is biased to plate current cutoff and the control grid is at cathode potential. A positive pulse applied to the suppressor cancels the bias, and the tube operates as an amplifier yielding a negative output ramp. At the end of the input pulse the tube is cut off and C discharges through the grid-cathode diode. The circuit is then ready for another actuating pulse.

The Miller integrator produces a linear ramp nearly as large as the plate supply voltage because of the operational-amplifier feedback action. It is superior to a simple relaxation oscillator in this respect. The voltage excursion in a relaxation oscillator cannot exceed a small fraction of the supply voltage if linearity is to be preserved. Furthermore, the initiation and duration of the ramp are easily controlled by the input trigger pulse in a Miller integrator. The slope of the ramp is determined by the values of R and C. Practical circuits cover a range of ramp speeds by inserting different values using a multitap switch.

Circuits similar to the Miller sweep are often used in *triggered-sweep* oscilloscopes, which are particularly useful for examining waveforms of transient signals. A typical block diagram of the sweep circuit for such an oscilloscope, Fig. 10-20, starts with a Schmitt trigger activated by the input signal applied to the vertical deflection amplifier. The output of the Schmitt trigger is differentiated and clipped to produce a sharp negative pulse suitable for triggering a monostable multivibrator. The multivibrator generates a square pulse input to the Miller integrator. The output ramp is clamped at a voltage level such that the sweep starts at the desired place on the oscilloscope screen.

A number of adjustable controls are included to increase the flexibility of the circuit. For example, bias on the Schmitt trigger can be adjusted to permit the circuit to trigger on input signals of different amplitudes (*trigger amplitude*, in Fig. 10-20). Similarly,

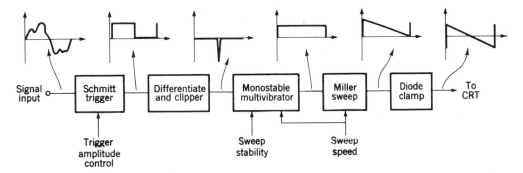

FIGURE 10-20 *Block diagram and typical waveforms of triggered-sweep circuit used in oscilloscopes.*

the bias of the multivibrator is variable (*sweep stability*) so that it may also be operated as a synchronized astable multivibrator to produce recurring sweeps. The sweep speed is altered by changing the charging capacitor (and/or resistor), as described above. At the same time, it is necessary to change the time constant of the multivibrator (also by switching capacitors) so that the sweep duration is commensurate with the sweep speed.

10-9 Pulse regeneration

It is often necessary to regenerate pulse waveforms that have become distorted after passing through various stages of a circuit. As we have seen in Fig. 10-13, the Schmitt trigger performs this function very well. Similarly, circuits such as the blocking oscillator can provide new output pulses once triggered by an imperfect input pulse. The same result can be obtained in several simpler ways, however.

A properly biased diode clipper, Fig. 10-21a, transmits a slice

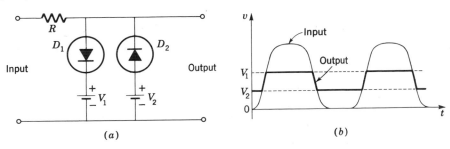

FIGURE 10-21 (a) *Diode clipper used for pulse regeneration, and* (b) *input and output waveforms.*

of the input waveform, Fig. 10-21b, and severe rounding of the pulses is eliminated. Diode D_1 is reverse-biased to clip the positive peaks of the waveform at a voltage level V_1 while D_2 is forward-biased so that the output voltage never drops below V_2. A narrow slice, produced by making V_1 just slightly greater than V_2, yields a good pulse shape, although subsequent amplification may be necessary to regain the desired pulse amplitude. Actually, it is preferable to introduce amplification ahead of the *slicer* so that the output pulse amplitude $V_1 - V_2$ is the desired value. In this way the output pulse waveform is not immediately degraded by limitations of a practical amplifier.

A second alternative, illustrated in Fig. 10-22a, is useful in

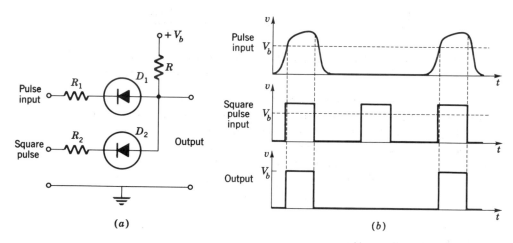

(a) (b)

FIGURE 10-22 (a) *Alternate pulse regeneration circuit, and* (b) *input and output waveforms.*

digital-computer circuits where the presence or absence of a pulse and the exact starting time are particularly significant. Here the diodes are biased forward through the resistance R. The output voltage is zero if $R \gg R_1, R_2$. If now positive pulses larger than V_b are applied to both inputs, the diodes are reverse-biased and the output voltage rises to V_b. Note that if only one input is activated, the other diode still holds the output at zero voltage. Therefore, an output pulse is present only while both input signals are present. If one input is derived from a square-pulse generator, the output waveform, Fig. 10-22b, has the good waveform of the pulse generator, but output pulses occur only when an input signal pulse is present. Extensive digital circuits may employ pulse regeneration at several places in the circuit. In this situation it is feasible to use a common source of square pulses for each pulse regenerator.

COUNTERS

10-10 Binary and decade scalers

A single binary circuit produces one output pulse for every two input trigger pulses. This is so because two trigger pulses cause the binary to shift from one stable state to the other and then back to the first state again. If the output pulse of one binary is used to trigger the input of a second binary, a total of four input pulses produces one output pulse, as will be examined in greater detail presently. Thus, a series of cascaded binary circuits divides, or scales down, the input pulse rate by a factor depending upon the number of cascaded stages. One major application of such a *scaler* is to reduce the pulse rate to the point where the output pulses can be recorded by an electromechanical register. A scaler may also be looked upon as an electronic *counter*. The state of each binary tells the total number of input pulses at any time.

Consider the four-binary scaler of Fig. 10-23. Each binary is similar to Fig. 10-9 except that a separate base bias voltage is used rather than an emitter bias resistor, and triggering is accomplished with steering diodes in the base circuit. A pulse amplifier is used at the input to provide trigger pulses of sufficient amplitude to cause a transition in binary B_1. Similar trigger amplifiers are often placed between the binaries in order to isolate each stage and also to assure reliable triggering action. Suppose that, initially, the V_2 transistors are all conducting and the V_1 transistors are cut off. This condition is achieved using the *reset* switch. When the switch is opened momentarily a strong forward bias is placed on all V_2 transistors, which assures that they conduct. With the reset switch closed, the binaries perform normally.

For convenience, we designate the state of any binary as state 0 if the output transistor V_2 is saturated. Similarly, when the output transistor is cut off, the binary is said to be in state 1. Starting from the condition in which all four binaries are in state 0, consider the waveforms at the output transistors of each binary as a result of a regular sequence of input trigger pulses, Fig. 10-24. The first input pulse causes binary B_1 to make a transition from state 0 to state 1. This means that the output transistor goes from saturation to cutoff and the output voltage increases. This positive step is blocked from triggering the second binary by the steering diodes coupling B_1 to B_2. Therefore the result of one input pulse is to put B_1 in state 1 while the other binaries remain in state 0.

At the second input pulse, B_1 returns from state 1 back to state 0. The resulting negative output voltage step triggers B_2 from state 0 to 1. Binary B_3 remains in state 0 because the output voltage from B_2 is a positive signal. The net result of two input pulses is that B_2 is in state 1, while the other three are in state 0. This

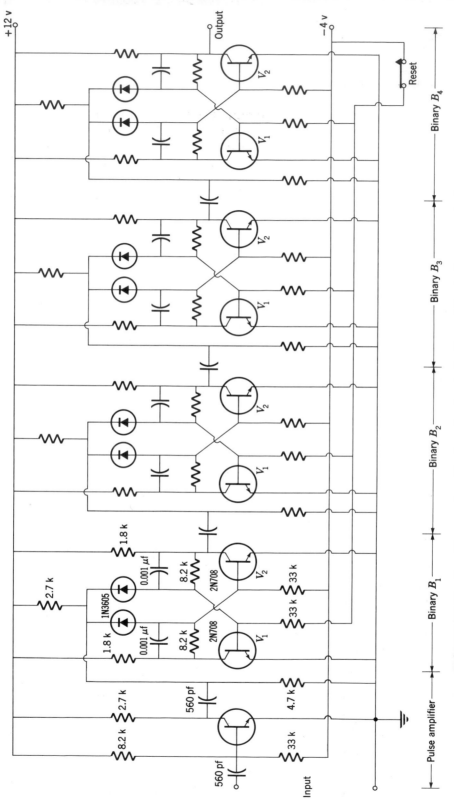

FIGURE 10-23 *Four-binary scaler. Component values in B_2, B_3, and B_4 are the same as in first stage.*

process continues with further input pulses as illustrated in Fig. 10-24 until at the sixteenth pulse a negative output pulse is produced. The cascade combination of four binaries is, accordingly, called a *scale-of-16* counter. Greater scaling factors are achieved simply by adding additional binary stages.

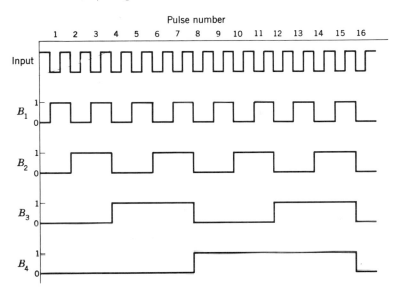

FIGURE 10-24 *Waveforms in scale-of-16 counter.*

Because of the two stable states of each stage, a binary scaler basically counts by 2s, or, rather, by powers of 2, a process which is explored in greater depth in a later section. It is somewhat inconvenient to determine the total number of counts corresponding to any given combination of 0 and 1 states for each binary in a scaler because we are not familiar with the binary number system. Rather, we prefer to count in the decimal system, and for this purpose *decade scalers* are used. The scale of a binary counter may be converted to a decade counter by several feedback arrangements which return pulses from certain stages to preceding binaries in the cascade.

For example, a decade counter based on a scale-of-16 binary is illustrated in Fig. 10-25. In this vacuum-tube version the method of coupling trigger pulses from one binary to the next differs from the one previously explained. Trigger pulses are developed across a resistor R in series with both plates of the succeeding binary. Thus, when the preceding binary changes states, a positive pulse or a negative pulse is applied to both plates. As noted previously, a binary is triggered best by turning off the on tube, so that only the negative trigger pulses are effective. To convert the scale-of-16 counter into a decade counter, two feedback circuits are added: one from the output of B_3 to the grid of V_1

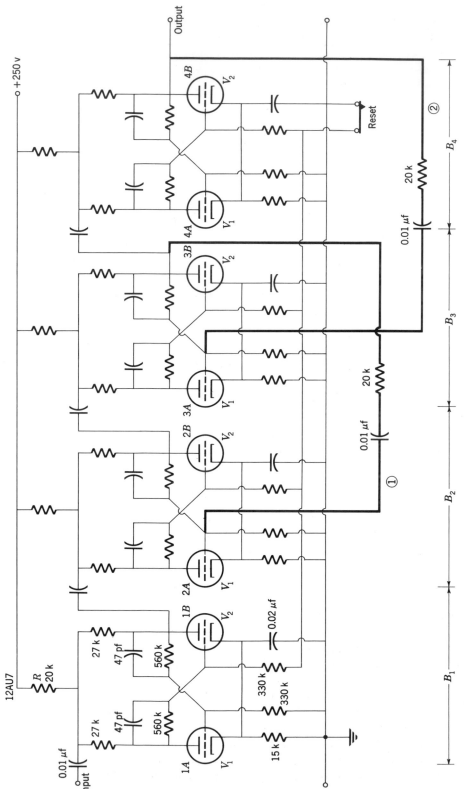

FIGURE 10-25 Scale-of-10 counter produced by feedback paths (heavy lines) in conventional four-binary scaler.

in binary B_2; the other from the output of B_4 to the grid of V_1 in binary B_3. These feedback paths are shown by the heavy lines in Fig. 10-25.

The operation of the decade counter is best understood by examining the plate voltage waveforms at each output tube, Fig. 10-26. Through the third count the circuit operates as a normal

FIGURE 10-26 *Waveforms in decade counter.*

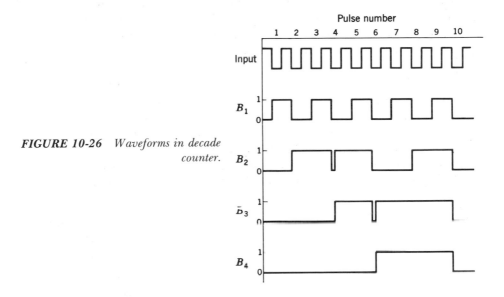

scaler. At the fourth input pulse binary B_1 makes a transition from state 1 to 0; this triggers binary B_2 into a similar transition, and the output of B_2 causes B_3 to make a transition from state 0 to state 1. At this time the positive pulse from the output of B_3 is coupled back through the first feedback path to the grid of V_1 in binary B_2. Since B_2 is in the 0 state, V_1 is cut off and the positive feedback pulse induces a transition from state 0 to 1 in B_2. Similarly, at the sixth input pulse binary B_3 first makes a transition from state 1 to 0 and subsequently reverses in response to the feedback pulse from B_4 through the second feedback path. The net result is that a negative output pulse is delivered by the last binary at the tenth count. That is, the circuit is a decade scaler.

Note that at the fourth count B_2 must settle in state 0 before the feedback pulse arrives to reverse the state. The delay between these two events is provided by the inherent transition time of the B_3 stage. A similar comment applies to the double transition in B_3 at the sixth input pulse. The necessary delay limits the rate at which the counter can reliably follow rapid input pulses. Alternative techniques have been devised to convert binaries into decade counters which improve this limitation. In every case, however, feedback pulses are employed and the various methods do not differ in principle from the typical circuit discussed here.

Most often, the output of a scaler is recorded by an electrome-chanical ratcheting register. A power output stage driven by the last binary is usually necessary to provide sufficient energy to actuate the register. Since a mechanical register typically cannot operate faster than about 10 pulses per second, a scaling factor at least sufficient to reduce the input pulse rate to this magnitude is required. Conversely, the maximum useful scaling factor is that which reduces the maximum input pulse rate to the limiting rate of the mechanical register. The maximum input pulse rate is set by the resolving time of the first binary stage, as discussed earlier.

The mechanical register totals the number of output pulses. The total number of input pulses is the product of the register total times the scaling factor plus the number of counts represented by the state of each binary in the scaler. In vacuum-tube circuits the state of each binary is indicated by a small neon lamp. The lamp is in series with a current-limiting resistor connected between each output tube plate and ground, Fig. 10-27. With the binary

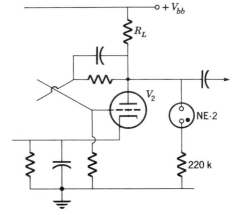

FIGURE 10-27 *Neon-lamp indicator lights when binary is in state 1 with V_2 cut off.*

in state 0, V_2 is conducting and the plate voltage is insufficient to light the lamp. When the binary makes a transition to state 1, V_2 is cut off and the plate voltage rises sufficiently to light the lamp. The neon bulbs connected to the four binaries in a scale-of-16 counter are labeled 1, 2, 4, and 8, respectively. The count is de-termined by adding the numbers associated with those neon bulbs which are lit.

In decade scalers a neon bulb is associated with each digit from 0 to 9 and the count is indicated directly in the decimal system. A method for interconnecting the 10 neon bulbs to a decade counter to provide this display is considered in Exercise 10-9. When three or four decade counters are cascaded, the neon in-dicator lights for a given decade are conventionally arranged in a vertical column parallel to the lights of the preceding decade.

Thus the number of counts in the system is indicated directly in terms of the units, tens, hundreds, thousands, etc., corresponding to each decade column.

Several indicator schemes have been developed that display the actual number corresponding to the count in a decade scaler. One of these, called a *Nixie* tube, is basically a 10-cathode neon tube in which each cathode is a wire shaped into the form of one of the digits from 0 to 9. These are connected to the scaler in a fashion similar to that used for the 10 individual neon bulbs, so that only one cathode is lit at a time. The characteristic neon glow covers the entire cathode wire and this numeral appears at the face of the tube, Fig. 10-28. Thus, one Nixie tube is associated

FIGURE 10-28   *Nixie-tube numerical indicator.*
(Courtesy Burroughs Corporation.)

with each decade and when the tubes corresponding to cascaded decades are arranged in a row, the count is indicated directly as a decimal number. Several other schemes which also present a numerical digit display are in use.

The potentials in transistor circuits are normally low compared with the voltages needed to light a neon bulb, and an auxiliary switching circuit is used to turn on the neon bulb or Nixie. A typical circuit, Fig. 10-29, uses a transistor switch activated by the collector potential of the binary output transistor. When V_2 is conducting, its collector potential is low and the base bias on V_3 is so small that it is cut off. Therefore, the Nixie does not light. V_3 is turned on when the binary is in state 1 and the collector potential of V_2 rises sufficiently to provide base bias for V_3. With V_3 saturated the full 250-volt power supply potential is applied across the Nixie, which causes it to light. Note that the voltage swing at the collector of the switching transistor need only be somewhat greater than the difference between the breakdown and maintaining voltage of the neon tube. That is, it is not necessary for the transistor to be capable of withstanding the full power-supply potential. Note also that a switching circuit similar to Fig. 10-29 is required for each of the separate cathodes of a Nixie tube.

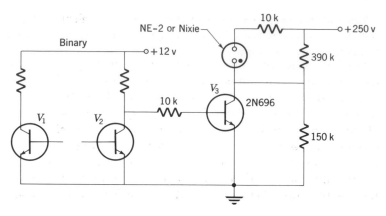

FIGURE 10-29 *Switching transistor used to light neon or Nixie indicator in transistor counters.*

10-11 The Dekatron counter

A very useful decade counter that requires a minimum of components is based on the Dekatron tube. This is a gas-filled discharge tube containing a central anode and 30 cathodes arranged around its periphery. Successive input pulses cause a glowing spot to move circumferentially around the face of the tube, thus indicating the number of counts. At the tenth input pulse the Dekatron delivers an output pulse which may be used to trigger a succeeding stage.

The movement of the glowing spot may be understood by referring to Fig. 10-30. The Dekatron contains a single anode, 10 glow cathodes (K_0, K_1, K_2, . . . , K_9), 10 1G guide cathodes ($1G_0$, $1G_1$, $1G_2$, . . . , $1G_9$), and 10 2G guide cathodes ($2G_0$, $2G_1$, $2G_2$, . . . , $2G_9$). K_0 is the output terminal, and cathodes K_1 to K_9 are tied together and brought to a single base pin. Similarly, all 1G electrodes are connected together, as are all 2G cathodes. A small positive bias is applied to the 1G and 2G cathodes and a normally closed reset switch is included in the K_1-K_9 lead.

Opening the reset switch momentarily causes a discharge between K_0 and the anode, since K_0 is then the most negative cathode. With the reset switch closed, the circuit is set to count pulses. A negative input pulse of about 100 volts applied to 1G causes the discharge to transfer from K_0 to $1G_0$. Although all 1G cathodes experience the same large anode-cathode potential resulting from the negative pulse, cathode $1G_0$ is nearest to the discharge previously existing at K_0. Gas ions remaining in the space near K_0 preferentially continue the discharge at $1G_0$. Just at the termination of the pulse on $1G_0$ a second negative pulse is applied to the 2G cathodes. The discharge now transfers to $2G_0$, since it is closest to $1G_0$. Finally, at the end of the second pulse the discharge jumps to K_1 because it is then at a lower potential than $2G_0$. The net result of the duality of negative pulses is that the glowing cathode spot has moved from K_0 to K_1. The spot remains in this

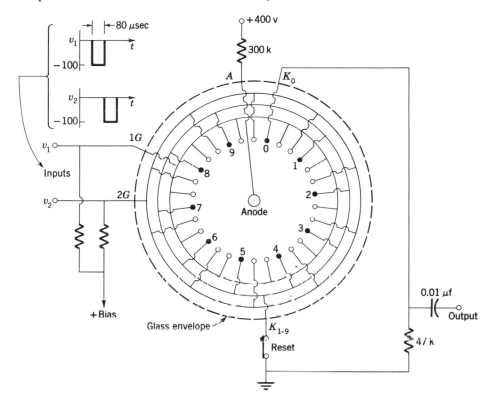

FIGURE 10-30 *Dekatron counter tube.*

position until a second pair of trigger pulses is applied to $1G$ and $2G$, at which time the spot moves to K_2. The sequence continues until at the tenth input pulse pair the discharge returns to K_0. The discharge current through the cathode resistor in series with K_0 results in a positive output pulse.

The circuit diagram of a three-stage, scale-of-1000 decade counter based on the Dekatron is shown in Fig. 10-31. Each counter stage is driven by a dual triode pulse-forming network which generates two properly timed negative pulses from a single positive input pulse. It is instructive to examine the way in which these pulses are produced. The output signal of each Dekatron (and the input to the scaler) is a 30-volt positive step. This is differentiated by the combination R_1C_1 to yield an exponential pulse with a time constant of $(2.2 \times 10^5)(680 \times 10^{-12}) = 150$ μsec. The positive peak is clipped by the grid-cathode diode of V_1 together with R_4 to give an approximately rectangular pulse 150 μsec long at the plate of V_1. This 130-volt negative pulse is applied to the $1G$ cathodes. The output of V_1 is differentiated by R_2C_2, producing

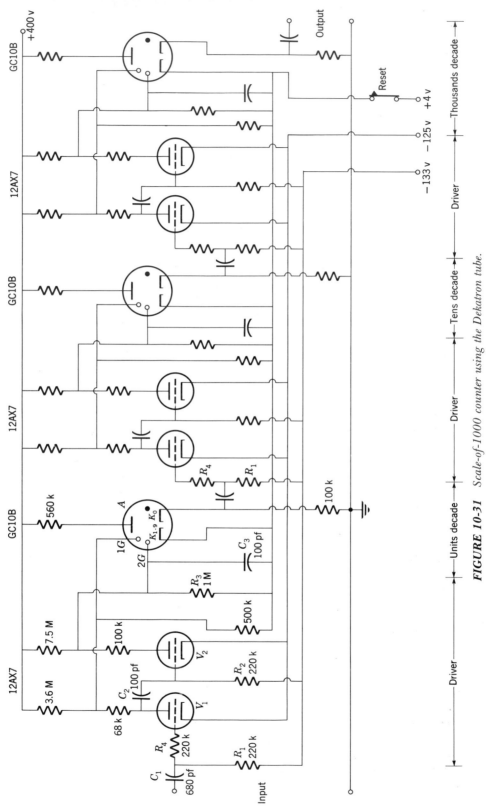

FIGURE 10-31 *Scale-of-1000 counter using the Dekatron tube.*

first a negative pulse followed by a positive pulse at the leading and trailing edges of the rectangular signal. The negative pulse cuts off V_2, but since this tube is biased nearly to cutoff anyway, the output signal is negligible. The positive pulse, $R_2C_2 = (2.2 \times 10^5) \times (100 \times 10^{-12}) = 22$ μsec long, is clipped by the grid-cathode diode of V_2 to yield a 130-volt negative rectangular pulse at the plate of V_2. The combination R_3C_3 integrates this output, making the pulse length $(1 \times 10^6)(100 \times 10^{-12}) = 100$ μsec, which is suitable to drive the 2G electrodes. Note that the 2G pulse starts at the trailing edge of the 1G pulse, as required for proper operation of the Dekatron. A more quantitative analysis of the driver circuit is undertaken in Exercise 10-10.

The Dekatron combines the functions of decade counting and display all in one unit, and comparatively simple scaling circuits are possible. The scale-of-1000 counter in Fig. 10-31, for example, employs a total of only six tubes, compared with at least twelve tubes for a decade counter based on binary circuitry. The major drawback of Dekatron scalers is the maximum counting rate, which is limited by the time required to transfer the discharge from one cathode to another. Note that a time interval of $150 + 100 = 250$ μsec is necessary to register one count. The input pulse interval cannot be a shorter time than this, so that the maximum counting rate is $1/250$ μsec $= 4000$ cps. Other Dekatrons are capable of proper performance up to 20 kc but even this rate is much lower than that possible with transistor and vacuum-tube binaries.

10-12 Frequency meters and timers

Counters are used to measure the frequency of an input signal by counting the number of cycles in the signal during an accurately known time interval. For this purpose the input signal is first converted into a series of negative pulses, one per cycle, by means of a Schmitt trigger followed by a differentiator and clipper circuit, as shown in Fig. 10-32. The output of the clipper is fed to a *gate* circuit which passes the pulses on to a decade counter only during the time a second signal, the *gate pulse*, is present. The number of input pulses during this interval is registered by the counter. If, for example, the duration of the gate pulse is 1 sec long, the frequency of the unknown signal is indicated by the decade counter directly.

A typical gate circuit using the suppressor grid of a pentode is shown in Fig. 10-32. The suppressor is biased to plate current cutoff so that, even with a signal impressed on the control grid, the output voltage is zero. A positive gate pulse applied to the suppressor permits plate current so an output signal is present during the gate pulse. Other gate circuits are also possible; in every case the purpose of the gate is to control the transmission of one signal by another signal. In the frequency counter an accurately timed gate pulse is derived by scaling down the output of a stable crystal oscillator. The positive pulse from the last binary of

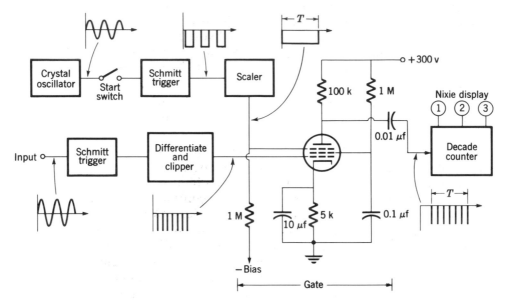

FIGURE 10-32   *Frequency meter that counts number of cycles in input signal during known time interval.*

the scaler is used directly as the gate pulse and the duration of the pulse is set by the oscillator frequency together with the scaling factor. Changing the scale factor alters the counting period and therefore the frequency range of the instrument.

The frequency meter is started by closing the start switch and subsequently opening it after one counting interval. In practical instruments internal control circuitry is included to open the start switch automatically after one gate pulse is generated. This prevents the counter from recording counts during more than one gate pulse. Alternatively, the control circuitry can be used to reset the decade counter after each gate pulse. In this mode the instrument periodically samples the input frequency and can, for example, detect slow frequency changes of the input signal.

The precision with which a counter measures frequency is ± 1 cycle during the gate interval, depending upon the time the gate opens relative to the input frequency pulses. An extra count is registered if the gate pulse starts during an input pulse compared with the count recorded if the gate opens between input pulses, as illustrated in Fig. 10-33. Because of this one-count uncertainty, it is desirable to maximize the number of input pulses during the gate interval. This can be done by adjusting the gate duration by means of the oscillator scaling factor. Alternatively, low-frequency input signals are measured by deriving the gate pulse from one period of the input signal and counting the number of oscillator pulses during this time. The period of the input signal is determined from the known oscillator frequency. This approach is considered further in Exercise 10-11.

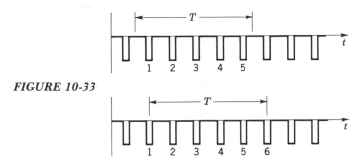

FIGURE 10-33

A less precise, but much simpler, frequency meter based on the diode pump is shown in Fig. 10-34. According to Eq. (10-22) the output current of a diode pump is a linear function of the signal

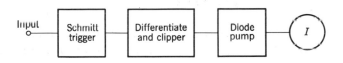

FIGURE 10-34 *Frequency meter based on diode pump.*

frequency, assuming only that individual pulses have the same shape and amplitude. A Schmitt trigger followed by a differentiator and clipper produces uniform negative pulses independent of the input signal waveform. The frequency range of the instru-

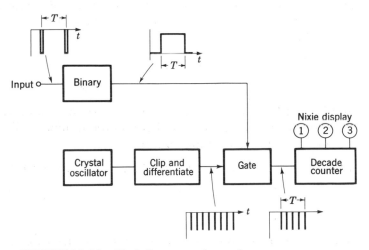

FIGURE 10-35 *Block diagram and waveforms in time-interval meter.*

ment is conveniently altered by changing the value of C_1 in Eq. (10-22). This circuit is commonly employed in portable nuclear-radiation detectors called survey meters, as well as in simple laboratory frequency meters.

The time interval between two signal pulses can be accurately measured by counting the number of cycles of a stable oscillator during the time between the pulses. This is accomplished, Fig. 10-35, by triggering a binary with the input pulses to provide a gate pulse of duration equal to the interval between pulses. If the oscillator frequency is 1000 cps, the decade counter reads the time interval directly in milliseconds. The timing accuracy depends upon the oscillator stability and is subject to the same one-cycle uncertainty as the frequency-counter circuit.

DIGITAL CIRCUITS

10-13 Binary numbers

Pulse waveforms are used in digital circuits to represent the digits of numbers. This permits mathematical operations such as addition and subtraction to be carried out by electronic circuits. It proves convenient to represent numbers by waveforms which have only two amplitudes, called state 0 and state 1, or off and on. In this way the stability advantages of pulse circuits are used most effectively. Since only two digits are available, the *binary number* system is used, rather than the more familiar *decimal* system based on the use of 10 digits. Although the binary system is less familiar, there is no difference in principle between the two. Consider, for example, the meaning of the decimal number 528. This array of decimal digits is a shorthand notation for the increasing powers of ten in the number. Thus,

$$528 = (5 \times 10^2) + (2 \times 10^1) + (8 \times 10^0)$$
$$= \quad 500 \quad + \quad 20 \quad + \quad 8 \quad = 528$$

Similarly, the two digits in the binary system, 0 and 1, tell the number of increasing powers of two in the number. The binary number 10110, for example, means

$$10110 = (1 \times 2^4) + (0 \times 2^3) + (1 \times 2^2) + (1 \times 2^1) + (0 \times 2^0)$$
$$= \quad 16 \quad + \quad 0 \quad + \quad 4 \quad + \quad 2 \quad + \quad 0$$
$$= \quad 22$$

That is, the binary number 10110 represents the same quantity as the decimal number 22.

Table 10-1 contains the decimal-binary equivalents for the numbers from 0 through 16. The binary-number representations in this table are identical to the states of the four-binary counter of Fig. 10-23. The correspondence can be established by noting the

TABLE 10-1

BINARY AND DECIMAL NUMBERS

Decimal number	Binary number
0	0000
1	0001
2	0010
3	0011
4	0100
5	0101
6	0110
7	0111
8	1000
9	1001
10	1010
11	1011
12	1100
13	1101
14	1110
15	1111
16	10000

state of each binary at every input count using the waveforms in Fig. 10-24. This is the basis for the earlier statement that a binary scaler counts by powers of 2. It is one illustration of the convenience attendant on using the binary-number representation in electronic digital circuits.

Arithmetic manipulations with binary numbers involve mathematical logic quite familiar from decimal numbers. Addition and subtraction operations involve digits that are carried and borrowed in an analogous fashion, recognizing that $01 + 01 = 10$, etc. For example, the sum of 0110 and 0101 is written

$$
\begin{array}{ll}
0110 & 6 \\
+0101 & +5 \\
\hline
1011 & 11
\end{array}
\qquad (10\text{-}23)
$$

Similarly, subtraction is straightforward, after noting that $10 - 01$ $= 01$. For example,

$$
\begin{array}{ll}
1110 & 14 \\
-0101 & -5 \\
\hline
1001 & 9
\end{array}
\qquad (10\text{-}24)
$$

Other examples are undertaken in the Exercises.

Binary digits are represented by voltage waveforms with regularly spaced pulses of uniform amplitude. Conventionally, the pulses corresponding to increasing powers of 2 appear in time sequence beginning with 2^0. The waveforms of the binary numbers 1011 and 0011 are illustrated in Fig. 10-36, together with their

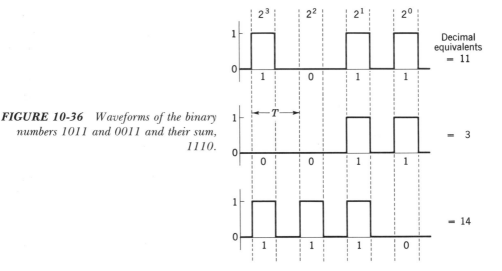

FIGURE 10-36 *Waveforms of the binary numbers 1011 and 0011 and their sum, 1110.*

sum, 1110. Note that the pulse lengths of both 0 and 1 digits are equal. One digit, be it a 0 or a 1, is termed a *bit*, which is a contraction for *binary digit*.

It should be noted in passing that the waveform of the sum bears no simple relationship to the waveforms of the two numbers. That is, the waveform of the sum is not obtained simply by adding the voltages of the waveforms representing the individual binary numbers. This points up the fact that waveforms in digital circuits are a coded representation of numbers and the voltages of the waveforms have no significance in themselves.

10-14 Logic gates

The various operations performed on digital waveforms are accomplished using circuits termed *logic gates* which have two or more inputs and one output. The output waveform of a logic gate may have little or no resemblance to any of the input signals except that the input-output characteristics of the circuits are described in terms of mathematical logic.

Consider the so-called AND gate illustrated in Fig. 10-37. Diodes

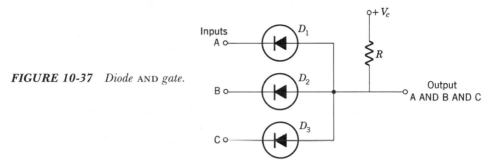

FIGURE 10-37   *Diode* AND *gate.*

D_1, D_2, and D_3 are biased in the low-resistance forward direction and the output voltage is zero. If positive pulses with amplitudes somewhat greater than V_c are applied simultaneously to all three inputs the diodes are reverse-biased and the output voltage rises to V_c. Note, however, that if even one input pulse is absent, the corresponding diode continues under forward bias and there is no output signal. This action is logically described by saying that an output pulse is present only when there are A *and* B *and* C input pulses.

One application of the AND gate has already been presented in connection with pulse regeneration, Fig. 10-22. The gate is also widely used in nuclear-radiation pulse circuits, where it is called a *coincidence circuit* since, in effect, it detects the coincidence of pulses presented to the inputs. An AND gate may employ transistors or multigrid vacuum tubes rather than diodes. The diode circuit is simplest, however, and adequately describes the logical operation of interest. In addition, diode logic circuits are extensively used in practice.

The operation of the AND gate should not be confused with the mathematical operation of addition. That is, the output of an AND gate is not the sum of the input signals, as is illustrated graphically by comparing AND-gate output waveforms with true sum waveforms in Exercise 10-16. Circuits which perform the addition operation are considered in a later section.

The OR gate, Fig. 10-38, yields an output pulse when the input is A *or* B *or* C. It is basically a mixing circuit that brings several pulse waveforms into a common output with minimum interaction between the pulse sources. Note, for example, if only input A receives a positive pulse, diode D_1 is biased forward and an output pulse is present. At the same time diodes D_2 and D_3 are reverse-biased by the input pulse and little effect is fed back to inputs B and C.

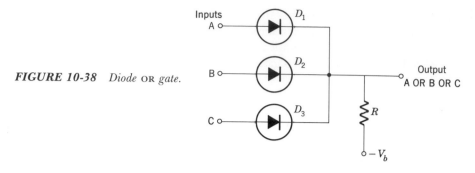

FIGURE 10-38 *Diode OR gate.*

In binary logic the operation NOT inverts the polarity of a wave-form, as illustrated in Fig. 10-39. The meaning of this operation is as follows. A digital waveform has only two states, 0 and 1. If

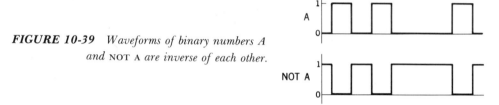

FIGURE 10-39 *Waveforms of binary numbers A and NOT A are inverse of each other.*

at any given instant the waveform has, say, the value 1 it may be said to be in state NOT 0. The NOT operation converts a state 0 into state 1 (NOT 0) and vice versa in any waveform. The usefulness of this operation is made evident in subsequent sections.

Consider the logic circuit employing a single transistor shown in Fig. 10-40. The 180° phase shift in the transistor produces, in

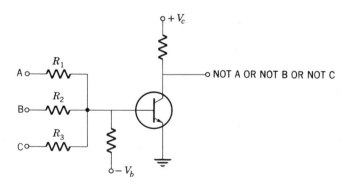

FIGURE 10-40 *Simple NOR gate performs the combined operation NOT-OR.*

effect, the NOT inversion. It is possible to include several input terminals, as shown, so that the waveform at each input may appear at the output, as in an OR circuit. Therefore this gate is a NOT-OR, or NOR, gate. Resistors R_1, R_2, and R_3 are sometimes replaced with diodes as in the diode OR gate, Fig. 10-38. This is only necessary if it is desirable to minimize input circuit interactions to the greatest extent possible.

The NOR gate is extremely versatile. It is, in fact, possible to achieve all logical operations by proper use of NOR gates alone. As an example, we show how three NOR gates are interconnected to make an AND gate in Fig. 10-41. It is easiest to understand the

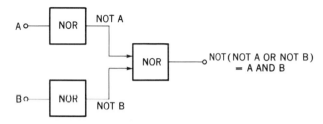

FIGURE 10-41 *Three* NOR *gates can be connected to produce an* AND *gate.*

operation of this circuit by examining typical input and output waveforms at various places in the circuit. Suppose, for example, the A input is the digital waveform representing the number 1101, as in Fig. 10-42, and the B input represents 1011. The waveforms for NOT A and NOT B obtained from each NOR gate are derived immediately with reference to the NOT operation. When NOT A and NOT B are applied to the third NOR gate, the output may be expressed as NOT (NOT A *or* NOT B). The output waveform is determined by noting that whenever the transistor base is driven with a positive pulse, the output is zero, and whenever the base input is zero the output is a positive pulse. Thus, Fig. 10-42, the first

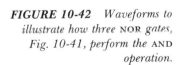

FIGURE 10-42 *Waveforms to illustrate how three* NOR *gates, Fig. 10-41, perform the* AND *operation.*

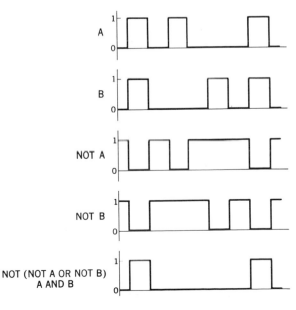

digit is 0 for both NOT A and NOT B, so that the output pulse is state 1. The second digit is zero for NOT A but positive for NOT B, so the output is zero. A similar situation exists at the third digit, except that the inputs are reversed, and the fourth digit is the same as the first digit. The output waveform is just A *and* B, as may be verified by forming the output waveform corresponding to the AND operation directly.

Using three NOR gates to achieve what a simple AND gate can do appears uneconomical. It is, however, advantageous to assemble extensive circuits from combinations of one single basic subunit. This greatly simplifies construction and maintenance procedures. Furthermore, if many simple AND gates are used in one circuit amplification is necessary anyway. It is then more convenient to include the transistor amplifier directly in the logic circuit itself.

One further common logic gate is a combination of a NOR and an AND gate, Fig. 10-43, sometimes referred to as a NOT-AND gate.

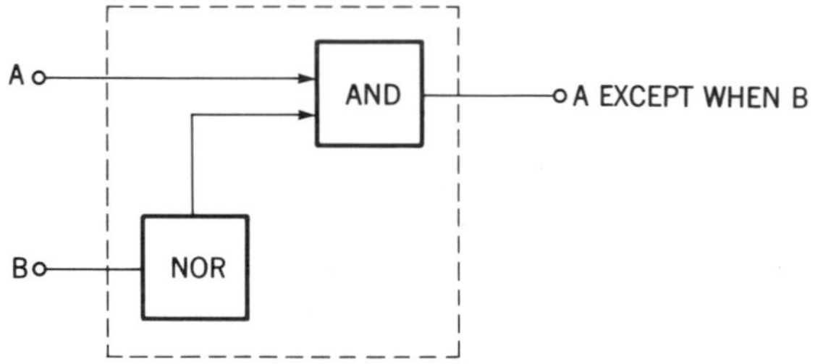

FIGURE 10-43 *A* NOT-AND *gate, also called an anticoincidence circuit.*

The function of this circuit is to pass the A waveform except when a pulse is present at the B input. That is, the B input inhibits the output and for this reason the circuit is also called an *inhibitor* gate. In pulse applications it is termed an *anticoincidence circuit* by analogy with the coincidence circuit. Detailed operation of this gate is considered in Exercises 10-17 and 10-18 by examining waveforms in the circuit.

We now consider how these simple logic circuits are combined to carry out arithmetic operations. It is most pertinent to examine the addition of digital numbers. Multiplication can then be accomplished simply by repeated additions. Subtraction circuits are very similar to addition circuits and can also be used to carry out division. It is, in fact, possible to base all numerical calculations on the single operation of addition.

Electronic digital addition of two numbers A and B is done in two steps: first the digits in each column are added, and then the carry digits in any column are added to the column representing the next higher power of 2. This procedure is identical to conventional addition, as illustrated by Eq. (10-23). Because of the two-step operation, it is convenient to split the adding circuit into two parts, each of which is termed a *half-adder*. Two half-adders in cascade result in a complete ADD logic gate.

We first consider the logic operations that must be accomplished by a half-adder. Considering each bit of the two numbers A and B, the *truth table* describing addition, Table 10-2, is constructed. Note

TABLE 10-2

TRUTH TABLE FOR ADDITION OF BITS

A *bit*	B *bit*	*Bit sum*	*Carry bit*
0	0	0	0
0	1	1	0
1	0	1	0
1	1	0	1

that only in the case of the last entry in the table is a *carry bit* produced. A half-adder logic circuit that accomplishes the results called for in the truth table is shown in Fig. 10-44. This can be

FIGURE 10-44 *Half-adder logic circuit composed of* NOR *gates. Numbers in parentheses and circles trace bits through circuit.*

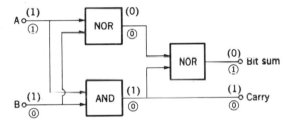

established, for example, by following 1 bits for both A and B through the circuit, as indicated by those bits in parentheses. The bit sum output is 0 while the carry output is 1, in agreement with the bottom line of Table 10-2. Similarly, a 1 bit at the A input together with a 0 bit at the B input, as encircled in Fig. 10-44, results in a 1 bit output and a 0 carry, as also required by the truth table. The remaining two entries in the truth table can be checked in identical fashion.

The way in which two half-adders are cascaded to produce the full sum is shown in Fig. 10-45. The second half-adder adds the

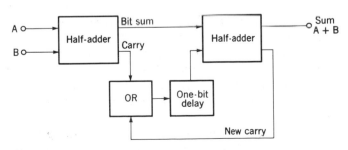

FIGURE 10-45 *Complete digital* ADD *gate.*

carry output and the bit-sum output of the first half-adder. The carry pulse, if any, is delayed by a time equal to the time interval between bits of the digital number (indicated by T in Fig. 10-36). This has the effect of adding the carry to the bit representing the next higher power of two. The carry output of the second half-adder is returned through the one-bit delay in order to account for the possibility that adding the original carry bit produces a new carry bit of 1. The output of the second half-adder is the required sum A + B. It is instructive to follow typical waveforms through the entire ADD gate to show that the output is, in fact, the correct sum waveform (see Exercise 10-19).

Subtraction is handled in an analogous fashion. The truth table for subtraction, Table 10-3, shows that the remainder-bit column

TABLE 10-3

TRUTH TABLE FOR SUBTRACTION OF BITS

A *bit*	B *bit*	*Bit remainder*	*Borrow bit*
0	0	0	0
0	1	1	1
1	0	1	0
1	1	0	0

is similar to the sum-bit column in Table 10-2, which means that the same basic half-adder circuit used for addition is also applicable to subtraction. It is, however, necessary to derive and use the borrow bit in a somewhat different fashion. The net result is a subtraction circuit that is not markedly different from the complete ADD gate.

10-15   The digital computer

A *digital computer* is a complex array of logic gates and associated circuitry organized to perform arithmetic computations by manipulating waveforms representing digital numbers. The great power of electronic digital processing stems from the variety of phenomena that can be represented numerically and analyzed arithmetically. Typical examples range from scientific computations which obey some physical law to bookkeeping activities which follow the principles of accounting. Because the speed of electronic circuits is so great, digital computers can complete extremely complex and extensive calculations in practical lengths of time.

The circuits of digital computers are designed to carry out numerical calculations of all kinds. Therefore, the machine is furnished specific instructions pertaining to any desired computation, in addition to all the digital numbers involved. These instructions are represented by pulse waveforms similar to those representing numbers. A complete set of instructions, together with the numbers associated with a given problem, is called the *program*.

A digital computer comprises five major parts: input, output, memory, control, and arithmetic units, Fig. 10-46. The input and

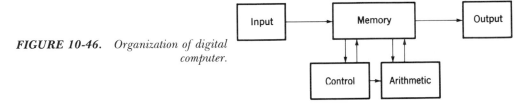

FIGURE 10-46. *Organization of digital computer.*

output units present the program to the machine and retrieve the final results. Most often these are magnetic tape recorders which are capable of recording and reproducing the digital waveforms representing the instructions and numbers of the program as well as the waveforms representing the results. The recorded output signals are subsequently converted into printed form by passing the output magnetic tapes through a separate unit, called a *printer*. In effect, the input and output units are the means by which human operators communicate with the machine.

The computer *memory* stores each instruction and number of the program until needed during the course of the computation. In one type of memory, individual bits are stored by magnetizing a small ring, or core, of magnetic material in either the clockwise or counterclockwise direction. Information is retrieved by sensing the direction of magnetization in each core and generating a corresponding signal waveform. The instructions of the program are stored separately from numbers since the two are used in fundamentally different ways in the calculation. The location of each number is specified by an *address* which is used to tell the machine where a particular number is stored in the memory.

The *arithmetic* unit contains logic circuits such as ADD gates which actually perform the numerical calculations specified by the program. The arithmetic unit also includes *registers* for temporarily storing a digital number. The reason for this is that, ordinarily, only one number at a time is recalled from the memory. If two numbers are to be added, the first one must be stored until the second one is available before they can be presented simultaneously to the ADD gate. A common form of register is a series of cascaded binaries which, as was shown earlier, can represent a digital number by the state of each binary in the cascade.

The function of the *control* unit is to interpret each instruction and set the circuits of the computer accordingly. It is the most heterogeneous part of the computer and is composed of logic gates, registers, and a *clock* circuit which regulates the basic speed at which the machine operates. The clock provides a continuous train of pulses which are used in connection with the various logic gates to direct the digital waveforms through the various parts of the computer. Clock pulses are used, for example, to sense the magnetization of the magnetic cores in the memory; this means that the time interval between bits of a number read from the memory is the same as that of the clock pulses.

A digital computer is operated by first inserting the program into the memory. When the machine is started, the control unit reads the first instruction, prepares the circuits of the computer accordingly, and causes the proper number to be read from the memory as specified by the address in the instruction. At the completion of the indicated operation, the result is returned to the memory at the address also specified in the program. The control unit then passes on to the next instruction. The machine proceeds sequentially through the instructions, placing final results in the output unit until the final instruction *stop* is reached. At this point the computation is finished and the desired result is located in the output unit.

It is useful to illustrate by means of a rudimentary example how the control unit prepares the circuits of the machine in accordance with the instructions. Consider the partial block diagram, Fig. 10-47, in which either of two numbers can be operated upon and

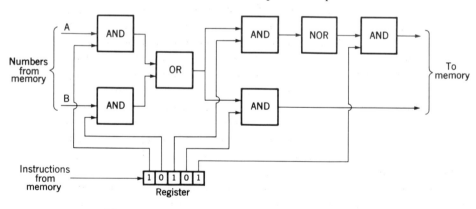

FIGURE 10-47 *Illustrating how an instruction determines path of number through circuit as in digital computer.*

returned to the memory, depending upon the instruction. Suppose the instruction 10101, as shown, is abstracted from the memory and stored in a register connected to the several AND gates. This means that the number A passes through the circuit, emerges as NOT A, and is returned to the memory. The number B is not used since it does not pass the first AND gate. Other instructions cause different operations to be performed, as may be determined by following the path through the circuit in each case:

Instruction	Interpretation
10101	Take A and return NOT A to memory
10010	Take A and return A to memory
01101	Take B and return NOT B to memory
01010	Take B and return B to memory

In effect, instructions set up signal paths through the computer by activating logic gates of the control unit.

It is not feasible, or necessary, to trace the entire signal path for each instruction through the complete circuit when preparing a program. In the design of the machine, a tabulation of the instructions to carry out various operations is developed, corresponding to the control logic circuits. This *dictionary of machine language* is used to write programs. It obviates the need to refer to the circuits of the computer itself. Nevertheless, because each minute step must be detailed in the instructions, the preparation of a program is a long and arduous task and programming errors are frequent. For example, transposing a 0 for a 1 in any one instruction may result in a "nonsense" instruction, or, more seriously, in a false instruction, and such errors are difficult to locate.

Large-scale digital machines are provided with a previously prepared *compiler* program which allows programs to be written in a special, stylized algebraic language that can be read and understood by the person preparing the program. As this program is typed on a special electric typewriter, an encoded punched-paper tape is prepared simultaneously. When this tape is passed through the computer input the compiler program in the memory operates to produce a magnetic-tape output which is a computer program in machine language. In effect, the computer compiles its own program by translating the stylized language program into machine language. Subsequently, the machine-language program is run on the computer in standard fashion. This technique is feasible because most programs comprise a large number of similar, repetitive steps. The net result is that programs can be prepared by relatively unskilled operators with much less effort than would be required if machine language were used directly.

10-16   Digital instruments

Digital instruments use the same logic circuits that make up a digital computer. The main advantage of digital over analog instruments is that digital data is decisive—the least significant bit must be either a one or zero so that precision can be increased simply by employing additional digits. Furthermore, digital signals can be amplified indefinitely and stored accurately.   Lastly, because of the off-on character of digital circuits, drift and stability problems are inherently nonexistent.   On the other hand, digital instruments tend to be more complex than their analog counter-parts.   Mathematical operations such as integration, differentia-tion, and addition, require elaborate logic circuits, whereas simple *RC* circuits suffice for analog signals.   Despite this inherent com-plexity, and attendant higher cost, the advantages of digital instru-ments are sufficient to assure their ever-expanding use in measure-ment and control applications.

One basic feature of digital instrumentation is the conversion of voltage signals into digital data.   A number of different techniques for *analog-to-digital* conversion have been devised.   We examine here a typical circuit employed in one type of *digital voltmeter*, an instrument which provides a direct-reading digital display of the voltage under measurement.

Consider the simplified block diagram of a digital voltmeter sketched in Fig. 10-48.   An unknown dc voltage applied to the

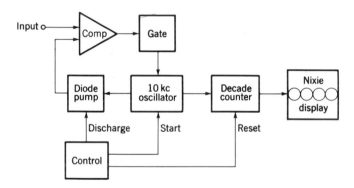

FIGURE 10-48   *Simplified block diagram of digital voltmeter.   (Courtesy Princeton Applied Research Corporation.)*

input terminals is compared with a staircase voltage waveform produced by a diode-pump circuit fed from a 10-kc oscillator. When the staircase signal is equal to the input voltage, the com-parator circuit gates off the oscillator.   The parameters of the diode pump are selected so that the height of each step of the stair-case is equal to 1 mv.   Therefore, the number of steps is directly equal to the unknown voltage in millivolts, and the steps are counted by a three-decade counter.   The Nixie display of the counter, therefore, shows the numerical value of the input voltage directly in millivolts.

Control circuits subsequently discharge the diode-pump capaci-tor, reset the counter, and start the oscillator, so that the cycle repeats.   A new reading is attained in about 1 sec, which means that the unknown voltage is sampled once each second.   Actually, in practical instruments the control circuit has other functions as well. It is possible, for example, to change input-multiplier resistors automatically so that voltages from 100 mv to 999 volts can be measured with the same one-digit (or 1 percent) precision. In addition, the circuit can automatically adjust to either input voltage polarity.

A somewhat different analog-digital conversion technique is considered in Exercise 10-20. Other typical digital instruments include the frequency counter, Fig. 10-32, and the time-interval meter, Fig. 10-35, discussed earlier. In control applications of digital circuits it is quite common for the digital data to be reconverted to analog form after the desired processing steps have been completed. The analog output signal is then used to adjust the system being controlled.

SUGGESTIONS FOR FURTHER READING

W. C. Elmore and M. Sands: "Electronics," McGraw-Hill Book Company, New York, 1949.

F. J. M. Farley: "Elements of Pulse Circuits," John Wiley & Sons, Inc., New York, 1963.

I. H. Gould and F. S. Ellis: "Digital Computer Technology," Reinhold Publishing Corporation, New York, 1963.

J. Millman and H. Taub: "Pulse and Digital Circuits," McGraw-Hill Book Company, New York, 1956.

Samuel Weber (ed.): "Digital Circuits," McGraw-Hill Book Company, New York, 1964.

EXERCISES

10-1 Select appropriate square-wave test frequencies to confirm that an amplifier has a passband extending from 20 to 20,000 cps. Sketch the expected output waveforms at both frequencies.

10-2 Sketch the voltage waveforms at the collector and base of both transistors of the astable multivibrator, Fig. 10-4, if $C_2 = 0.05 \, \mu f$. Compare with the waveforms in Fig. 10-5.

10-3 Replace the 12AU7 in the astable multivibrator of Fig. 10-7 with a 12AX7 and make $R_L = 100,000 \, \Omega$. Plot the grid and plate waveforms for each triode and compare with Fig. 10-8.

10-4 Make $C_2 = 0.05 \, \mu f$ in the astable multivibrator of Fig. 10-7 and plot the grid and plate waveforms for each triode. Compare with Fig. 10-8.

10-5 Show by plotting the grid voltage waveform of an astable multivibrator how positive pulses applied to the grid synchronize the frequency of oscillation. *Hint:* Refer to Fig. 9-15.

10-6 Verify that the vacuum-tube binary of Fig. 10-11 has only two stable states by determining the grid and plate voltages for both triodes. What is the magnitude of the output voltage swing? What is the minimum trigger pulse voltage necessary for reliable triggering?

Ans.: 37 volts, 200 volts, 60 volts, 100 volts; 100 volts; 2 volts

10-7 Astable multivibrators are often used as light flashers to mark road barricades and construction work, etc. Qualitatively describe the operation of a typical circuit, Fig. 10-49, starting from

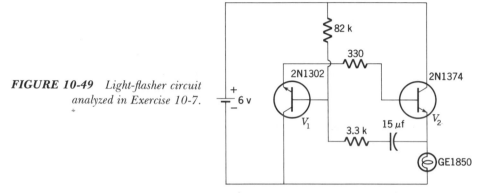

FIGURE 10-49 *Light-flasher circuit analyzed in Exercise 10-7.*

the time when V_1 and V_2 are off and V_1 is starting to turn on.

10-8 What scale factor is needed to count pulses having a repetition rate of 1000 pulses per second if the maximum rate of the mechanical register is 10 counts per second? Is there any advantage in a greater scale factor? *Ans.*: 100; no

10-9 The neon-tube display for a decade counter uses the circuit of Fig. 10-50 in conjunction with the counter in Fig. 10-25. The voltages indicated correspond to the reset condition when the count is at zero. With the aid of the waveform chart, Fig. 10-26, show that with this circuit the proper neon tube lights corresponding to the indicated count. Assume that the breakdown voltage of the neon tubes is 65 volts and the maintaining voltage is 55 volts.

10-10 Analyze the Dekatron driver tube circuit, Fig. 10-31, semiquantitatively by using an equivalent circuit in which each tube is represented by a switch in series with a battery representing the cathode-plate voltage in the saturated state. Plot the output waveforms.

10-11 Devise a block diagram, analogous to Fig. 10-32, for an instrument capable of measuring the period of signal frequencies of the order of 1 cps to an accuracy of 1 percent.

10-12 Draw the complete circuit diagram including component values of a diode-pump frequency meter based on Fig. 10-34. The instrument is to be capable of measuring frequencies from 1000 to 10,000 cps on a single meter scale.

10-13 Determine the binary number equivalents of 25, 50, and 100. Sketch the waveform representations.

Ans.: 11001; 110010; 1100100

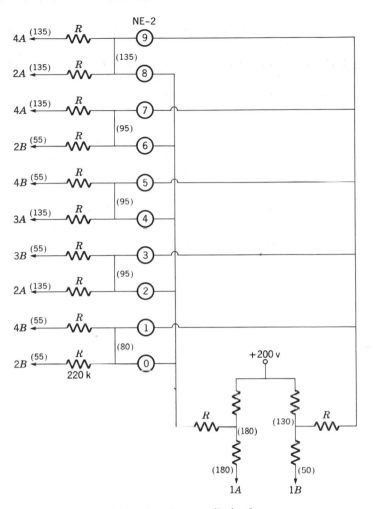

FIGURE 10-50 *Decade neon display for counter in Fig. 10-25 is analyzed in Exercise 10-9. Voltages in parentheses correspond to count of zero.*

10-14 Carry out the binary additions for $20 + 14$, $15 + 34$, and $56 + 25$. Check by forming the binary numbers of the decimal sums. Sketch the waveforms of the individual numbers and their sums.
Ans.: 100010; 110001; 1010001

10-15 Carry out the binary subtractions for $25 - 14$, $35 - 16$, and $12 - 3$. Check by forming the binary numbers of the decimal subtractions. Sketch the waveforms of the individual numbers and their differences.
Ans.: 1011; 10011; 1001

10-16 Sketch the waveforms of the binary numbers 1101 and 1001 and their sum. Compare the waveform of the sum with the output waveform of an AND gate with 1101 and 1001 as input signals.

10-17 Draw the waveform at each point and the output waveform of the anticoincidence gate, Fig. 10-43, if the A input is the waveform representing the binary number 1101 and the B input represents 1001.

10-18 Draw the block diagram of an anticoincidence circuit comprised of only NOR gates. Repeat Exercise 10-17 for this circuit.

10-19 Using input waveforms representing the binary numbers 1101 and 1001 as in Exercise 10-17, plot the waveforms at each point in the ADD gate of Fig. 10-45, including the block diagram of the half-adder, Fig. 10-44. Do not forget the one-bit delay in the carry circuit. Verify that the output waveform represents the sum of the inputs.

10-20 Devise a block diagram of a digital voltmeter in which the output of a ramp generator is compared with the unknown voltage and the time from the beginning of the ramp to the equality point is measured by a time-interval meter.

11

MEASUREMENT CIRCUITS

Electrical techniques are used to measure a wide variety of physical phenomena in both laboratory research and industrial control applications. Indeed, it is modern measurement practice to convert the phenomenon of interest to an electric signal at the earliest opportunity so that subsequent processing can be performed electronically. The great versatility of electronic circuits to amplify, process, record, and detect electric signals is the principal reason they enjoy such widespread use. Several techniques for generating electric signals corresponding to variations in physical parameters are investigated in this chapter. In addition, the problems associated with transmitting this signal from its point of origin to an electronic circuit, or from one circuit to another in a complete measurement system, are considered.

TRANSDUCERS

Devices that produce electric signals in accordance with changes in some physical effect are called *transducers*. A typical example is a microphone which generates a voltage waveform corresponding to the variations of sound pressure impinging on a diaphragm. Other transducers, such as the strain gauge, operate by changing some circuit parameter (e.g., resistance) rather than by generating a voltage. A great variety of transducers have been developed so that it is often possible to generate a signal in more than one way. The deciding factor in any given situation is the accuracy with which the transducer output represents the physical parameter being measured.

11-1 Mechanical transducers

A useful transducer for sensing mechanical motion or position is the *differential transformer*, Fig. 11-1. This device is a transformer

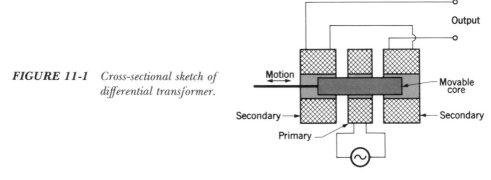

FIGURE 11-1 *Cross-sectional sketch of differential transformer.*

having two secondaries and a movable magnetic core. A sinusoidal current in the primary produces an equal voltage in each secondary when the core is positioned midway between them. Since the windings are connected in series opposition, the output voltage is zero. Displacing the core to the left causes more magnetic flux to link the left-hand secondary, and the output voltage rises. Similarly, a displacement to the right produces an output signal with opposite phase, because the voltage of the right-hand secondary exceeds that of the left.

With proper mechanical design the output voltage can be a linear function of the displacement over a reasonable distance, say, ~0.1 in. A phase-sensitive detector is commonly used to sense the direction of the displacement, where this is necessary. Alternatively, if motion in only one direction need be measured, a simple ac voltmeter can be used.

Another position-sensitive transducer measures the separation between a movable and a fixed plate by their mutual capacitance.

Variations in capacitance accompanying a change in the plate separation are detected with a capacitance bridge. Alternatively, the capacitor can be made part of the resonant circuit of an oscillator. Displacements of one plate relative to the other are reflected in frequency changes of the oscillator output. If it is only necessary to detect departures from an equilibrium position, simply connecting the capacitor in series with a resistor and a dc voltage is sufficient, as in the *condenser microphone*, Fig. 11-2.

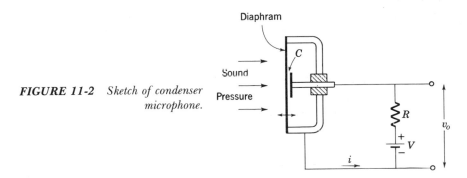

FIGURE 11-2 *Sketch of condenser microphone.*

Variations in sound pressure cause the diaphragm to deflect, thus changing the capacitance C, and generating a current in the external circuit,

$$Q = CV \tag{11-1}$$

$$i = \frac{dQ}{dt} = V \frac{dC}{dt} \tag{11-2}$$

The output signal is

$$v_o = RV \frac{dC}{dt} \tag{11-3}$$

The capacitance transducer can be adapted to measure mechanical force, as in Fig. 11-3. Here the position of an arm to

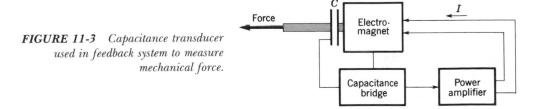

FIGURE 11-3 *Capacitance transducer used in feedback system to measure mechanical force.*

which the force is applied is detected by the capacitance between the arm and the pole face of an electromagnet. Any applied force displaces the arm, and the change in capacitance is detected by a capacitance bridge. The unbalance voltage of the bridge provides a signal for an amplifier feeding the coils of the electromagnet.

The magnetic force pulls the arm back to the equilibrium position against the external force. Thus, the magnet current is a direct measure of the applied force.

A system that strives to return to the equilibrium, or *null*, position is very commonly used in measurement circuits. Two comments are worthy of note. First, the system is basically a feedback network and may be analyzed as such. Secondly, the system always returns to its equilibrium position so it is not necessary for the transducer to have a linear relation between input action and output signal. As a matter of fact, it is not even essential that the transducer calibration be known, since it is not deflected in the equilibrium position.

Mechanical stress in structural members and materials is conventionally measured by means of a resistance *strain gauge*. One common strain gauge is a 1-mil metal wire bent back and forth and fastened to a thin paper backing, as in Fig. 11-4. The gauge is

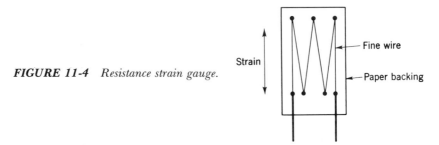

FIGURE 11-4   *Resistance strain gauge.*

cemented directly to the surface of the structural member under test so that changes in length are detected by changes in the resistance of the gauge. The magnitude of the change in resistance can be determined from

$$R = \rho \frac{L}{A} \tag{11-4}$$

where L is the total length, A is the cross-sectional area, and ρ is the resistivity of the wire. Taking the logarithm and the differential of both sides,

$$\log R = \log \rho + \log L - \log A$$

$$\frac{\Delta R}{R} = \frac{\Delta \rho}{\rho} + \frac{\Delta L}{L} - \frac{\Delta A}{A} \tag{11-5}$$

Introducing Poisson's ratio σ for the wire material,

$$\frac{\Delta A}{A} = -2\sigma \frac{\Delta L}{L} \tag{11-6}$$

into Eq. (11-5) yields

$$\frac{\Delta R}{R} = \frac{\Delta L}{L}(1 + 2\sigma) + \frac{\Delta \rho}{\rho} \tag{11-7}$$

Finally, the *gauge factor* $K = (\Delta R/R)/(\Delta L/L)$ is

$$K = 1 + 2\sigma + \frac{\Delta \rho}{\rho} \frac{L}{\Delta L}$$

$$K = 1 + 2\sigma + \frac{L}{\rho} \frac{d\rho}{dL} \tag{11-8}$$

According to Eq. (11-8) the change in resistance arises from changes in the wire dimensions because of mechanical strain plus the possibility of changes in resistivity. In metal-wire gauges, the third term is negligible and $K \cong 2$. The gauge resistance may be approximately 100 Ω and the strains of interest are of the order of 10^{-3}, so that the total resistance change is, from Eq. (11-7),

$$\Delta R = RK \frac{\Delta L}{L} = 100 \times 2 \times 10^{-3} = 0.2 \ \Omega$$

which is a fairly small value. *Silicon strain gauges* have much larger gauge factors, of the order of 150, as a result of change in resistivity with strain. The reason for this is that the number of current carriers in a semiconductor is sensitive to mechanical strain. Therefore, the conductivity changes significantly in response to elastic deformation. Because of their increased sensitivity, silicon strain gauges are becoming ever more popular.

Semiconductor strain gauges are sensitive to temperature changes, however, because of the exponential change in resistivity with temperature characteristic of semiconductors. Actually, temperature effects are important in wire strain gauges as well. Although the change in resistivity of a metal with temperature is quite small, the changes caused by mechanical strains are small as well. Bridge circuits are universally used to measure the change in resistance of strain gauges because small resistance changes can be measured and temperature compensation is easily effected. Most often, two identical strain gauges are used in the bridge, Fig. 11-5. One is subjected to the mechanical strain and the other is

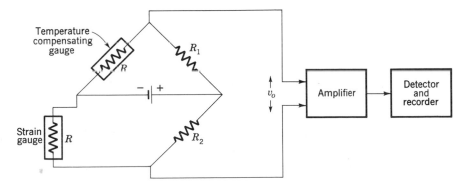

FIGURE 11-5 *Strain-gauge bridge circuit uses second gauge for temperature compensation.*

isolated from the strain but positioned so that its temperature environment is the same as that of the strain detector. Thus, changes in temperature influence each gauge equally, and the bridge remains balanced.

For maximum bridge sensitivity $R_1 = R_2 = R$, the output voltage is zero, and the voltage across resistance R_1 is $V/2$ in the unstrained condition. The gauge resistance becomes $R + \Delta R$ in the presence of strain and the voltage drop across the gauge is

$$V_g = \frac{V}{R + R + \Delta R} (R + \Delta R) \tag{11-9}$$

Therefore, the output voltage signal resulting from strain is

$$v_o = \frac{V(R + \Delta R)}{2R + \Delta R} - \frac{V}{2} = \frac{\Delta R}{4R + 2\Delta R} V \tag{11-10}$$

Neglecting ΔR in comparison with $2R$,

$$v_o = \frac{\Delta R}{4R} V \tag{11-11}$$

Finally, introducing the gauge factor, the output signal is written,

$$v_o = \frac{KV}{4} \frac{\Delta L}{L} \tag{11-12}$$

which shows that the output signal is a direct measure of the mechanical strain.

Since $\Delta L/L \cong 10^{-3}$, the output signal is of the order of 10 mv or less, so that usually some amplification is necessary. The bridge can be excited with an oscillator so that an ac-coupled amplifier can be used to avoid the drift problems of a dc amplifier. Synchronous detection provides low-noise operation and also detects both positive and negative strains.

Mechanical vibrations in structures and machines are determined with transducers called *accelerometers*. An accelerometer measures the forces on a small mass caused by accelerations of the object to which the transducer is fastened. The inertial force $F = ma$ is counterbalanced by the restoring force of a spring supporting the mass,

$$ma = kx \tag{11-13}$$

where k is the spring constant. The deflection x is detected by the voltage generated in a piezoelectric crystalline material such as rochelle salts or barium titanate. As discussed in Chap. 9, piezoelectric materials generate a voltage proportional to the mechanical strain on the crystal. Actually, as illustrated in Fig. 11-6, the piezoelectric element is formed from two parallel slabs such that, for example, a vertical deflection of the mass puts the upper slab in compression and the lower slab in tension. The output terminals on the flat faces of the two slabs are connected in parallel.

The result of this *bimorph* construction is a more sensitive transducer than can be obtained with only a single element.

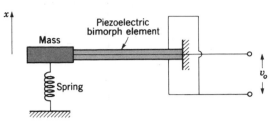

FIGURE 11-6 *Elementary piezoelectric accelerometer.*

Since the output voltage is proportional to the deflection *x*, Eq. (11-13) can be written

$$a = \frac{kc}{m} v_o \qquad (11\text{-}14)$$

where *c* is the piezoelectric constant. The useful frequency range of an accelerometer ranges up to the mechanical resonant frequency of the mass and the supporting spring combination. An upper frequency limit of 2 kc is typical. Extended performance can be obtained, at a sacrifice in sensitivity, by eliminating the mass and spring altogether. In this case the mass and elastic constant of the bimorph piezoelectric element alone are used and the upper frequency limit is set by the mechanical resonance of the cantilever beam geometry of the element itself.

The output voltage of an accelerometer can be integrated electronically to develop a signal proportional to velocity. A second integration yields the displacement. Such accelerometers form an important part of inertial guidance navigation systems in missiles and aircraft. Three mutually perpendicular accelerometers are arranged to measure the displacement of a missile from a known starting point.

11-2 The pH meter

The acidity or alkalinity of a solution is determined by measuring the concentration of hydrogen ions in the liquid with a *pH meter*. This instrument is based on the potential developed by the solution with respect to a standard electrode, which is given by

$$V = -\frac{RT}{F_y} \ln a_\mathrm{H} \qquad (11\text{-}15)$$

where *R* is the universal gas constant, *T* is the absolute temperature, F_y is a quantity of electric charge called the faraday, and a_H is the activity of hydrogen ions which is, in effect, equal to their concentration. Actually, the quantity defined by the expression

$$\mathrm{pH} = -\log a_\mathrm{H} \qquad (11\text{-}16)$$

is used in practice because the numerical values so obtained are more convenient to handle. The pH of a neutral solution, for example, is equal to 7, whereas $a_H = 10^{-7}$, according to Eq. (11-16).

Standard electrode conditions pertaining to Eq. (11-15) are inconvenient in practice, so the usual pH meter employs the electrode scheme depicted in Fig. 11-7. The potential of an unknown

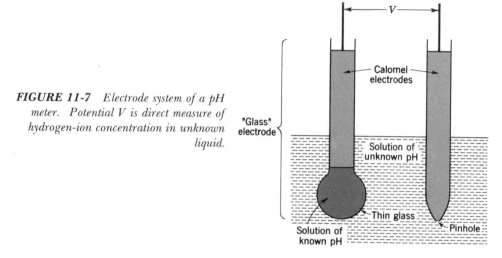

FIGURE 11-7   *Electrode system of a pH meter. Potential V is direct measure of hydrogen-ion concentration in unknown liquid.*

liquid is compared with that of a solution of known and constant pH. Electric contact to both liquids is achieved with standard electrodes called *calomel* electrodes. The electrochemical properties of a calomel electrode (a mixture of Hg, HgCl, and KCl) are very stable and easily reproduced in the laboratory. The solution of known pH is commonly a mixture of Ag, AgCl, and HCl contained in a thin-walled glass vessel. The thin glass wall permits only hydrogen ions in the unknown solution to migrate through the system. Therefore, the potential developed results only from the hydrogen-ion concentration in the unknown even though other ions may be present as well. The combination of a calomel electrode with the standard solution is known commercially as a "glass electrode." Electric connection between the other calomel electrode and the unknown solution is provided by a tiny pinhole, as noted in Fig. 11-7.

In terms of the voltage developed by this standard arrangement, the pH of the unknown solution is, from Eqs. (11-15) and (11-16),

$$\text{pH} = \frac{V + 0.106}{0.0592} \tag{11-17}$$

where the constant 0.106 volt refers to the calomel–standard-solution potential difference, and the denominator is the quantity RT/F_y evaluated at room temperature. Note that the pH is a linear function of the potential difference between electrodes, and that the potential of a neutral solution is $7 \times 0.0592 - 0.106$

≅ 0.3 volt. This potential difference must be measured with a meter having an extremely large input impedance to avoid loading the cell and thereby reducing the terminal voltage. Even the small hydrogen ions migrate through the glass wall only with considerable difficulty and this produces a very large internal resistance. Voltmeters having a suitably large input impedance, called *electrometers*, are described in a later section.

11-3 Ion gauges

The most sensitive method of determining the gas pressure in a vacuum system is by ionizing gas molecules with high-energy electrons and then measuring the positive-ion current. This is accomplished in the Bayard-Alpert *ion gauge*, Fig. 11-8, with a

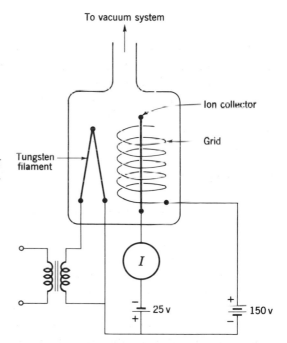

FIGURE 11-8 Ion gauge for determining gas pressure in vacuum system.

three-electrode device connected to the vacuum system. Electrons emitted from a hot tungsten filament are accelerated toward a positive gridlike electrode and produce ions upon collision with gas molecules. The grid structure is designed so that most of the electrons pass through. As they approach a negative central electrode, they are decelerated, reversed, and attracted back toward the grid. The electrons oscillate back and forth past the grid many times before finally being collected, thus making their total distance of travel much greater than the dimensions of the gauge. The probability of an ionizing collision with a gas molecule is increased by this long path, and the sensitivity of the gauge is correspondingly greater. Positive ions produced by electron collisions drift to the negative collector wire, where they are detected as an electric current.

The positive-ion current is proportional to the pressure over many decades, as illustrated in Fig. 11-9 for a typical ion gauge.

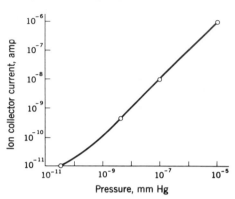

FIGURE 11-9 Calibration characteristic of ion gauge showing that ion current is proportional to gas pressure.

At the lowest pressures, quite feeble ion currents are encountered that are best measured by electrometer circuits. Most often, the electrometer circuit and a power source to provide the proper electrode potentials for the ion gauge are contained in a single instrument. The circuit is connected to the gauge by a multi-conductor cable.

11-4 Photocells

Light energy from infrared to ultraviolet wavelengths is detected and measured with various forms of *photocells*. A simple, though extensively used, photocell is a small piece of semiconductor provided with two electric contacts. The resistance of the semiconductor between contacts depends upon the intensity of light energy impinging upon the surface. Absorbed photons produce electrons and holes that act as current carriers in the semiconductor. The response of a semiconductor photocell is zero for photon energies less than the width of the forbidden energy gap because such photons have insufficient energy to promote electrons from the valence band to the conduction band across the forbidden energy gap. The photoresponse is also small at short wavelengths (high photon energies) because photons are so heavily absorbed in the surface layers that most of the semiconductor is inactive. Therefore, the response is a maximum at photon energies corresponding to the width of the forbidden energy gap, as illustrated for the common photoconductor materials CdS, CdSe, and CdTe in Fig. 11-10. Note that CdS photocells are useful in the visible region of the spectrum, CdSe is most sensitive to red light, and CdTe responds to near-infrared radiation. Other semiconductors commonly used as infrared detectors are PbS and PbSe, which are useful at 3.0 μ and 4.5 μ, respectively, corresponding to forbidden energy gaps of 0.37 and 0.27 ev. In addition, InSb, with a

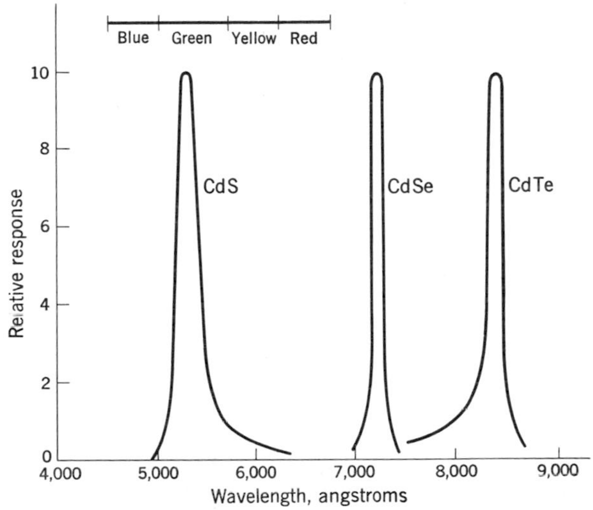

FIGURE 11-10 Wavelength response of CdS, CdSe, and CdTe photocells. Maximum response is obtained at photon energies equal to width of forbidden energy gap.

forbidden energy gap of only 0.18 ev, responds to radiation at wavelengths as long as 7 μ.

A useful measure of the sensitivity of a photocell at the peak of the wavelength response curve is the *gain G*. The gain is the ratio of the number of current carriers generated by illumination to the number of absorbed photons per second. Expressed in terms of the photocurrent I the gain is

$$G = \frac{I/e}{F} \tag{11-18}$$

where e is the electronic charge, and F is the rate of photon absorption. The photocurrent can be written in terms of an applied voltage V and the dimensions of the semiconductor using Ohm's law and the relation between resistance and carrier density, expressed by Eqs. (1-16) and (1-21),

$$G = \frac{1}{e}\frac{V}{R}\frac{1}{F} - \frac{1}{e}\frac{V}{\rho L/A}\frac{1}{F} = \frac{n\mu A}{L}\frac{V}{F} \tag{11-19}$$

where n is the carrier density, μ is the carrier mobility, and A and L are the cross-sectional area and length of the photoconductor, respectively. Equation (11-19) is further simplified by noting that the total number of carriers nAL is equal to the rate at which carriers are produced by photon absorption times the average time τ an electron spends in the conduction band before recombining with a hole in the valence band,

$$F\tau = nAL \tag{11-20}$$

so that, using Eqs. (11-19) and (11-20),

$$G = \frac{\mu V \tau}{L^2} \tag{11-21}$$

Finally, the transit time of a carrier between the contacts on the semiconductor is the distance between the electrodes L divided by the average carrier velocity. The carrier velocity is the mobility times the electric field, so that

$$T = \frac{L}{\mu(V/L)} = \frac{L^2}{\mu V} \tag{11-22}$$

where T is the transit time. Inserting Eq. (11-22) into Eq. (11-21), the gain becomes simply

$$G = \frac{\tau}{T} \tag{11-23}$$

According to Eq. (11-23), high sensitivity implies a sluggish response. That is, a large value of gain is achieved by increasing the time constant τ, and τ also determines the speed of response of the photoconductor to sudden changes in light intensity. Where speed is of secondary importance simple photoconductors are widely used because they are extremely sensitive. Most often, the change in resistance of the photocell accompanying incident illumination is measured by connecting the photocell in series with a dc voltage source and a load resistor. The voltage drop across the load resistor corresponds to the resistance changes in the semiconductor resulting from photon absorption.

High sensitivity together with rapid response time is achieved in a vacuum-tube photocell called a *photomultiplier* or PM tube which consists of a photosensitive cathode and a number of additional electrodes called dynodes, Fig. 11-11. The dynodes are at successively higher voltages so that electrons emitted from the photocathode, or from a preceding dynode, are attracted to the next dynode with sufficient energy to dislodge electrons from the surface. The surfaces of the dynodes are especially processed so that more than one electron is emitted for each incident electron and the number of electrons is multiplied accordingly as they proceed from dynode to dynode. The electrons are finally collected as an output current at the anode. Gains of the order of 10^6 are achieved in PM tubes so that it is possible to detect the emission of only a single electron from the photocathode. Furthermore, the response time depends upon the transit time of the electrons and is correspondingly rapid. Useful response at frequencies of the order of hundreds of megacycles is possible using a PM photocell.

Both photoconductors and PM tubes suffer from the disadvantage of nonuniform wavelength response since photon energies must be sufficient to create electron-hole pairs in the one case and to cause photoelectric emission in the other. This means, in particular, that the response to far-infrared radiation, where photon energies are small, is negligible. *Thermistor bolometer* detectors, which measure the temperature change produced by the

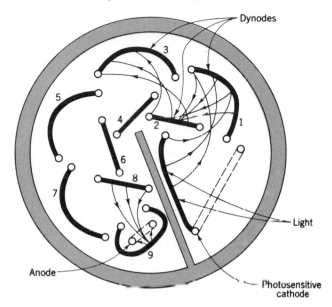

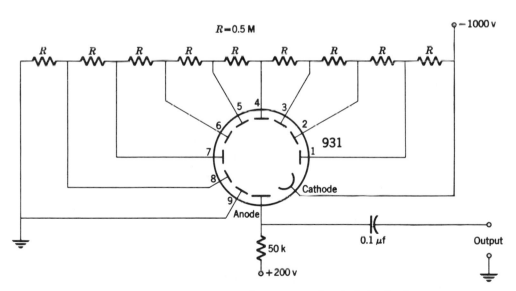

FIGURE 11-11 *Internal structure and typical circuit of photomultiplier tube.*

incident radiation, have a uniform, though comparatively small, response at all wavelengths. Conventional thermistors (the name comes from a contraction of "thermally sensitive resistors") are composed of an oxidic semiconductor material and have the rapid exponential variation of resistance with temperature that is characteristic of semiconductors. The detector consists of a small thermistor thermally insulated from its surroundings so that incident radiation increases the temperature of the sensitive element alone. Since the temperature increase depends only upon the amount of energy absorbed, independent of the individual photon energy, response is obtained at all wavelengths. Indeed, thermistor bolometers are used even at microwave frequencies.

The change in resistance of a thermistor bolometer is most often measured with a dc bridge similar to the one illustrated for strain gauges in Fig. 11-5. It is common practice to include a second thermistor to compensate for changes in ambient temperature, again as in the case of the strain gauge. Usually this compensating thermistor is mounted in the same housing as the detector element but is shielded from the incident radiation. Although not as sensitive as the other photocells previously discussed, a thermistor bolometer can detect a change in infrared radiation from an object corresponding to a variation in the object's temperature of as little as one degree centigrade. In addition, thermistors are often used as electric thermometers and are capable of measuring temperature differences as small as 10^{-6} °C.

Many semiconductor photocells having rapid response and good sensitivity are based on a reverse-biased pn junction. Photons absorbed in the region of the junction create electrons and holes that are swept to the opposite sides of the junction, as in Fig. 11-12.

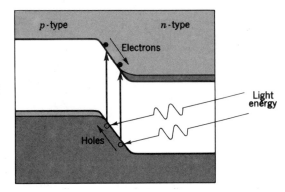

FIGURE 11-12   *Energy-band model of pn-junction photocell.*

The collected carriers are observed as an increase in reverse current. Since the width of a pn junction is very small, the transit time T in Eq. (11-23) is also small, and a reasonable value of G can be attained even for fast response times. The pn-junction structure has the additional advantage that the reverse current in the dark is very small compared with the current in a simple piece of semiconductor at the same applied voltage. This means that the additional carriers produced by photon absorption can be detected with greater sensitivity. For this reason InSb infrared detectors are universally of the pn-junction type. In addition, it is common practice to cool such detectors in order to reduce the reverse current in the dark and obtain ultimate sensitivity.

Note that electrons and holes created in the region of the junction are collected even in the absence of an applied voltage because of the internal potential rise at a *pn* junction, Fig. 11-12. This means that an illuminated *pn* junction can act as a battery. An open-circuit voltage equal to the internal potential step exists between terminals applied to the *n*-type and *p*-type regions. The short-circuit current of the battery depends upon the illumination intensity at the junction. This is the principle of the *solar battery* used as an energy source on space satellites. Silicon solar batteries are most often used because the width of the forbidden energy gap in silicon corresponds favorably with the wavelength distribution of radiant energy from the sun. Similar photocells are also used in automatic-iris cameras and exposure meters.

Highly ionizing radiation such as β rays and α rays are detected by a *pn* junction. If an α particle strikes the junction, its energy is consumed in creating electrons and holes which are subsequently collected by the field at the junction. The output current pulse corresponding to this event is a measure of the energy of the incident particle. Therefore, a *pn-junction radiation detector* not only signals the presence of nuclear radiation, but also measures the energy of the individual particles. Most often, it is desirable to employ detectors having a wide *pn* junction to assure that the particle is completely absorbed in the junction region. Furthermore, the junction must be very near the surface of the semiconductor so that little energy is lost in creating carriers far from the junction where they cannot be collected. These requirements have led to special fabrication procedures for *pn*-junction radiation detectors which are different from those normally used in transistor production. Junction detectors are used with the pulse amplifiers and counter circuits described in the previous chapter.

TRANSMISSION LINES AND WAVEGUIDES

Usually the components of a measuring system are physically separate from one another. For example, it may not be convenient or possible to locate an amplifier immediately adjacent to the transducer. Similarly, several distinct electronic instruments may be connected together in cascade to make a measurement. The signal must then be transported from the output of one unit to the input of the next. This is done by connecting the various circuits with *transmission lines*. In the simplest case a transmission line is just two wires, as has been implicitly assumed in previous chapters. A transmission line must, however, faithfully transmit the signal between instruments with a minimum of waveform or amplitude distortion. If this is not the case, the ultimate output of the system may be erroneous.

In low-frequency and dc systems it is only necessary to consider the resistivity of the conductors in the transmission line, as well as, perhaps, shunt resistance between conductors. These effects are examined by straightforward circuit analysis as studied in Chap. 1. Even a straight piece of wire has associated with it a small inductance, however, and there is also a small capacitance between the two conductors. At high frequencies the reactances of these unavoidable inductances and capacitances become significant and influence signal propagation along the transmission line. This is particularly important in pulse circuits because of the high frequencies associated with pulse waveforms. In many practical high-frequency circuits transmission lines only a few inches long introduce objectionable waveform distortions.

11-5 Characteristic impedance

It is useful to represent the incremental impedances of a short section of transmission line by a series resistance r_1 and inductance l per unit length together with a shunt resistance r_2 and capacitance

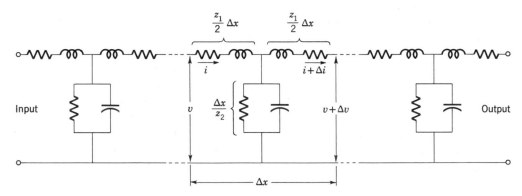

FIGURE 11-13   *Representation of transmission line in terms of series and shunt impedances per incremental length.*

c per unit length, as in Fig. 11-13. Thus the series and shunt impedances of a small section Δx of the line are

$$z_1 \, \Delta x = (r_1 + j\omega l) \, \Delta x$$

$$\frac{1}{z_2} \, \Delta x = \left(\frac{1}{r_2} + j\omega c\right) \Delta x \qquad\qquad (11\text{-}24)$$

Variations of voltage and current along the transmission line are produced in response to an input signal. Consider one section Δx of the line for which the input voltage is v and the output voltage is incrementally different, $v + \Delta v$. Similarly, the input and output currents of the line element are i and $i + \Delta i$, respectively. The voltage equation around the outside loop of this circuit is then

$$v - i \frac{z_1}{2} \Delta x - (i + \Delta i) \frac{z_1}{2} \Delta x = v + \Delta v \tag{11-25}$$

Dividing through by Δx,

$$\frac{\Delta v}{\Delta x} = -z_1 i - \frac{z_1}{2} \Delta i \tag{11-26}$$

In the limit as $\Delta x \to 0$, $\Delta v / \Delta x$ becomes the derivative dv/dx and the second term on the right side of Eq. (11-26) vanishes,

$$\frac{dv}{dx} = -z_1 i \tag{11-27}$$

Similarly, the voltage equation including the shunt path is

$$v - i \frac{z_1}{2} \Delta x - [i - (i + \Delta i)] \frac{z_2}{\Delta x} = 0 \tag{11-28}$$

$$v - i \frac{z_1}{2} \Delta x + \frac{\Delta i}{\Delta x} z_2 = 0 \tag{11-29}$$

In the limit, $\Delta x \to 0$, Eq. (11-29) reduces to

$$\frac{di}{dx} = -\frac{1}{z_2} v \tag{11 30}$$

Differentiating Eq. (11-27) with respect to x and using Eq. (11-30), the result is

$$\frac{d^2 v}{dx^2} = -z_1 \frac{di}{dx}$$

$$\frac{d^2 v}{dx^2} = \frac{z_1}{z_2} v \tag{11-31}$$

Similarly, differentiating Eq. (11-30) with respect to x and using Eq. (11-27) yields an equation in i alone,

$$\frac{d^2 i}{dx^2} = \frac{z_1}{z_2} i \tag{11-32}$$

Equations (11-31) and (11-32) are called the transmission-line equations. Their solutions yield the current and voltage at any point along the line.

The general solution of Eq. (11-31) is

$$v = A e^{-\gamma x} + B e^{\gamma x} \tag{11-33}$$

where A and B are constants that depend upon the input and output conditions of the transmission line, and γ is called the *propagation constant*. The propagation constant is a complex number with a real part α and an imaginary part β given by

$$\gamma = \alpha + j\beta = \sqrt{\frac{z_1}{z_2}} \tag{11-34}$$

as can be verified by substituting Eqs. (11-33) and (11-34) into the differential equation (11-31).

Since the differential equation for i, (11-32), is identical in form to the voltage equation, (11-31), the solution also has the same form. It is possible to evaluate the arbitrary constants in terms of A and B by using Eq. (11-30). The result is

$$i = \frac{A}{Z_c} e^{-\gamma x} - \frac{B}{Z_c} e^{\gamma x} \tag{11-35}$$

where

$$Z_c = \sqrt{z_1 z_2} \tag{11-36}$$

is called the *characteristic impedance* of the line. Equations (11-33) and (11-35) give the variation of voltage and current with distance along the line. We postpone examination of their significance to consider the meaning of the characteristic impedance.

Suppose a transmission line d meters long is terminated in its

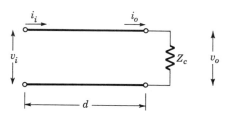

FIGURE 11-14 *Transmission line terminated in its characteristic impedance.*

characteristic impedance, as in Fig. 11-14. Using Eqs. (11-33) and (11-35), the output voltage v_o can be written

$$v_o = i_o Z_c$$

$$A e^{-\gamma d} + B e^{\gamma d} = Z_c \left(\frac{A}{Z_c} e^{-\gamma d} - \frac{B}{Z_c} e^{\gamma d} \right) \tag{11-37}$$

which means

$$B = -B = 0$$

At the input end $x = 0$, so that

$$v_i = A$$

Therefore, the voltage and current equations become

$$v = v_i e^{-\gamma x}$$

$$i = \frac{v_i}{Z_c} e^{-\gamma x} \tag{11-38}$$

In particular, the input impedance of the line is

$$Z_i = \frac{v_i}{i_i} = \frac{v_i}{v_i / Z_c} = Z_c \tag{11-39}$$

This means that the input impedance of a transmission line

terminated in its characteristic impedance is simply equal to the characteristic impedance, independent of the length of the line. For this reason, as well as an equally significant one discussed subsequently, a transmission line is most often terminated in its characteristic impedance.

In many applications the series and shunt resistances of the transmission line can be neglected in comparison with the reactances. Thus, if $r_1 \ll \omega l$ and $1/r_2 \ll \omega c$, the characteristic impedance, Eq. (11-36), reduces to

$$Z_c = \sqrt{z_1 z_2} = \sqrt{\frac{r_1 + j\omega l}{1/r_2 + j\omega c}} = \sqrt{\frac{l}{c}} \tag{11-40}$$

which is a pure resistance.

The magnitude of Z_c depends upon the geometry of the line since both l and c are functions of the wire size, shape, separation, etc. In particular, the characteristic impedance of a transmission line comprising two parallel wires is given by

$$Z_c = 276 \log \frac{D}{a} \tag{11-41}$$

where D is the separation between the wires and a is the radius of each conductor. A transmission line commonly used to connect television antennas to television receivers has $D/a = 10$, so that $Z_c = 276 \ \Omega$. Actually, such "twinlead" has a characteristic impedance closer to 300 Ω. The difference is attributable to the dielectric constant of the insulation separating the two conductors. Equation (11-41) applies to the case of air (dielectric constant of unity) between the wires.

Coaxial transmission lines are also commonly employed. The characteristic impedance of a coaxial line is given by

$$Z_c = 138 \log \frac{b}{a} \tag{11-42}$$

where b is the radius of the outer conductor and a is the radius of the central wire. A common value for the characteristic impedance of a coaxial line is 72 Ω, although other values are also commercially available.

11-6 Delay time

According to Eq. (11-38) the voltage along a transmission line terminated in its characteristic impedance is given by

$$v = v_i e^{-j\beta x} \tag{11-43}$$

if the series and shunt resistances can be neglected. Suppose that the input signal is sinusoidal. Then, recognizing that

$$e^{-j\beta x} = \cos \beta x - j \sin \beta x \tag{11-44}$$

Eq. (11-43) becomes

$$v = V_i \sin \omega t (\cos \beta x - j \sin \beta x) = V_i \sin \omega t \angle -\beta x \qquad (11\text{-}45)$$

This can be written equivalently as

$$v = V_i \sin (\omega t - \beta x) \qquad (11\text{-}46)$$

Equation (11-46) represents a wave that is periodic both in time and in space.

A plot of Eq. (11-46) for one cycle when $t = 0$ is illustrated in Fig. 11-15. Similarly, plots of Eq. (11-46) when $t = T/4$ and $t = T/2$

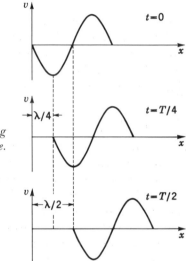

FIGURE 11-15 *Motion of sinusoidal signal along transmission line.*

(where T is the period of the input signal) shows that the input signal moves away from the input end of the line. The *wavelength* λ of the signal at any given time is the distance along the line at which the voltage has gone through one complete cycle of 2π radians. Therefore, from Eq. (11-46)

$$\lambda = \frac{2\pi}{\beta} \qquad (11\text{-}47)$$

Note that, according to Fig. 11-15, the input signal moves a distance $\lambda/4$ in a time $T/4$, a distance $\lambda/2$ in a time $T/2$, etc. Therefore, the speed with which the input signal is transported along the line is

$$v = \frac{\lambda/4}{T/4} = \frac{\lambda}{T}$$

$$v = \lambda f \qquad (11\text{-}48)$$

where f is the frequency of the input signal. Equation (11-48) is a fundamental relation among the wavelength, frequency, and velocity of any propagating phenomenon.

The time required for an input signal to travel from the input of a transmission line to the output end is given by, using Eq. (11-48),

$$t_d = \frac{d}{v} = \frac{d}{\lambda f}$$

$$t_d = \frac{d}{\lambda} T \tag{11-49}$$

where d is the length of the line. According to Eq. (11-49), the time delay in terms of the period of the input signal depends upon the length of the line in terms of the wavelength. The time delay is a function of the parameters of the line since $\lambda = 2\pi/\beta$ and β depends upon the line geometry.

The propagation characteristics of transmission lines are often used to introduce a given time delay between input and output signals. One such example is the one-bit delay necessary in an ADD gate, as explained in connection with Fig. 10-45. Such *delay lines* are also constructed with actual inductances and capacitances connected according to Fig. 11-13. This is necessary if long delay times are required, since the delay time increases when l and c are large.

11-7 Reflections and resonance

We now consider a transmission line that is not terminated by an impedance equal to its characteristic impedance. As a useful illustration, consider the case when the output end is short-circuited so that $v_o = 0$. Thus at $x = d$, where d is the length of the line,

$$0 = Ae^{-j\beta d} + Be^{j\beta d} \tag{11-50}$$

Similarly, from Eq. (11-35),

$$i = \frac{A}{Z_c} e^{-j\beta d} - \frac{B}{Z_c} e^{j\beta d} \tag{11-51}$$

Solving Eqs. (11-50) and (11-51) for A and B yields

$$A = \frac{i_o Z_c}{2} e^{j\beta d} \tag{11-52}$$

and

$$B = -\frac{i_o Z_c}{2} e^{-j\beta d} \tag{11-53}$$

Using Eq. (11-33) the voltage on the line is

$$v = \frac{i_o Z_c}{2} e^{j\beta d} e^{-j\beta x} - \frac{i_o Z_c}{2} e^{-j\beta d} e^{j\beta x}$$

$$v = \frac{i_o Z_c}{2} \left(e^{-j\beta(x-d)} - e^{j\beta(x-d)} \right) \tag{11-54}$$

Similarly, the current is, from Eq. (11-35),

$$i = \frac{i_o}{2} \left(e^{-j\beta(x-d)} + e^{j\beta(x-d)} \right) \tag{11-55}$$

Comparing Eqs. (11-54) and (11-55) with Eq. (11-38) we interpret the second term in Eqs. (11-54) and (11-55) as a wave traveling from the receiving end to the input end. That is, the incident wave is *reflected* at the output of the line because of the improper termination at the receiving end. Reflections are avoided in pulse applications particularly since pulses that are reflected back and forth between the input and output ends of the line completely obscure the true input signal. This is the second major reason why a transmission line is normally terminated in its characteristic impedance.

A short-circuited transmission line does have useful properties, however, as can be illustrated by computing the input impedance. According to Eqs. (11-54) and (11-55) the input impedance is

$$Z_i = \frac{v_i}{i_i} = Z_c \frac{e^{j\beta d} - e^{-j\beta d}}{e^{j\beta d} + e^{-j\beta d}} \tag{11-56}$$

Using Eq. (11-44), this becomes

$$Z_i = Z_c \frac{\cos \beta d + j \sin \beta d - \cos \beta d + j \sin \beta d}{\cos \beta d + j \sin \beta d + \cos \beta d - j \sin \beta d}$$

$$= jZ_c \tan \beta d$$

$$Z_i = jZ_c \tan 2\pi \frac{d}{\lambda} \tag{11-57}$$

According to Eq. (11-57) the input impedance of a short-circuited transmission line is equal to zero when the length of the line is such that $d = \lambda/2$, because $\tan \pi = 0$. Of particular importance is the case when $d = \lambda/4$, for which $Z_i \to \infty$. That is, the line acts as a parallel resonant circuit at the frequency corresponding to $d = \lambda/4$. Such quarter-wavelength lines are often used as resonant circuits at very high frequencies. This is useful since normal parallel resonant circuits consisting of a single inductance and capacitance are not possible at extreme frequencies because of the very small inductance and capacitance values required. Analogous results can be achieved with transmission lines that are open-circuited at the receiving end (see Exercise 11-6).

11-8 Waveguides

At very high frequencies, where the signal wavelength is of the order of the spacing between conductors, parallel-wire and coaxial transmission lines do not efficiently transport signals from the input to the output end.   Such signal frequencies are propagated in hollow conductors, called *waveguides*. Analysis of the transmission properties of waveguides is accomplished by focusing attention on the electric and magnetic fields in the interior of the hollow conductor, rather than on the currents in the conductor itself.   In effect, the signal is carried by waves of electric and magnetic fields and the function of the hollow conductor is to guide these waves from the transmitting to the receiving end.

Some appreciation of the electric-field configuration in a circular waveguide is attained by considering the situation in a coaxial line as the central conductor is made smaller and smaller until it vanishes altogether, Fig. 11-16.   When the central conductor is large, the electric field in the space between conductors is essentially radial, Fig. 11-16a, and currents are present in both conductors corresponding to the electric-field pattern.   A small central conductor results in an electric-field configuration that originates and terminates on the same conductor, Fig. 11-16b. This suggests that the central wire may be eliminated altogether; the electric-field pattern that results is shown in Fig. 11-16c.   One reason for the increased efficiency of the waveguide over that of the two-conductor line is the fact that resistance losses in the center wire are eliminated.

Waveguides with a rectangular cross section are more commonly employed than are circular waveguides because the electric-field configurations are somewhat less complicated.   This means that input and output terminations are simpler.   In both types the electric-field configuration is such that only signals of frequencies higher than a certain *cutoff frequency* can be propagated; that is, a waveguide acts as a high-pass filter.   For example, the longest wavelength that can be transmitted through a rectangular waveguide having the longer cross-sectional dimension a is given by

$$\lambda_c = 2a \qquad\qquad (11\text{-}58)$$

Minimum losses are achieved if the waveguide dimension is only just sufficient in cross section to pass the lowest signal frequency of interest.   For this reason, the size of a waveguide is a good indication of the signal frequency it is designed to transmit.   A relation analogous to Eq. (11-58) applies to circular waveguides also.

If the receiving end of a waveguide is short-circuited, a resonance effect identical in principle to that of a short-circuited transmission line is observed.   Most often, both ends of the waveguide are closed, which produces a *resonant cavity* useful as a resonant circuit at microwave frequencies.

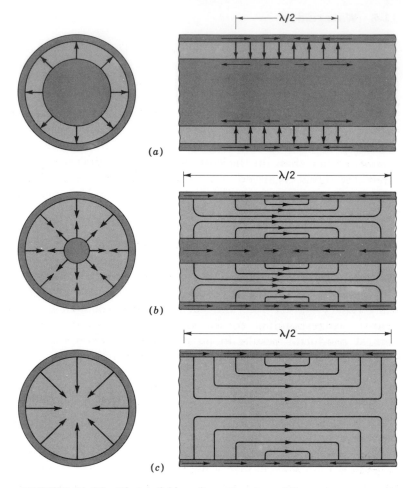

FIGURE 11-16 *Electric-field configurations (a and b) in coaxial transmission lines and (c) in hollow circular waveguide.*

ELECTRICAL MEASUREMENTS

Throughout previous sections of this book many circuits for measuring electrical parameters such as current, voltage, resistance, etc., have been described. Each circuit has its own particular features and is used in situations where its advantages are most useful. For example, a simple d'Arsonval meter is used for dc voltage measurements where potentials of the order of one to hundreds of volts are expected and where the loading effect of the meter is unimportant. A dc VTVM is used for high-impedance circuits over the same voltage range. Smaller dc potentials are best determined with the potentiometer circuit, and a self-balancing potentiometer (Chap. 8) is conventionally used in applications where a permanent chart record is desired. Similar comments apply to the measurement of ac voltages. As discussed previously, it is common practice to rectify the ac signal so that a dc instrument is ultimately used.

Many electrical-measurement circuits employ a comparison technique in which the unknown is matched against a calibrated known parameter. The potentiometer circuit is a prime example of a comparison measurement, as are dc and ac bridge circuits. As discussed in earlier chapters, bridge circuits are the most satisfactory way of determining accurate values of unknown resistances, capacitors, and inductances.

11-9 Electrometers

Feeble electric currents are most easily measured by determining the voltage drop across a high resistance. Consider the simple vacuum-tube circuit, Fig. 11-17, in which the change in grid voltage

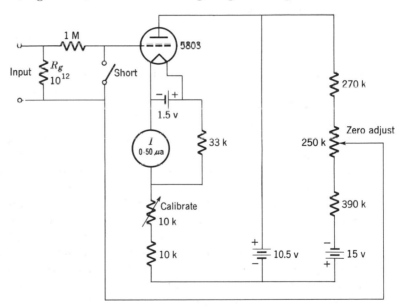

FIGURE 11-17 *Simplified circuit diagram of vacuum-tube electrometer. (Courtesy Keithley Instruments.)*

caused by the unknown current in the grid resistor is detected by a d'Arsonval meter in the cathode circuit. Note that the quiescent cathode current is balanced out so that the meter reading is zero in the absence of an input signal.

The advantage of this *electrometer* circuit over a sensitive d'Arsonval meter in determining minute direct currents is illustrated in the following way. The ultimate sensitivity of any system is limited by the inherent internal random noise level in the system. This means that the minimum current that can be detected by a meter is approximately equal to the Nyquist noise of the meter's internal resistance. Therefore, according to Eq. (7-22), the minimum detectable current of a d'Arsonval meter is given by

$$I_m = \frac{\sqrt{4kTrB}}{r} = \sqrt{\frac{4kTB}{r}} \qquad (11\text{-}59)$$

where r is the internal resistance of the meter and B is its effective bandwidth. Parenthetically, it should be noted that a meter of considerable mechanical inertia has a small effective bandwidth. This is an effective way of increasing sensitivity. The response of the meter is, however, correspondingly sluggish.

In the case of the electrometer circuit, the minimum current is determined by the magnitude of the grid resistor,

$$I'_m = \sqrt{\frac{4kTB}{R}} \qquad (11\text{-}60)$$

Comparing Eqs. (11-60) and (11-59),

$$I'_m = I_m \sqrt{\frac{r}{R}} \qquad (11\text{-}61)$$

According to Eq. (11-61) the minimum detectable current is reduced if $R \gg r$. That is, the inherent sensitivity of the electrometer circuit is a result of the high input impedance characteristic of a vacuum tube.

In order to attain the highest possible input resistance, special electrometer tubes have been designed. The glass envelope of an electrometer tube is treated to reduce leakage currents along the surfaces. The cathode is operated at low temperature to minimize radiant heating of the grid. This reduces thermionic emission of electrons from the grid and also minimizes photoelectric emission resulting from cathode light striking the grid wires. A low plate potential is employed to reduce ionization of residual gas in the tube by the plate current. If this is not done positive ions attracted to the negative grid result in unwanted grid current. With these precautions grid resistors as high as $10^{12} \, \Omega$ are feasible and currents of the order of 10^{-12} amp can be measured.

Since the electrometer is basically a dc VTVM, it is also used as a voltmeter when the high input impedance is an advantage, as in the case of a pH meter. In either application, there is a further advantage if the circuit is designed so that the electrometer-tube saturation current is less than that which will damage the meter. This means that, in spite of its great sensitivity, the instrument is not damaged if it is inadvertently subjected to an excessive input signal.

A more elaborate electrometer circuit with increased sensitivity and improved stability uses a vibrating capacitor to develop an ac signal. This signal is amplified, rectified, and fed back to the input circuit. The system is exactly analogous to the lock-in amplifier discussed in Chap. 7 and has the stability and sensitivity advantages of this circuit. Most often, the vibrating capacitor C_e, Fig. 11-18, is

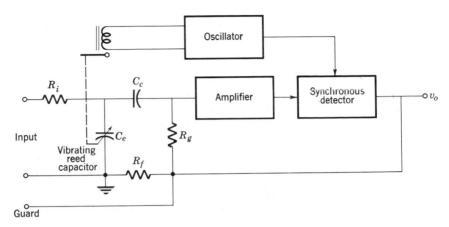

FIGURE 11-18 *Block diagram of vibrating-reed electrometer.*

a small metal reed electromagnetically vibrated by a sinusoidal voltage derived from an oscillator. The oscillator output also provides a signal for the synchronous detector to develop a dc output voltage in accordance with the input signal. The mechanical vibration of the reed results in a sinusoidal variation in capacitance of the reed in combination with an adjacent stationary electrode. A charge Q_e placed on the capacitance produces an ac voltage

$$v_e = R_i Q_e \frac{dC_e}{dt} \qquad (11\text{-}62)$$

which is presented to the amplifier input.

The operation of the *vibrating-reed electrometer* is analyzed in the following way, with reference to Fig. 11-18. A charge Q applied to the input terminals divides between the reed capacitance and the coupling capacitance C_c so that the charge on C_e is

$$Q_1 = \frac{QC_e}{C_e + C_c} \qquad (11\text{-}63)$$

The ac signal from the vibrating capacitor is amplified and rectified and appears as an output voltage v_o across the feedback resistor R_f. This voltage also produces a charge on C_e,

$$Q_2 = \frac{v_o}{1/C_c + 1/C_e} = \frac{v_o C_e C_c}{C_e + C_c} \qquad (11\text{-}64)$$

Therefore, the total charge on C_e is the sum of Eqs. (11-63) and (11-64), or

$$Q_e = Q_1 + Q_2 = \frac{C_e}{C_e + C_c} (Q + v_o C_c) \qquad (11\text{-}65)$$

We define the overall gain of the system A as the ratio of the output voltage to the dc voltage across the vibrating capacitor, so that

$$v_o = -A \frac{Q_e}{C_e} \qquad (11\text{-}66)$$

The gain involves the effective change in capacitance of the vibrating reed, Eq. (11-62), together with the amplifier gain and the rectifier efficiency. The minus sign signifies that negative feedback is employed. Introducing Q_e from Eq. (11-66) into Eq. (11-65) and solving for the output voltage, the result is

$$v_o = -\frac{Q}{C_c + (C_e + C_c)/A} \cong -\frac{Q}{C_c} \qquad (11\text{-}67)$$

which is true when A is large.

According to Eq. (11-67), the output voltage is a direct measure of the input charge. The output voltage is measured by a conventional d'Arsonval meter. Carefully designed vibrating-reed electrometers can measure charges as small as 10^{-16} coul, equivalent to a few hundred electrons. Minute currents can be measured by timing the rate at which C_c charges or by shunting the input terminals with a large known resistance. Currents of the order of 10^{-17} amp, a few hundred electrons per second, can be detected.

The input resistor R_i is present to isolate the instrument from the capacitance of the source. This is necessary because any fixed capacitance in parallel with C_e effectively reduces the ac signal developed by the vibrating reed since the net change in capacitance is reduced. The time constant $R_i C_e$ is made larger than the vibration period of the reed to accomplish this isolation. Note also that the feedback voltage is essentially equal to the input voltage. Therefore, the *guard* terminal, Fig. 11-18, can be used to reduce unwanted leakage currents between the upper input terminal and other points in the circuit. When these points are connected to the guard terminal the potential difference is negligible and stray leakage currents are eliminated.

11-10 Oscilloscopes

We have touched several times previously upon the circuits and applications of that most versatile instrument, the cathode-ray oscilloscope. The complete block diagram of a typical unit, Fig. 11-19, includes vertical and horizontal amplifiers coupled to the vertical and horizontal deflection plates of the cathode-ray tube, a triggered ramp generator to provide a linear horizontal sweep, and suitable power-supply circuits. In the most common mode of operation, the waveform of interest is applied to the vertical input terminals. The vertical amplifier increases the amplitude sufficiently to cause an appreciable vertical deflection of the electron

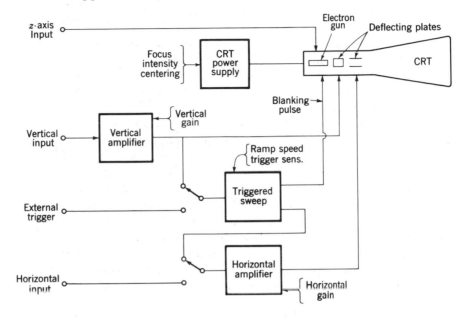

FIGURE 11-19 *Block diagram of oscilloscope.*

beam. A portion of the amplified signal is used to derive a trigger pulse for the sweep generator in order to synchronize the sweep signal with the input waveform. The output of the sweep generator is amplified and applied to the horizontal deflection plates. The sweep generator also provides a pulse to the electron gun of the cathode-ray tube (CRT) which blanks off the electron beam during retrace so that the spot can return to the starting point without leaving a spurious trace.

Sometimes it is advantageous to trigger the sweep generator with an external signal as, for example, if it is necessary to start the sweep before the vertical signal amplitude is large. For this purpose, an external trigger input is provided to which the generator input can be connected. When the linear sweep is not desired, as in the case of Lissajous figures (Chap. 2), the input of the horizontal amplifier is connected to the horizontal input terminals and external waveforms can be placed on both the horizontal and vertical deflection plates. It is also possible to modulate the intensity of the electron beam by altering the grid potential in the electron gun; this external terminal is conventionally termed the z-axis input to distinguish it from the horizontal (x-axis) and vertical (y-axis) inputs.

The vertical and horizontal amplifiers are quite often of the dc-coupled differential type illustrated in Fig. 7-41. Voltage-divider gain controls are included to adjust the amplitude of the deflection on the screen. Many different sweep circuits are in common use; the one in Fig. 10-20 is typical. Sweep-speed and trigger-sensitivity controls are necessary here in order to set the sweep for best waveform display. The power supply for the CRT is designed so that dc potentials applied to the electron-gun elements can be adjusted to achieve the optimum focus and intensity of the trace. Similarly, the quiescent position of the spot on the tube face is adjusted by altering the dc voltages on both the horizontal and vertical deflection plates.

The ability of a conventional oscilloscope to display very-high-frequency signals is limited by the high-frequency cutoff of the vertical amplifier and by the luminous efficiency of the cathode-ray-tube screen at high spot speeds. As one example of the versatility of CRT instruments, consider the so-called *sampling oscilloscope*, which can display repetitive waveforms at frequencies far in excess of a conventional instrument. The input waveform amplitude is sampled at successively later points in its cycle and then reassembled into a replica of the input waveform on the CRT screen. Since the input signal is repetitive, the sampling can be done every tenth cycle, as illustrated in Fig. 11-20, which means

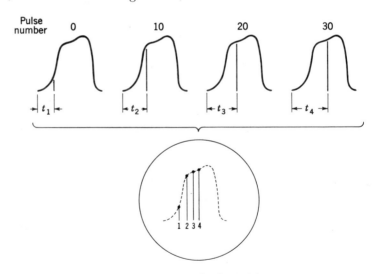

FIGURE 11-20 *By taking sample of repetitive input waveform every tenth cycle, waveshape can be reconstructed by circuits with maximum frequency response only 1/10 of the input frequency.*

the sampling and display circuits operate at only one-tenth of the input frequency.

The basic circuit diagram of a sampling oscilloscope, Fig. 11-21, employs a pulse generator to produce a series of successively delayed pulses and a gate which is opened during the pulse duration.

The gate output is passed through a low-pass filter and applied to the CRT. Note that although most of the circuit need not be capable of handling the signal frequency, the pulse generator must

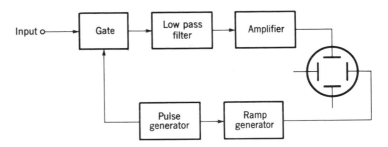

FIGURE 11-21   *Block diagram of sampling oscilloscope.*

produce very sharp pulses. As discussed in the previous chapter, several different circuits are available to perform this function. It proves easier to generate extremely narrow pulses than to design an amplifier with significant gain at corresponding frequencies.

11-11   The waveform analyzer

Complex waveforms may be thought of as combinations of harmonically related sine waves, according to the method of Fourier analysis discussed in Chap. 2. Instruments capable of determining the amplitude of the frequency components in a waveform, called *waveform analyzers*, in effect carry out Fourier analysis experimentally. As such, they are frequency-measuring instruments which complement the capabilities of digital frequency meters and frequency-sensitive ac bridges described in previous chapters.

A waveform analyzer is basically a sharply tuned ac amplifier-voltmeter which has a significant response at only one frequency. The input signal is heterodyned with the output of a variable-frequency sinusoidal oscillator to produce a signal at the response frequency of the amplifier, Fig. 11-22. That is, according to Eq. (4-38), two sine waves suitably mixed produce a sine wave at the sum (and difference) frequency. If the oscillator frequency is f_o while the input waveform has a frequency component f_i, the combination will result in an output signal if

$$f_i + f_o = f_a \qquad\qquad (11\text{-}68)$$

where f_a is the center frequency of the tuned amplifier. Thus, by tuning the oscillator frequency over a given interval, the output meter deflects each time Eq. (11-68) is satisfied for a frequency component of the input waveform. The magnitude of the meter deflection is proportional to the amplitude of each input-signal component. In this way, the entire frequency complement of the input waveform is determined.

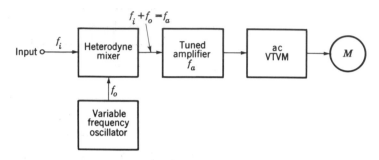

FIGURE 11-22 *Block diagram of waveform analyzer for determining frequency components in complex waveform.*

The heterodyne technique is used in preference to simply tuning the amplifier itself in order to obtain the greatest possible frequency coverage. An oscillator circuit capable of output frequencies over a wide band is simpler than a tunable amplifier covering the same frequency interval. Furthermore a fixed-tuned amplifier has a constant peak response and bandpass characteristic, both difficult to achieve in a tunable system. The frequency dial of the waveform analyzer is calibrated in terms of $f_a - f_o$, so that the unknown frequency is indicated directly.

RECORDERS

The ultimate purpose of any measuring circuit is an output indication characteristic of the input signal. It is often desirable to record the output reading permanently in some fashion. Recording schemes are as varied as are measuring instruments, ranging from pencil and paper in the hands of a laboratory scientist to the memory circuits of a digital computer. In every case, however, the objective is to preserve the measurement for future reference and analysis.

11-12 Chart recorders

A very common recording scheme employs a long strip of paper, or chart, on which is recorded the time history of the deflections of a d'Arsonval meter. The recording is produced by a pen attached to the meter pointer, Fig. 11-23, and the chart is moved uniformly by a clock mechanism. Such *chart recorders* take many forms depending upon the sensitivity of the d'Arsonval movement, the duration of the recording, etc. It is not unusual for a single chart to record the deflections of several meters so that a number of pertinent variables can be recorded simultaneously.

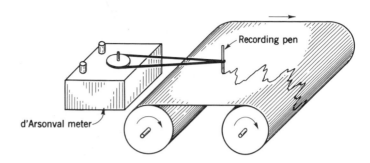

FIGURE 11-23 *Simple chart recorder employing d'Arsonval meter.*

The self-balancing recording potentiometer described in Chap. 8 is an example of a useful chart recorder. In another version of this instrument the chart is fixed and the recording pen is positioned in two directions by two independent potentiometer servo systems. This makes it possible to record the magnitude of one variable in terms of a second variable, independent of the time interval involved. Such an instrument is called an *x-y recorder*.

Chart recorders are essentially dc instruments, although rapid response to changes in signal level is often important. Limitations in response time are set primarily by the mechanical inertia of the recording-pen system, including the friction of the pen upon the chart paper. Through careful design it is possible to achieve sufficiently rapid movement that the writing speed of the pen system becomes the limitation. Nevertheless, chart recorders are restricted to signal frequencies below 10 cps or so, and most instruments are slower than this.

11-13 The oscillograph

The cathode-ray oscilloscope is the ideal instrument for recording ac signals, but it is limited in recording time by the width of the CRT screen. By contrast, chart recorders have a long-duration recording capability but are limited to dc or slowly varying signals. The *oscillograph* combines these features with the result that ac signals can be recorded for long time intervals. The oscillograph employs the basic principles of a d'Arsonval meter, but mechanical inertia is minimized to improve high-frequency response. The moving coil, Fig. 11-24, is a one-turn hairpin loop in the field of the magnet. Deflections of the coil are detected by a small mirror attached to the hairpin. A light beam reflected from the mirror falls on a moving chart of photosensitive paper and the position of the light spot on the chart depends upon the signal current in the coil.

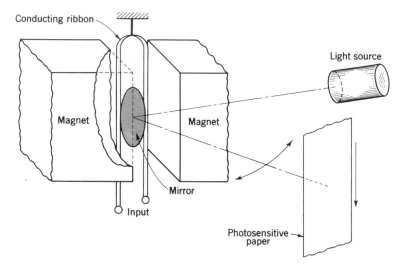

FIGURE 11-24 *Sketch of oscillograph.*

A long optical lever arm produces a useful deflection of the light spot on the chart for even minute deflections of the mirror. By this technique, as well as by minimizing the mechanical inertia of the meter, the upper frequency limit of an oscillograph may be 2 kc or more. Thus the instrument combines a modest high-frequency capability with long recording time.

11-14   Magnetic recorders

One of the most useful recording schemes is based on the *magnetic-recorder* principle in which an electric signal is recorded in the form of magnetization on a ferromagnetic chart, or tape. After recording, the tape is passed back through the instrument and a voltage signal corresponding to the original input is obtained. This makes it possible to observe the signal again and again, if necessary, and to analyze the waveform by as many different techniques as may be required.

The magnetic tape, most often in the form of a ferromagnetic oxide powder coated onto a plastic tape, is magnetized in accordance with the signal by the magnetic field of the recording head, Fig. 11-25a. Signal current produces a magnetic field at a sharply defined gap in the core of the recording head and this field permanently magnetizes the tape as it passes the gap. A high-frequency ac bias signal is also applied to the recording head to improve the linearity of the recording process. In playback, Fig.

11-25*b*, the tape is moved past the head again and the magnetic field of the tape induces a voltage in the coil of the head. Since the magnetization of the tape corresponds to variations in the

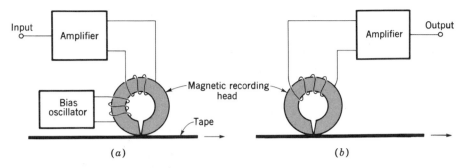

(a)   *(b)*

FIGURE 11-25   *(a) Recording and (b) playback of electric signals using magnetic recording techniques.*

original signal, voltages induced in the head replicate the input waveform. Playback does not change the tape magnetization, so that the signal can be reproduced as many times as desired.

The action of the ac bias frequency can be understood by considering the typical nonlinear properties of the magnetic tape as illustrated by the hysteresis loop in Fig. 11-26. In the absence of

FIGURE 11-26   *Action of ac bias is to cause magnetic tape material to traverse minor hysteresis loops as it passes under recording head. Remanent magnetization is then a linear function of signal field.*

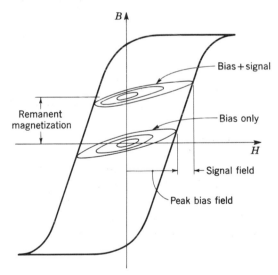

ac bias, the recorded magnetization is not a linear function of the signal field and the playback signal is strongly distorted. The ac bias causes the magnetization of the material to traverse minor hysteresis loops as shown. As an element of tape moves away from the recording gap, the size of the loops decreases to zero. Thus, in the absence of signal the resulting magnetization is equal to zero. The signal field displaces the minor loop so that the remanent magnetization is a finite value. Because of the straight sides of the major hysteresis loop, the relation between the remanent magnetization and the signal field is linear. The ac bias signal is of the order of five times the maximum signal frequency and the peak amplitude is approximately equal to the coercive force of the tape.

The highest frequency that can be recorded depends upon the tape speed and width of the gap in the record-playback head. Consider the enlarged view of the playback head shown in Fig.

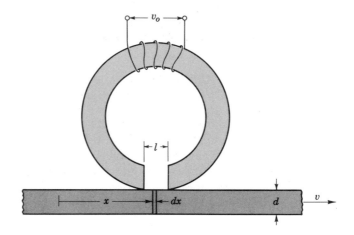

FIGURE 11-27 *Enlarged view of record-playback head showing resolution limit determined by width of gap.*

11-27 and assume that the tape has been recorded with a sinusoidal signal. The magnetic flux of the tape is then given by

$$\phi_t = Mdw \sin \frac{2\pi x}{\lambda} \tag{11-69}$$

where M is the peak magnetization, d and w are the thickness and width of the tape, respectively, and λ is the wavelength of the sinusoidal magnetic signal on the tape. The flux induced in the playback head due to an element of tape dx depends upon the reluctance of the air gap, so that

$$d\phi = \phi_t \frac{dx}{l} \tag{11-70}$$

The total flux in the playback head is found by integrating Eq. (11-70) over the length of the gap,

$$\phi = \int_{x-l/2}^{x+l/2} d\phi = \frac{Mdw}{l} \int_{x-l/2}^{x+l/2} \sin 2\pi \frac{x}{l} \, dx \tag{11-71}$$

Equation (11-71) can be integrated directly and the result simplified by means of a trigonometric identity to yield

$$\phi = -Mdw \sin \frac{2\pi x}{l} \frac{\sin (\pi l/\lambda)}{\pi l/\lambda} \tag{11-72}$$

The output voltage from the N-turn coil on the head depends upon the rate of change of flux caused by tape motion,

$$v = -N \frac{d\phi}{dt} = MdwN \frac{2\pi}{l} \frac{dx}{dt} \cos \frac{2\pi x}{l} \frac{\sin (\pi l/\lambda)}{\pi l/\lambda} \tag{11-73}$$

But $dx/dt = v$, the tape velocity, and $v = \lambda f$, where f is the playback signal frequency. After introducing $x = vt$, Eq. (11-73) can be put in the form

$$v = MdwN\omega \cos \omega t \frac{\sin \cdot (\pi l/\lambda)}{\pi l/\lambda} \tag{11-74}$$

Finally, the rms playback voltage is simply

$$V = M'dwN\omega \frac{\sin (\pi l/\lambda)}{\pi l/\lambda} \tag{11-75}$$

where M' is the rms magnetization on the tape. Putting Eq. (11-75) in terms of the playback frequency,

$$\frac{\pi l}{\lambda} = \frac{\pi l}{v/f} = \frac{\omega l}{2v} \tag{11-76}$$

the result is

$$V = M'dwN\omega \frac{\sin (\omega l/2v)}{\omega l/2v} \tag{11-77}$$

According to Eq. (11-77), the playback voltage is small at low frequencies, rises to a maximum, and falls sharply to zero where

$$\frac{\omega_m l}{2v} = \frac{2\pi f_m l}{2v} = \frac{f_m l}{v} = \pi \tag{11-78}$$

or

$$f_m = \frac{v}{l} \tag{11-79}$$

Since $f = v/\lambda$, Eq. (11-79) can also be written

$$\lambda_m = l \tag{11-80}$$

The meaning of Eq. (11-80) is that the minimum wavelength that can be played back is equal to the gap length. That is [Eq. (11-79)], the maximum frequency depends upon the tape speed. Experimental results, Fig. 11-28, are in general agreement with Eq. (11-77).

The falloff in playback signal at low frequencies is a result of the small rate of change of flux at long tape wavelengths. Uniform frequency response is achieved by a *compensated* playback amplifier that has large gain at low frequencies and decreasing gain at high frequencies. The high-frequency response depends upon the recording-head gap length and tape speed. With suit-

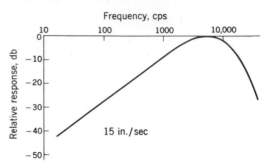

FIGURE 11-28 *Experimental frequency-response characteristic of magnetic recorder playback head. Fall at high frequencies is determined by size of the gap in head.*

able choice of parameters, frequencies as high as 10 Mc can be accommodated. This matter is considered further in the Exercises.

Although major use of magnetic recorders is in reproducing the amplitude and frequency characteristics of the input signal exactly, many other possibilities also exist. For example, according to Eq. (11-79) the playback frequency depends upon the tape speed. Therefore a very-long-duration, low-frequency recording can be played back at high tape speed. The resulting high-frequency signal can be analyzed in a much shorter time than required for the original recording. Conversely, a high-frequency recording can be played back at a slow tape speed with a corresponding reduction in the frequency components in the signal. In this way, the signal can be analyzed with instruments having only a low-frequency capability. Time compression or expansion ratios greater than factors of 1000 are possible.

SUGGESTIONS FOR FURTHER READING

M. B. Stout: "Basic Electrical Measurement," 2d ed., Prentice-Hall, Inc., Englewood Cliffs, N.J., 1960.

J. J. Studer: "Electronic Circuits and Instrumentation Systems," John Wiley & Sons, Inc., New York, 1963.

F. E. Terman and J. M. Pettit: "Electronic Measurements," 2d ed., McGraw-Hill Book Company, New York, 1952.

S. D. Prensky: "Electronic Instrumentation," Prentice-Hall, Inc., Englewood Cliffs, N.J., 1963.

EXERCISES

11-1 By using the Thévenin equivalent circuit for a bridge as developed in Chap. 1, verify that the most sensitive arrangement for a strain-gauge bridge is with all arms of the bridge equal to the gauge resistance.

11-2 Derive the current-voltage characteristic of a solar battery by noting that, according to Fig. 11-12, electrons and holes produced by light energy tend to bias the junction in the forward direction, resulting in a forward current given by Eq. (4-13). Therefore, the current generated by light energy I_g is equal to the load current plus the forward current. Plot the output current-voltage characteristic if $I_g = 40$ ma and the reverse saturation current of the cell is $I_o = 4 \times 10^{-9}$ amp.

11-3 Given that a typical thermistor has a 6 percent change in resistance per degree centigrade at room temperature, what is the minimum temperature change detectable by a 1000-Ω thermistor if the limiting factor is Nyquist noise in the thermistor resistance? Assume that 10 volts is applied to the thermistor and that the bandwidth is 10 cps.   *Ans.:* 2.2×10^{-8} °C

11-4 Show that maximum sensitivity is obtained in a simple photocell circuit consisting of a photocell in series with a load resistor and a battery when the load resistor is equal to the dark resistance of the photocell.

11-5 Calculate the time delay of a 100-Mc signal transmitted along a transmission line 10 m long. Assume the properties of the line are such that the wavelength on the line is 1 m.   *Ans.:* 10^{-7} sec

11-6 What is the input impedance of a transmission line if the output end is an open circuit? Compare the condition for parallel resonance with that corresponding to the short-circuited line, as given by Eq. (11-57).   *Ans.:* $-jZ_c \cot (2\pi d/\lambda)$; $\lambda/2$

11-7 Sketch a simple vacuum-tube oscillator circuit in which the parallel-resonance properties of a short-circuited transmission line are used to stabilize the frequency of the oscillator. If the propagation velocity along the line is 10^8 m/sec, how long a line is needed for a 300-Mc oscillator?   *Ans.:* 8.3 cm

11-8 Compare the relative merits of a VOM, an ac VTVM, and an amplifier-rectifier combination in measuring ac voltages. Consider ranges of voltage and frequency, as well as circuit impedances.

11-9 Compare the relative merits of the ac bridge, the frequency counter, and the waveform analyzer in measuring the frequency of unknown signals. Consider the accuracy, frequency range, and applicability to complex waveforms.

11-10 What is the minimum tape speed necessary if a magnetic recorder is used to record signals up to 1 Mc? Assume that the recording gap is 1 μ long.   *Ans.:* 1 m/sec

APPENDIX

1

Resistor and Capacitor Color Codes

Colored bands around the body of a resistor designate the nominal value of its resistance in ohms. Three colored bands grouped toward one end of the resistor, Fig. A1-1, are interpreted as a number having two

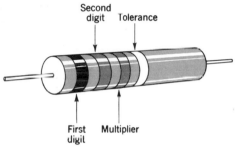

Second digit   Tolerance

FIGURE A1-1   *Resistor color code is series of colored bands.   (See also Fig. 1-6.)*

First   Multiplier
digit

significant figures and a multiplier factor. The band nearest the end of the resistor represents the first significant figure according to the color code in Table A1-1. The second band is the second significant figure, and the third band gives the number of zeros to add to determine the actual resistance. For example, a resistor whose bands are yellow, violet,

TABLE A1-1

RESISTOR COLOR CODE

Color	Number
Black	0
Brown	1
Red	2
Orange	3
Yellow	4
Green	5
Blue	6
Violet	7
Gray	8
White	9

and orange has a resistance of 47,000 Ω; green, blue, green signifies 5,600,000 Ω, or 5.6 MΩ, etc. Resistor values between 1 and 10 Ω are indicated by a gold third band, while a silver third band means the resistance is between 0.1 and 1 Ω.

A fourth band of either gold or silver tells the tolerance, or limit of accuracy, of the resistance value. A gold band indicates that the tolerance is ±5 percent, which means that the actual resistance may be any value within 5 percent of the nominal value. Similarly, a silver band signifies a tolerance of ±10 percent. If the fourth band is absent, the tolerance is understood to be ±20 percent.

The significant figures of standard resistor values commercially available in 5 and 10 percent tolerance are listed in Table A1-2. These values

TABLE A1-2

STANDARD RESISTOR VALUES

5% tolerance	10% tolerance	5% tolerance	10% tolerance
1.0	1.0	4.3	
1.1		4.7	4.7
1.2	1.2	5.1	
1.3		5.6	5.6
1.5	1.5	6.2	
1.6		6.8	6.8
1.8	1.8	7.5	
2.0		8.2	8.2
2.2	2.2	9.1	
2.4		10	10
2.7	2.7		
3.0			
3.3	3.3		
3.6			
3.9	3.9		

have been chosen so that there is a nominal value within 10 percent (or 5 percent) of any required resistance. Any other choice of nominal values requires many more values to cover the same resistance range. Those listed repeat in each decade so that, for example, 5.6-MΩ and 6.8-MΩ resistors are available in both 5 and 10 percent tolerance types, but a nominal 6.2-MΩ resistor only comes in 5 percent tolerance.

Capacitor color codes are not as universally accepted as is the case for resistors. The codes used differ somewhat among manufacturers and many manufacturers print the numerical value of capacitance on the body of the unit. Nevertheless, the majority of mica and ceramic tubular capac-

itors use the same color code as in Table A1-1 to indicate the nominal
capacitance value in picofarads, Fig. A1-2. For example, red, violet,

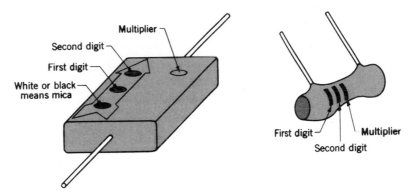

FIGURE A1-2　*Color-code scheme for mica (left) and
ceramic (right) capacitors.*

red signifies 2700 pf or 0.0027 μf; orange, orange, black means 33 pf,
etc. Other colored bands or dots are also used to indicate tolerance,
temperature coefficient of capacitance, and other parameters. These
also vary from manufacturer to manufacturer.

Effective Value
of Complex Waveforms

The *effective value* of a time-varying current is, by definition, equal to the direct current that produces the same joule heat in a resistor as the ac current. For example, the effective value I_e of a sinusoidal current waveform is found by computing the average power in the resistor and equating this to the dc power, or

$$I_e{}^2 R = \frac{1}{T} \int_0^T R I_p{}^2 \sin^2 \omega t \; dt \qquad \text{(A2-1)}$$

where T is the period and I_p is the peak value of the sine wave. Integrating,

$$I_e{}^2 = \frac{I_p{}^2}{T} \left[\frac{t}{2} - \frac{\sin 2\omega t}{4} \right]_0^T$$

$$= \frac{I_p{}^2}{2} \qquad \text{(A2-2)}$$

$$I_e = \frac{I_p}{\sqrt{2}} \qquad \text{(A2-3)}$$

Equation (A2-3) gives the relation between the peak and effective value of a sine wave. The effective value is also called the *root-mean-square,* or *rms,* value because the computation involves the square root of the average of the ac current squared. An expression identical to Eq. (A2-3) applies to ac voltages as well.

The rms value of any nonsinusoidal waveform is found by the same procedure. Consider, for example, the square wave of period T and maximum value I_p illustrated in Fig. A2-1. The effective current is just

$$I_e{}^2 = \frac{1}{T} \int_0^T I_p{}^2 \; dt = \frac{I_p{}^2}{T} \int_0^T dt = I_p{}^2 \qquad \text{(A2-4)}$$

or

$$I_e = I_p \qquad \text{(A2-5)}$$

This means that the effective value of a square wave is equal to the maximum value. Since the joule heat in a resistor depends upon the square of the current, the current direction is immaterial and Eq. (A2-5) is just what is expected.

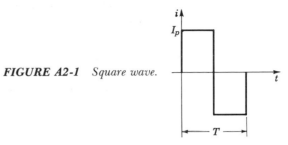

FIGURE A2-1 *Square wave.*

Consider next the simple triangular sawtooth waveform illustrated in Fig. A2-2. The current varies as

$$i = \frac{2I_p}{T} t \tag{A2-6}$$

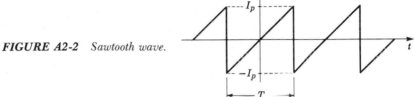

FIGURE A2-2 *Sawtooth wave.*

over the interval from $-T/2$ to $T/2$. Therefore, the rms value is

$$I_e{}^2 = \frac{1}{T} \int_{-T/2}^{T/2} \left(\frac{2I_p}{T} t\right)^2 dt = \frac{4I_p{}^2}{T^3} \int_{-T/2}^{T/2} t^2 \, dt$$

$$= \frac{4I_p{}^2}{T^3} \left[\frac{t^3}{3}\right]_{-T/2}^{T/2} = \frac{4I_p{}^2}{3T^3} \left[\frac{T^3}{8} + \frac{T^3}{8}\right] = \frac{I_p{}^2}{3} \tag{A2-7}$$

$$I_e = \frac{I_p}{\sqrt{3}} \tag{A2-8}$$

The result is used in Chap. 4 in connection with the ripple factor of a capacitor filter.

Another waveform of interest is the output of a full-wave rectifier. The effective value can be found by the usual procedure used above. The full-wave rectifier waveform, Fig. A2-3, has, however, a dc component, as can be shown by computing the average value,

$$I_{dc} = \frac{2}{T} \int_0^{T/2} I_p \sin \omega t \, dt = \frac{2I_p}{\omega T} \left[-\cos \omega t\right]_0^{T/2}$$

$$= \frac{4I_p}{\omega T} = \frac{4I_p}{2\pi} \tag{A2-9}$$

$$I_{dc} = \frac{2}{\pi} I_p \tag{A2-10}$$

This dc component contributes to the heating effect of the complete waveform.

For most purposes the rms value of the ac components alone is of interest. It is convenient to consider the Fourier series of complex wave-

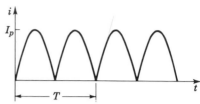

FIGURE A2-3   *Full-wave-rectified sine wave.*

forms. Since the heating effect of each frequency component is independent of the others, the effective value of any complex waveform is given by

$$I_e{}^2 = I_{dc}{}^2 + I_1{}^2 + I_2{}^2 + I_3{}^2 + \cdots \tag{A2-11}$$

where I_{dc} is the average value and $I_1, I_2, I_3, \ldots$ are the rms values of each frequency component. It is often sufficient to consider only the fundamental frequency, since it predominates.

The Fourier series of the full-wave rectified waveform is

$$i = \frac{2}{\pi} I_p - \frac{4I_p}{3\pi} \cos 2\omega t - \frac{4I_p}{15\pi} \cos 4\omega t + \cdots \tag{A2-12}$$

Note that the first term corresponds to Eq. (A2-10), in conformity with the definition of the dc component. The effective value of the ac components alone is, using Eqs. (A2-3) and (A2-11),

$$I_{rms}^2 = \frac{I_p{}^2}{2}\left[\left(\frac{4}{3\pi}\right)^2 + \left(\frac{4}{15\pi}\right)^2 + \cdots\right] \cong \frac{1}{2}\left(\frac{4I_p}{3\pi}\right)^2 \tag{A2-13}$$

$$I_{rms} = \frac{2\sqrt{2}I_p}{3\pi} \tag{A2-14}$$

Thus, the ratio of the rms value of the ac components to the dc component is

$$\frac{I_{rms}}{I_{dc}} = \frac{2\sqrt{2}I_p/3\pi}{2I_p/\pi}$$

$$\frac{I_{rms}}{I_{dc}} = \frac{\sqrt{2}}{3} \tag{A2-15}$$

This result is used in Chap. 4 in connection with the ripple factor of an L-section filter.

APPENDIX
3
Characteristic Curves of Tubes and Transistors

The following pages contain characteristic curves of tubes and tran-sistors discussed in the text and examined in the Exercises. These curves have been taken directly from manufacturers' publications and are typical of information available to circuit designers. Note the minor differences in terminology used in these curves compared with the text.

The vacuum-tube characteristics are reproduced with the permission of Radio Corporation of America, as are those for transistor types 2N35 and 2N175. Data for types 2N338, 2N930, 2N1719, and 2N2499 are reproduced with the permission of Texas Instruments, Inc. The General Electric Co. supplied the characteristic curves for the type 2N1415.

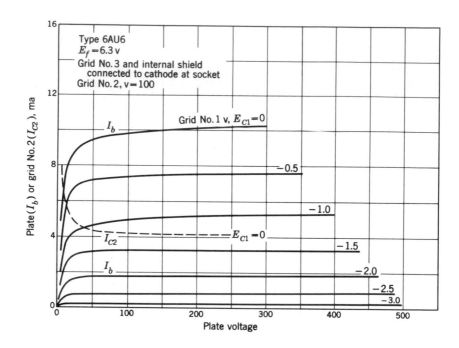

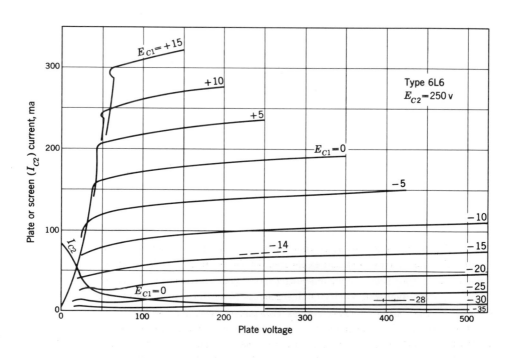

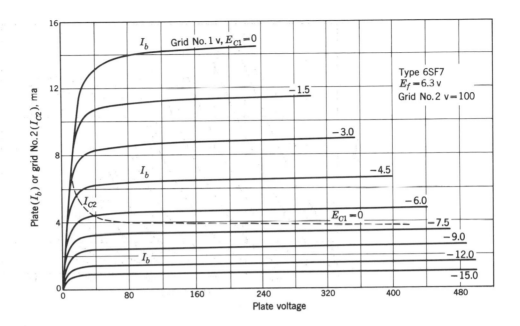

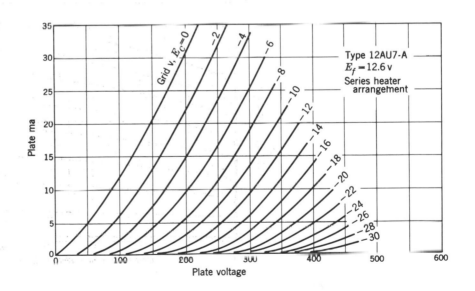

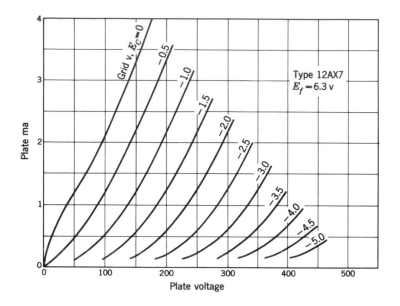

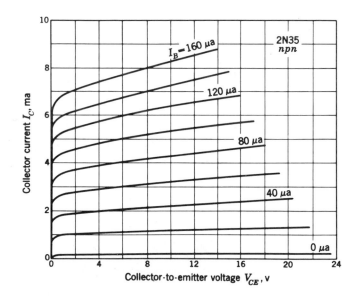

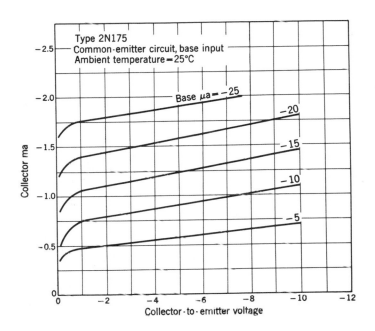

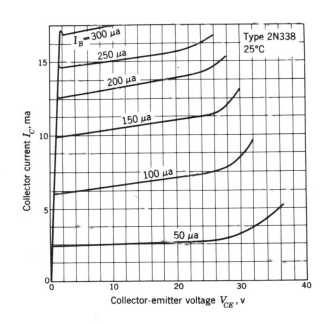

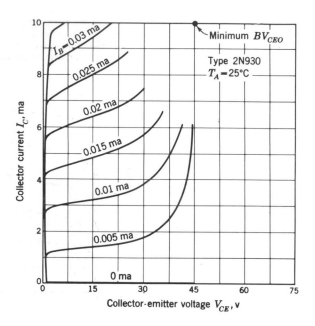

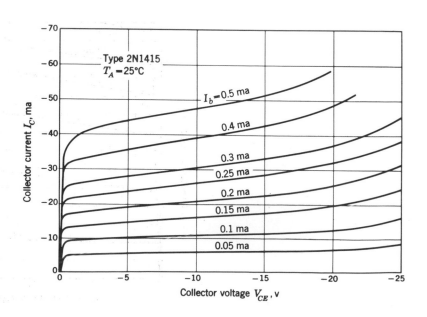

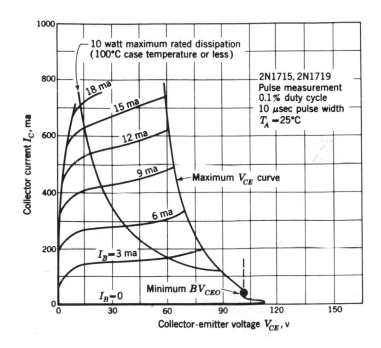

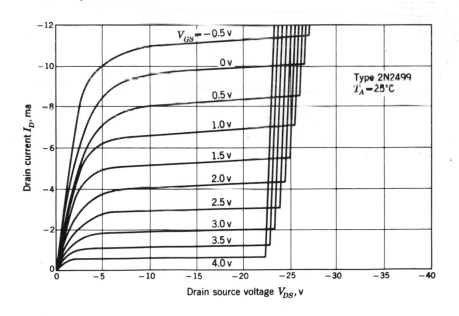

INDEX